MECHANISED FORCE
British tanks between the wars

KT-478-605

DISPOSED OF
BY LIBRARY
HOUSE OF LORDS

The ultimate accolade, four Medium C tanks follow the Tank Corps contingent over Westminster Bridge during the 1919 Victory Parade. Gen. Elles leads on the white horse with J F C Fuller alongside him.

THE TANK MUSEUM

MECHANISED FORCE

British tanks between the wars

David Fletcher

LONDON : HMSO

© Crown Copyright 1991
First published 1991

Applications for reproduction should be made to HMSO

ISBN 0 11 290487 4

British Library Cataloguing in Publication Data
A CIP catalogue record for this book is available
from the British Library

Front cover:
To an entire generation in Britain the word tank *conjured up this image.
From 1923, almost to the outbreak of the Second World War the Medium
Tank was the only machine worthy of the name. Shown here is a Medium
Mark II★★ of 5th Battalion Royal Tank Corps at Lulworth Camp in
Dorset.*

Back cover:
*The wide, uncultivated expanse of Salisbury Plain is a valuable military
training area. Between the two world wars it became, for a while, the
nursery for a new creed of armoured warfare. In this view a column of
Medium and Light tanks of 3rd Battalion, Royal Tank Corps, crosses a
public road.*

HMSO

HMSO publications are available from:

HMSO Publications Centre
(Mail and telephone orders only)
PO Box 276, London, SW8 5DT
Telephone orders 071-873 9090
General enquiries 071-873 0011
(queuing system in operation for both numbers)

HMSO Bookshops
49 High Holborn, London, WC1V 6HB 071-873 0011
(Counter service only)
258 Broad Street, Birmingham, B1 2HE 021-643 3740
Southey House, 33 Wine Street, Bristol, BS1 2BQ 0272-264306
9–21 Princess Street, Manchester, M60 8AS 061-834 7201
80 Chichester Street, Belfast, BT1 4JY 0232-238451
71 Lothian Road, Edinburgh, EH3 9AZ 031-228 4181

HMSO's Accredited Agents
(see Yellow Pages)

and through good booksellers

Printed in the United Kingdom for HMSO
Dd 0293211 C30 7/91 3735

Contents

Abbreviations

ACC	Armoured Car Company
ACV	Armoured command vehicle
AEC	Associated Equipment Company
AFV	armoured fighting vehicle
bhp	brake horsepower
BSA	Birmingham Small Arms Company
Co	Company
Coy	Company (military)
CIGS	Chief of the Imperial General Staff
CTA	Cemented Tank Armour
FOO	forward observation officer
GS	General Staff
hp	horsepower
in	inch
KRRC	King's Royal Rifle Corps
LAMBS	Light Armoured Motor Batteries
LMS	London, Midland and Scottish Railway Company
LTC	Light Tank Company
MEE	Mechanisation Experimental Establishment
MGO	Master General of Ordnance
mm	millimetre
MWEE	Mechanical Warfare Experimental Establishment
NAP	normal air pressure
pr	pounder
QF	quick firing
RAC	Royal Armoured Corps
RAF	Royal Air Force
RAMC	Royal Army Medical Corps
RAOC	Royal Army Ordnance Corps
RASC	Royal Army Service Corps
RE	Royal Engineers
ROF	Royal Ordnance Factory
rpm	revolutions per minute
R/T	radio telephony
RTC	Royal Tank Corps
RTR	Royal Tank Regiment
TOG	The Old Gang
TTS	Tank Testing Section
W/T	wireless telegraphy

Introduction

On 19 July 1919 a great Victory Parade was held in London. Crowds gathered to watch as groups representing the armed forces of Britain and her allies marched past the sovereign on a route that took in Whitehall and Westminster Bridge. Among the contingents the Tank Corps was represented by its field commander, Maj-Gen. Hugh Elles, some 70 men and four Medium C tanks. Although they had not seen active service the Mediums were the very latest tanks and provided a fitting reminder of the progress made in just three years. Tanks had first seen action on 15 September 1916 and their development since then had been astounding.

Yet now the Tank Corps was shrinking fast. The battalions were disbanded or reduced to cadres as they came home from France and the men who formed them returned to their civilian lives. In no time at all, if certain influential factions had their way, the Corps would cease to exist altogether and the ugly, noisy machines would be tossed onto the scrap-heap. Even so, not everyone wanted to be a civilian, and there was still useful work for armoured vehicles to do; there might be no great battles but the Armistice of 1918, and the confirmation of victory that followed, was no guarantee of a peaceful world. An Army of Occupation was still required in Germany, as much to preserve civil order as prevent the war from starting again, and the Tank Corps had units in Solingen and Cologne which took their Mark Vs onto the streets now and then, just in case anyone needed reminding what it was that had so effectively helped to scupper the Kaiser's plans.

In Ireland too there was dissention to be reckoned with. Republican ambitions had largely been submerged in the greater war effort, but now that was over men were coming home to unemployment and heavy-handed administration. There was plenty of mischief for idle hands to do, so both tanks and armoured cars were shipped to Dublin in small numbers to try and contain the situation. Further afield Britain found itself with a new and forlorn commitment in Russia. Even before the Armistice was signed British troops had been despatched to that country, ostensibly for the purpose of preventing Germany from providing more than just moral support to the revolutionary forces. Now three small tank detachments were sent to support the White Russians as they attempted to stem the Bolshevik tide. The South Russian Tank Detachment (Mark Vs and Medium As) entered the country via Batum on the Black Sea in April 1919. The North West Russian Tank Detachment (Mark Vs and Medium As) arrived at Reval, Estonia, in July, while a month later the North Russian Tank Detachment disembarked at Archangel with four Mark Vs and two Medium Bs to protect the main Allied base. In theory the other two detachments were there to provide training before handing their tanks over to Russian crews, but it was largely a waste of time. Even if the Russian officers could not recognise a

lost cause their men did, and such efforts as they made to learn were uninspired. The force marching out of Estonia attempted to take Petrograd with three tanks but they had no more luck than the Germans, more than 20 years later when they tried to capture the city – now Leningrad – with a good deal more enthusiasm and armour. Where success was achieved it was only temporary but, in South Russia at least, spectacular. Turning a blind eye to their orders one British crew led a successful attack on Tsaritsin with a single Mark V; something the Germans singularly failed to do with a number of Panzer divisions when the place was called Stalingrad. British armoured cars were still in action in the Middle East and India, although not yet under Tank Corps control and there was even a partial mobilisation in Britain. Some Medium C tanks were rushed up to Glasgow in 1920 when a coal strike was feared to be the first sign of imminent revolution.

Yet all this time, like some tottering business empire, the Tank Corps lurched from crisis to crisis while its future remained uncertain. Presenting the Army Estimates for 1920 to the House of Commons, Winston Churchill, the Minister of War, spoke first of a new, high speed tank capable of 20mph which the Government had just ordered, but then went on to say that for the present only NCOs and other ranks serving with the Tank Corps could regard themselves as permanently attached. Officers would just serve on detachment from their original regiments until the future status of the Corps was decided. During this period of turmoil the original battalions suffered disbandment while a mere six were reborn. These were the 1st (Depot) Battalion stationed in and around Bovington to handle enlistment and training; 2nd, 3rd, 4th and 5th, which became operational tank battalions; and the Workshops Training Battalion, which supplied fitters to the others. This last was permanently disbanded in 1925 when the Royal Army Ordnance Corps (RAOC) took over responsibility for the issue and maintenance of armoured fighting vehicles. From 1920 onwards 12 armoured car companies were formed, either at Bovington or abroad, which provided exciting employment for many redundant tank men and also absorbed the surviving Light Armoured Motor Batteries (LAMBS) that had been created during the war. Now, at last, all armoured vehicles, where ever they were stationed came under Tank Corps control, which made a great deal of sense, especially when the Machine Gun Corps was disbanded in 1922. A year later, on 12 September 1923, the Tank Corps was officially established on a permanent basis and, just over a month after that, with the approval of Buckingham Palace, it became the Royal Tank Corps (RTC).

What follows is, in the main, a history of this Corps until, as the Royal Tank Regiment (RTR), it went to war again in 1939. It is by no means a dull story, peace is only ever a relative term, and there are many exciting events to record. However, the regimental aspect has been chronicled before by far abler pens so, in keeping with other titles in this series, the aim here is to approach the subject through the tanks and armoured cars themselves. It is here, perhaps, that the real excitement lies for anyone with an interest in mechanical things. For the years between the wars were the truly formative years. With very little past experience to guide them but massive technological strides to carry them on their way, the designers had free rein. Nearly every idea, no matter how bizarre, was developed at least to prototype state and evaluated, and more often than not found wanting, but it resulted in the appearance of some amazing armoured vehicles that deserve to be recorded for their own sake.

While the RTC grew in strength and experience it gained confidence, but the period is also characterised by economy; false economy as it turned out, for by 1939 the heady promise of the early, inventive years had evaporated into virtual stagnation, both in ideas and designs. Many of the reasons why the British Army passed through the Second World War with some inferior tanks can be traced to the inter-war years and the same might be said of the way they were used. In a sense it was the independence which the RTC fought so hard to attain that can be blamed for the fact that many of Britain's senior commanders, in the first years of the war, failed to appreciate the value and correct usage of armour. Conversely it may be said that much of Germany's apparent aptitude for armoured warfare, which appeared to have sprung from nowhere in 1939, can be attributed to lessons they learned by studying British tank exercises held on Salisbury Plain in the same period.

Outside the Corps other matters are recorded. The gradual mechanisation of the cavalry evokes enough pathos to suit a Victorian melodrama when viewed through reactionary eyes; but it was a logical step which led, in April 1939, to the formation of the Royal Armoured Corps. On the sidelines the seemingly curious adoption of armour by certain ground-based elements of the RAF is mentioned along with developments in the Commonwealth. One of the most significant chapters deals with commercial matters. In addition to building machines for its own army Britain maintained a thriving export trade, it is a subject that has received very little attention until now. Yet even this brief study reveals that British influence in tank design had a world-wide effect due, almost entirely, to the efforts of one manufacturer which, at the time of writing, once again holds much of Britain's destiny as a tank producing nation in its hands.

While every effort has been made to present this book as complete and readable in itself, there is no doubt that it leans, to some extent, on two previous titles: *Landships*★ and *War Cars*†. Likewise another title, *The Great Tank Scandal* ‡ carries the story forward from 1939 and, in its turn, leans on this work.

★Fletcher. *Landships: British Tanks in the First World War*. HMSO, 1984.
†Fletcher. *War Cars: British Armoured Cars in the First World War*. HMSO, 1987.
‡Fletcher. *The Great Tank Scandal: British Armour in the Second World War, Part 1*. HMSO, 1989.

1 Medium Tanks: Backbone of the Corps

In the summer of 1918, shortly before the battle of Amiens, the Ministry of Munitions formed a Tank Board to replace the earlier Tank Committee. Its main purpose was to decide on tank policy for the supposed victory year of 1919. To guide its deliberations it had, as one of the Tank Corps' members, Col. J F C Fuller, who carried the battle plan for 1919 in his head and had the facts and figures at his fingertips. Plan 1919 called for a new type of high-speed tank, the Medium D. It was no more than an idea at this stage and Fuller was realistic enough to appreciate that it might not be ready in time. He therefore advocated increased production of the slower Medium C as a workable, if inferior substitute, while a tank to fulfil the Medium D requirement was developed. As things turned out, of course, the war ended far sooner than anyone could have predicted, even the visionary Fuller who was soon in for another big shock.

The first post-war meeting of the Tank Board took place on 14 November 1918, just three days after the Armistice came into effect, and it began with an announcement by Gen. Seeley to the effect that the War Cabinet had instructed the Army Council to stop all further work on tanks. Fuller was moved to protest. He pointed out that most of the tanks then in service were battle-worn and unfit for much more use, while those few that might be delivered before the ban came into effect would hardly be sufficient to equip the future Tank Corps, whatever form that might take. He also pointed out that the new Medium D was in an advanced state of development and that tank design was passing through a dramatic period of change, all of which would be jeopardised unless this drastic scheme was modified.

Fuller's comments were passed back to Gen. Wilson, Chief of the Imperial General Staff (CIGS), and the Secretary of State for War, Winston Churchill, who in turn reported to the Army Council early in December. Here it was agreed that a total halt to tank production would be unwise, and instead the following plan should be adopted: 250 assorted tanks already on the production line should be completed, along with a further 250 of the Medium C type. Experimental work on the Medium D should continue and the best possible use be made of the surviving tanks in France. Clearly the Treasury would have to be consulted but, in view of the fact that some 8,600 tanks were originally required for 1919 under war conditions, the odd 500 in peacetime was hardly an unreasonable request. But that was to reckon without the Treasury. The civil servants, even after four years of war, remembered something that these politicians and soldiers had forgotten – the annual vote. It was firmly pointed out that with the Armistice the wartime policy of unrestricted financial support for the services ended, to be replaced by the pre-war system of annual estimates. It was calculated that the Army Council's proposal would cost around

£2.5 M: which was probably more than the Treasury visualised spending on all three services for 1919! Seeing the strength of this argument Fuller revised the plan to one which was agreed at another Army Council meeting on 16 December 1918. This called for only 175 assorted wartime tanks to be completed and the requirement for 250 Medium Cs to be dropped in favour of 500 Medium Ds and for experimental work on this type to continue under a new Department of Tank Design and Experiment. To this the Treasury replied that 175 miscellaneous tanks might be acceptable, but that working from the Ministry of Munitions estimate of £4,500 per Medium D, finding some £2 M for these new machines would be impossible.

At this point the Ministry of Munitions stepped in and explained that, due to unforseen circumstances, the minimum number of wartime tanks still under construction which had to be completed for economic and contractural reasons would be 263, not 175. Since this would further upset the costings they suggested that orders for Medium Ds should be placed at the rate of ten per month, thus limiting the expenditure to £550,000 per year. This proposal caused the Master General of Ordnance (MGO) to point out that, at that rate, it would take four years to equip the Tank Corps, by which time, he had no doubt, even better machines would have been developed.

The great advantage of all this argument, at least to the Treasury, was that while it went on no money was spent at all, apart from that already committed to existing orders. Whether this was adopted as a tactical manœuvre or not is unclear, but it is interesting to note that it was July 1919 before the matter was raised again, and when it came it was another bombshell from the Ministry. They, for some reason, had been working on the assumption that at least 75 Medium D tanks would be ordered, which they now reckoned would cost £12,250 each – £7,750 more than the original estimate *per tank*! This was not a case of runaway post-war inflation, German style, but a serious miscalculation due, once again to the reversion to peacetime practice. Pressed by Churchill the Ministry explained that their original figure was based upon a price which did not take into account the cost of engine, transmission system or armament of any kind. In other words all the Tank Corps would have got for £4,500 was an armoured shell on tracks which looked like a tank but could neither move nor fight. Churchill stormed at the Ministry's attitude and inefficiency, threatening retribution at the highest level, but the War Office was seriously embarrassed; its tank programme was in tatters.

Worse was to come. In September 1919, after due consideration, the Treasury announced that it could not sanction the new tank programme. It pointed to the War Cabinet's conclusion that no major European war could be expected for at least ten years as a reason for delaying new construction, and offered its own view that the Army should retrench and 'live off its fat' for the time being. The most they were prepared to find was £30,000 for development work. Churchill now turned on the Treasury in the person of Austen Chamberlain, Chancellor of the Exchequer. Did Chamberlain realise, he wanted to know, that in taking this attitude the Treasury was playing directly into the hands of those reactionary soldiers who loathed tanks but would end up costing the country even more money before they had finished? By his somewhat convoluted argument these men deplored mechanisation because it saved on manpower, and commanding large bodies of men was all these old fuddy-duddies understood. To add weight Churchill claimed the backing of the Prime Minister and War Cabinet, who were actually trying to *save* money while the Treasury supported the expensive, pre-war element. The Chancellor countered with the same rehearsed arguments about using up the tanks already available, to which Churchill replied towards the end of October. Backed up by a statement of tanks actually available he explained that his mechanisation programme was designed to render existing cavalry forces redundant – and the Chancellor knew how expensive cavalry regiments were. Finally he resorted to threats; as Secretary of State for War he fully realised that he was up against the entrenched anti-tank opinions of the military establishment which he could not override unless he had the tanks to do it with. He reminded Chamberlain that he was only pursuing the Prime Minister's policy and, if the Treasury continued to obstruct him, there would be no alternative but to place the whole matter before the Cabinet. This seemed to have the desired effect. Chamberlain assured the Secretary of State that he believed in tanks too, and wanted the Army to have them, but would it be possible to spread the cost over two years? Since 12 months had already been wasted arguing about it this did not seem much to ask and Churchill agreed. Treasury approval was given on 8 December 1919 for an initial batch of 20 tanks, but the sum to include sufficient for 60 Rolls-Royce engines already set aside for the purpose by the Ministry of Munitions.

If this fiscal preamble seems dull and irrelevant it is perhaps worth labouring some of the points raised, and studying the effect they appear to have had on future developments. It could well be that many problems which later beset British tank production can be traced right back to this undignified series of exchanges that livened up 1919. In the first place of course it has long been recognised that the pro-tank lobby, especially as personified by Fuller, had the very effect Churchill had noted: of stirring a strong reactionary movement at the War Office. But what Fuller achieved there it seems Churchill also did at the Treasury. Chancellors may come and go but senior civil servants remain and they know how to dig in, just as old soldiers do. Indeed there may even have been collusion in clubland, for the cause of mechanisation was hindered by a shortage of funds for the next 20 years – and the cavalry remained.

As things turned out Churchill might just as well not have bothered to press the case so hard because there never were even 20 Medium D tanks built, and probably never could have been. Fuller, blinded by the promise of advanced technology as non-technical men often are, misled his advocate and gave the Treasury an opportunity for revenge that it was not slow to

take. The origins of the Medium D are recounted in the final chapter of *Landships*, but just to recap: Lt-Col. Philip Johnson, the Tank Corps' Experimental Officer, had returned from France in 1918 to establish the Department of Tank Design and Experiment which would evolve the high-speed tanks for Plan 1919. Settling, in due course, at Charlton Park, Woolwich in the summer of 1919, they continued with experimental work while contracts for ten Medium D tanks were placed: four with John Fowler & Co, the traction engine builders of Leeds, and six with Vickers Ltd, through their subsidiary company Wolseley Motors of Birmingham. The first of these appeared, ready for testing, in about June 1919. It was clear at once that here was a revolutionary machine, long and narrow with a fixed crew compartment at the forward end and track frames arranged, contrary to normal practice, to be higher at the back than the front. This curious arrangement was adopted in order to give the driver a clear view of the ground ahead and the gunners a good field of fire, but it meant that any attempt to surmount a high obstacle like a bank would have to be done in reverse, which offended just about every tactical precept ever written. Although Rolls-Royce engines had been specified, and even put aside, these first tanks used the six-cylinder Wolseley Puma from Bristol Fighter aircraft, and a transmission that employed separate three-speed epicyclics to drive the rear-mounted sprockets. But it was the suspension that really set these tanks apart. Until this time no production British tank had any suspension at all, and a cautious engineer might have opted for something more conventional, but Johnson was the type who threw caution to the winds. His was probably the most sinuous suspension system ever devised for a tank, and the key to his concept of what a high-speed tank should be. It consisted of a train of small roller wheels, attached to pulleys which, in turn, ran on lengths of flexible steel wire rope that stretched from one end of the tank to the other. Springs, in the conventional sense, were done away with: they were only used to tension the ends of the cable. The result was a system that permitted the rollers to rise and fall in sequence over a small obstacle without disturbing the running of the tank at all. By virtually eliminating springs Johnson also saved a lot of weight, which was important, but he was creating nightmare complications. His tracks were just as odd. They consisted of a series of narrow shoes threaded onto a core of cable in such a way that they could twist to accommodate rough ground and flex laterally to conform with a turning movement. This was Johnson's solution to the problem of steering tracked vehicles. With conventional tracks the resistance set up during a skid turn was enormous, it created a great deal of stress and wastage of power which caused a tank to slow, almost to a halt, each time it changed direction. On a Medium D, lateral movement in the suspension, coupled to the curving of the tracks, eased this situation dramatically, especially at speed, if it worked. Like his American contemporary Walter Christie, Philip Johnson was obsessed by speed, almost to the exclusion of everything else, and he achieved it. When it was running well a Medium D could reach 20mph on favourable ground, compared with 8mph for an unsprung Medium C. Yet if all this technology was not complex and fragile enough in its experimental state these tanks were designed to swim, without any special modifications, at least on inland waterways, and this facility raised the complexity level, with its attendant risk of failure, to even greater heights.

Unfortunately, now that the war and Plan 1919 were history, priorities within the Tank Corps had changed. They now wanted something simple and reliable to train on, that could fight if necessary. When Hugh Elles, the Tank Corps commander, first saw a Medium D he was horrified by the scant attention its designer had paid to combat potential. The crew compartment at the front was a cramped, oval structure, pierced to mount just three Hotchkiss machine-guns covering the front and sides, while the driver sat above and behind the gunners, his head protruding through a protective cupola, his view taking in the entire roof of the fighting compartment before he could see the road. To Elles this appeared to be an unsatisfactory arrangement in every respect and he was backed up in this opinion by Lt-Col. H B Thorpe, a Tank Corps officer now serving on the General Staff, in a well reasoned paper that demanded a gun in every tank. Looking back on the first four years of tank design Thorpe criticised the wartime system of male and female tanks and the illogical tradition which decreed that medium tanks only required machines-guns. Punctuating his paper with upper case sentences to drive the point home, he urged repeatedly that every tank, no matter what its role, should mount a proper gun. At a Tank Board meeting on 28 November 1919 Elles recommended the old, long (40 calibres) 6pr, as fitted to the very first tanks. Johnson appeared to agree, although he warned that such a tank might not float. However, as criticism mounted, he took a more defensive posture over the entire subject of driver location and potential, arguing that he should first be permitted to get the new tanks working properly and only worry about these other matters when that was done. Now it seemed that with the War Office and Treasury against tanks in general, the Treasury and Tank Corps had it in for the Medium D in particular. Things did not improve when the great Landships Committee veteran, Sir Eustace Tennyson D'Eyncourt, speaking for the Admiralty, announced that from their calculations a Medium D, however armed, would be unstable in the water.

The first Medium D was destroyed by fire shortly after it arrived at Christchurch for trials; the remainder were dogged by mechanical troubles and only four were built: two by Fowlers, and two by Wolseley Motors. In an effort to overcome the stability problem when afloat two more of the Wolseley tanks were modified at the production stage. One appeared late in 1919 as the Medium D★, a widened version which still appears to have had stability problems in the water. The other was even wider and also had an extra bulkhead at the rear of the hull. It appeared in 1920 as the Medium D★★ and during trials at Christchurch this tank proved it could float by crossing the river Stour at the Experimental Bridging Establishment. There is some evidence to suggest that this tank was also used for transmission trials. As built it had a four-speed sliding gearbox driving through a pair of cam-operated steering clutches designed by another famous Tank Corps engineer, J G Rackham. In 1921 it is recorded as having been modified to take hydraulic steering apparatus of the Variable Speed Gear type, otherwise known as the Williams-Janney system.

It was, of course, the Medium D that Churchill was referring to when he presented the 1920 estimates to the House of

1 A Medium DM tackling an obstacle at Charlton Park. If it was behaving true to its designer's intentions it should actually be reversing over this heap of stones.

Commons, but it was 1921 before they were ready to enter production, and the arguments had still not ended. Working on the basis of Medium D★★ being the successful prototype Johnson now produced a design for what he called the Medium DM (or D Modified), two of which were built close to Charlton Park at the Woolwich Ordnance Factory. They were powered by the Rolls-Royce Eagle V12 engine rated at 260hp, but each tank is said to have had a different type of transmission, although neither is specified. Similar in outline to the earlier prototypes they can best be identified by the two cupolas on the cab roof and the round 'manhole' type hatches in the hull sides. The former feature may have been added by Johnson in response to the complaint from Elles that, unless he was also the driver, the tank commander could not see out and therefore had no idea what was going on. If that is the case then the advantage gained was a dubious one since the presence of the extra cupola partly obstructed the driver's view and made his task more difficult! The two tanks retained the wire rope suspension and cable tracks, as well as the amphibious capability, at least in theory, for a report suggests that one of them sank during trials in the Thames. In terms of armament these tanks were no improvement on the prototypes and they would still have to take a steep obstacle in reverse, prompting Elles to note that a rear-firing gun might not be a bad idea either.

Following further juggling with figures it was decided to place an order for 42 of these tanks: 36 to equip a tank battalion and six reserves. Writing from Bovington Gen. Elles sounded another note of caution. His main point was that, as it stood, the Medium DM was a very complex machine that required a degree of skill from both officers and men of the Tank Corps which very few could aspire to. He wrote, 'I think I may safely say that it will be at least a year before we could man a first issue of 42 D machines and then only by picking the best personnel out of the existing battalions.' Indeed in this context it is worth recording a comment made in the *Royal Tank Corps Journal* some years later which explained that Philip Johnson was the *only* person who could drive these tanks properly. An exaggeration, obviously, but probably stemming from a grain of truth. Returning to Elles and his comments, he clearly appreciated that there was no alternative but to proceed with this first order, although he considered that any second order placed at this stage would be folly. He need not have worried. The Medium DM was classed by the General Staff as a cavalry tank. That is a high-speed machine capable of working in the mobile exploitation and scouting roles normally allotted to cavalry. What was needed now was an infantry tank, capable of direct frontal assault on enemy positions, presumably at a slower pace to operate alongside the foot soldiers. The Department of Tank Design and Experiment was ordered to produce a plan.

Before discussing this tank it would be instructive to examine Philip Johnson's position at this time – say about the summer of 1921. Johnson may safely be described as an engineering genius, with all that implies; but a genius can be as much a liability as an asset if he cannot be properly controlled. Working under tight financial restraints with a Government establishment one might assume that Johnson's activities were adequately controlled, but it seems that they were not. In addition to his mainstream work designing the tanks so far

described, Johnson and his team were engaged upon a whole range of other experiments, all directed towards more or less the same ends: the production of an entire family of tracked vehicles. If they could be made to work then the British Army would soon have a range of fast, tracked vehicles, including everything from ambulances to motorcycles. This work was carried out on a pitifully small budget and even then Johnson was obliged to scrounge wrecked or worn out vehicles from Army dumps and adapt them as best he could. The tracked motorcycle was probably a rather light-hearted experiment, but his Light D series of modified motor cars formed part of a serious development programme while his most bizarre concept, the so-called Rigid Rail Machine was, or ought to have been, a major step forwards in tracked vehicle technology. Johnson and most of the officers working under him at Charlton Park had already retired from active duty, but they must have known they faced an uncertain future. In any case Johnson had ambitions in the world of transportation that went beyond what the War Office would permit him to do and he had taken the precaution of founding a company, Roadless Traction Ltd, which would be activated when his official career came to an end.

Whether it was this, or simply frustration with the penny-pinching restrictions he had to work under, that prompted Johnson's next move we may never know, but it seems that his desire to perfect the ultimate high-speed tank overrode his sense of duty to supply the War Office with what it asked for; either that or the whole plan was a conspiracy with the Tank Board to continue the work by any name. Certainly the Light Infantry Tank, which appeared in November 1921, was in no way suited to the role its title implies, although it did embody many new features. It was light, weighing a mere eight tons against 18 for a Medium DM, but where the infantry part came into it is anybody's guess. Similarity with other tanks in the Medium D series was evident; although this machine was much shorter and did not have the tail-high configuration, the fighting and driving conditions were exactly the same, as Elles noted critically when he saw the tank at Charlton Park on 5 April 1921. Reporting next day from Bovington he claimed that the driver, in his elevated position, was blind within seven yards of his tank and very uncomfortable. Again he was also effectively the commander since the other crew members, the

2 The Light Infantry Tank during trials at Farnborough. The driver's head can just be seen above the No. 4 on the body and it is also possible to make out the system of pulleys and cable that served for a suspension.

machine-gunners, were limited to what they could see through the sighting apertures of their weapons. 'Generally speaking,' he wrote, 'the cab has most of the defects of the Medium D; and few of the suggestions made in regard to the cab of the Medium D have been incorporated.' In particular he remarked upon the lack of a proper gun and the inability of the tank to fire to its rear. The Light Infantry Tank was powered by an American Hall-Scott aero engine, rated at 100hp, driving through a four-speed gearbox and Rackham steering clutches, but the greatest innovation again lay in the suspension and tracks. The former still employed wire rope but incorporated a cam device which kept the cable taught and prevented a slack portion from creeping to the rear end. For the tracks Johnson abandoned wire rope in favour of a system of lubricated ball joints. Each track shoe was an oval steel plate, welded to a tubular segment of backbone, linked to its neighbours by a ball and socket joint packed with grease. This was the famous Snake Track. It retained the all-round flexibility of the rope type but was far more robust and gave far better surface contact although it wore badly because the lubricant seeped out and attracted grit into the joints. The tank was evaluated by the Tank Testing Section at Farnborough and underwent amphibious trials on the nearby Fleet Pond. It clocked 30mph in Long Valley and, mechanically at least, appears to have been a great success, assuming that it was what the Tank Corps was looking for. But was it? The answer might be found in the fact that no more were ordered. In passing it is worth noting that two suspension units and a few links of Snake Track, now on display at the Tank Museum, are all that remain of this, or indeed any of the Johnson tanks, although an American tank, built to the Johnson concept, is preserved. It is known that the French, too, showed some interest in the design.

In 1922 Johnson took two of the original Medium D machines out to India for tropical trials, as will be discussed later, and the trip resulted in what turned out to be his final tank designs for the War Office. The actual orders were placed in 1921 and reflect the view held by the General Staff that a European war was unlikely in the forseeable future while India and other warm locations posed a more immediate threat. Armoured cars had already proved their worth on the Frontier but they were largely road-bound so tracked vehicles would clearly have their uses. Johnson was instructed to prepare designs for a family of vehicles and strictly enjoined by the MGO to keep experimental features to a minimum; perhaps the Light Infantry Tank had been a bit of a confidence trick after all. Four machines were built: a tank, artillery transporter, supply carrier and amphibian of indeterminate purpose, all on basically similar chassis. The power train comprised a 45hp Tylor water-cooled engine, four-speed gearbox and Rackham steering clutches. Wire rope suspension was retained although the tracks were of a more conventional pattern. Only the tank concerns us here, and it was an ugly looking thing, in reality more of a tracked armoured car than a tank in the true sense. The driver sat alongside the engine in an armoured cab at the front, while the other two crew members occupied small machine-gun turrets; not unlike those fitted to the old wartime Austin armoured cars, except that these turrets were offset, rather than parallel, to give a better field of fire. Built at Woolwich the tank – known as the Tropical Tank 8-20-10 – never got to India; indeed it never went much further than Farnborough where it was briefly tested until recorded as

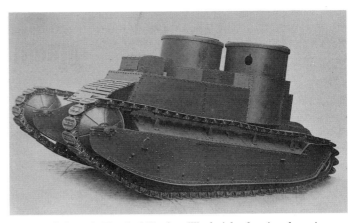

3 *Philip Johnson's Tropical Tank at Woolwich, showing the twin turret layout.*

'ceased running', after completing only 238 miles, in June 1922.

Johnson's department was officially closed down in March 1923. This may have been largely a Treasury inspired decision but there is no doubt that the MGO – Sir Noel Birch – whose department was responsible for tank design and construction, was being heavily pressed to produce some workable machines; for the Tank Corps was getting fed up with the succession of exotic prototypes that spent more time in workshops than they did running. Add to that the opinions expressed by Gen. Elles and others who could point out that none of the recommendations they made were ever taken into account, and closure seems to have been a foregone conclusion. Only Fuller remained constant. He described Johnson as:

the most able designer of tanks we ever had; certainly he aimed high, and perhaps too high for the imagination of soldiers, yet it is my firm conviction that had he been granted another two years wherein to perfect his machines, we should today [and Fuller was writing in 1935!] have a tank at least 300 percent superior to anything we have got.

Considering that Fuller had been pressing urgently for new tanks just after the Armistice it seems strange that he should later counsel waiting until 1925 for something suitable.

Yet Fuller was not just writing from hindsight, he was also endeavouring to show his part in those events in the best light and probably still smarting from the result. In December 1921 Fuller was acting as General Staff representative on the Tank Board. The Board's purpose was to serve as a link between the General Staff – which specified what kind of tanks the Army needed – and the MGO, whose duties have already been explained. Thus, in theory at least, no new tank could be specified, let alone built, without General Staff approval; yet in that December Fuller claims to have learnt, to his dismay, that a branch of the MGO's office had been working on the design of a light tank with Vickers Ltd. In Fuller's view they had no right whatever to do this, but it is a contentious point. It really depends on how specific a GS specification had to be; if it was drawn up in great detail then Fuller had a point, but if only an outline requirement is given – and this is normal practice – then the MGO had every right to place orders where ever he saw fit, as long as the resulting machine fulfilled the General Staff's expressed intentions. If the Department of Tank Design and Experiment was failing to deliver then there was clearly a crisis in the offing since the money Churchill had fought so hard to squeeze out of the Treasury would be forfeit when the financial year ended. A deal with Vickers must have been the obvious alternative.

Such evidence as there is for the case against Fuller may be found in a series of discussion documents that passed between the CIGS and MGO in 1921. The latter started the ball rolling by pointing out that in August of that year the tank policy formulated by the General Staff had stood for 18 months, and much had changed in that time. Basically, as we have seen, the General Staff called for two classes of tank: a fast type to work in the cavalry role and a slower one to work with the infantry, along with some sort of cross-country supply carrier. They do not appear to have gone into greater detail, merely stating that such tanks should meet reasonable standards of performance and reliability since, it was reasoned, they were bound to be better than any foreign types since there were few enough of them anyway. Working on the basis of prospective trouble spots – among which they included Russia, India, South Africa and the Balkans – the case was even better since none of these places had much in the way of tanks at all. If this was agreed, and suitable designs finalised, they proposed that production should start as soon as possible to a total of 84 machines, being sufficient to equip two battalions (36 tanks plus six reserves each), one for cavalry and one for infantry support. When operational they could be used for training and to intervene in any minor wars – the General Staff expression – that might occur. With this in mind it was recommended that such tanks should be especially suitable for operations in hot climates.

There was broad agreement from the MGO and Tank Corps although it was pointed out that professional tank men would prefer all tanks to carry a proper gun, rather than the old male and female variations. Beyond this the General Staff were not prepared to look. They felt that the future of tank warfare contained so many imponderables that experimental work was largely a waste of time and should be limited to design work and small scale experiments only. The point that the MGO was now making was that a third battalion was due for re-equipping in 1923 and unless experimental work was continued, at least on the present scale, there would be no progress at all. Looking at the other side of the coin the MGO also commented on anti-tank weapons and suggested that a 3pr, shot-firing gun would be the best. Taking this a stage further it was reasoned that the ideal anti-tank mounting would probably turn out to be another tank; a conclusion that still holds good today, although self-propelled guns were also mentioned. The tactical handling of this new equipment, in the view of the MGO, could best be evolved by forming an experimental brigade and, he added, by keeping a close watch on developments abroad, notably in France, the United States and, for some unexplained reason, Japan. All in all these documents, which even touch upon such matters as tank landing craft, present a far more positive image than Fuller, or many later commentators would allow. Clearly Britain was seen to have established a lead in tank design and meant to keep it.

If this makes Fuller's case look shaky it is undermined even further by a letter addressed to Gen. Elles from the Tank Board, dated October 1921. In it he is informed that the Light

4 This side view of the Vickers No 1 tank shows its rather archaic profile. Just to the right of the turret cupola may be seen the anti-aircraft ball-mount for a Hotchkiss gun.

Infantry Tank and a new tropical model were available for inspection at Charlton Park, while a new infantry tank was nearing completion at the Vickers works in Erith, Kent. When he had examined all three Elles was urged to discuss his preferences with the Board as soon as possible because £220,000 had been allocated by the Treasury for the construction of 42 tanks and if it was not spent they would lose it. It is rather hard to believe that Fuller, as a member of the Tank Board and a close colleague of Elles, should have known nothing at all of this, unless both sides, knowing his views, decided to keep it from him, but presumably it suited Fuller's purpose to give that impression.

Bearing in mind the things Elles had said already about the Johnson tanks it might be supposed that the task of choosing would not prove too difficult, but it rather depended on what the Vickers tank was like. In fact an order had been placed for three of them and the first one was completed early in November 1921. Vickers own documents actually speak of it being 'launched', but they also comment that it was too noisy and not dependable. Nevertheless it was sent to the Tank Testing Section at Farnborough in December. Thus when Gen. Elles first saw it, it was close to completion, but not yet running. Compared with the Johnson designs it was a heavy, bulky looking thing but at least it had a turret and looked as if it was meant to fight. It shared the floor of the Erith factory with some armoured cars that Vickers were building for India and, like them, featured a dome-shaped turret. This contained four mountings for Hotchkiss machine-guns, one of which pointed skywards, and was topped off with a drum-shaped cupola. The hull was high and flat-sided, reminiscent in profile of the wartime tanks but on a smaller scale and rounded at the nose. The suspension might not have been as revolutionary as Johnson's wire rope, but it had the merit of simplicity and it worked. It consisted of a series of independent units, called bogies, each of which ran on a cluster of four little rollers like a child's roller skate. These were attached to a bracket at the base of a short stem which was topped by a coil spring contained within an upright tube so that it was free to move up and down like a piston. Deflection was minimal, but sufficient for a 10-ton tank that was designed to travel at 15mph. The tracks were very basic, appearing from the photographs to have wooden sole plates riveted into a pressed steel tray connected to its neighbours by short pins. The flimsy construction and smooth outer face suggest that they would not grip very well or last long in service. Power was provided by a rear mounted six-cylinder Wolseley engine of modest power output, and so far, it may be said, everything about this design suggested sound, if rather pedestrian engineering; especially when compared with the Johnson approach. Yet in the matter of transmission the designers seem to have taken a more adventurous line, although not a very original one. They chose to adopt the Williams-Janney hydraulic equipment which had been tried, and to some extent found wanting, in the Mark VII tank of 1918. It was also being tested at this time in a Medium D machine although details of this experiment are not known. Variable Speed Gears Ltd of Crayford, who made the Williams-Janney equipment was, like Wolseley Motors at that time, part of the Vickers group, and this may have influenced their choice, but it was not a happy one. In theory the system was ideal for tanks because it gave an infinitely variable range of

speeds for each track, without the need to change gear, being controlled by a pair of handwheels in the driver's cab. In practice it tended to generate a lot of heat within the confines of a tank hull and probably explains why, in photographs of the tank moving, it is always seen with the engine and transmission covers wide open. The fighting compartment at the front was spacious, and sealed off from the engine and transmission by an internal bulkhead. Access for the crew was provided by large doors in the hull sides and the driver's seat was a sumptuous affair described as having barber's chair controls to adjust it for the correct position.

The records show that Vickers had quite a lot of trouble with the transmission, even before it left Erith, but when it arrived at Farnborough it was entered in a race where it was convincingly outstripped by the Light Infantry Tank. Fuller adds mischievously that it was even overtaken by a Medium C, but even allowing for his bias it is obvious that the new tank was far from ideal. It spent the best part of 1922 back at Erith, where it was fitted with a more powerful Wolseley engine and better tracks, but there is every reason to believe that it was still riddled with faults that would take a good deal of time to remedy. In fact it was not considered worthwhile to try. The tank was received back at Farnborough in October 1922 and is recorded as being stored derelict by the following March. But time was fast running out if that £220,000 was to be spent to some purpose and not forfeit to the Treasury. Clearly we have reached a critical point, not just in immediate history but in the entire story of British tank development. However before the next stage is examined, the tale of these first three Vickers tanks can be completed. Work on the second one began in July 1922 but it was not completed until twelve months later and by that time other events had rendered it obsolete. It looked, as one might expect, much like its older sister, but with one big difference: it mounted a 3pr gun in the turret. It may be that there was still an intention to build both male and female types, despite the wishes of the Tank Corps, but it could simply be that the tank was being used as a test mount for a new weapon. The whole subject of tank armament was under review at this time, and one of the contenders was a 3pr, semi-automatic quick-firing type, capable of delivering 20 rounds a minute. A naval 3pr was also available, with an even better performance but, like the old wartime 6pr, which still dominated Tank Corps thinking, this was a heavy weapon not best suited to the turret of a light tank. If it seems strange to find a 47mm weapon being selected in preference to a 57mm type it should be borne in mind that the former had a much higher muzzle velocity, and consequently a flatter trajectory, than the larger weapon, which made it much more suitable for use against other tanks. Memoranda on the subject flowed thick and fast for a while, culminating in a letter to Gen. Elles from Col. J T Dreyer on behalf of the Director of Artillery. Dated 15 March 1922, it informs the General that, 'each future tank is to carry, in addition to machine-guns, a quick firing (QF) gun'. No size is mentioned although there is a reference to a 3pr in an earlier paragraph and it may be assumed that this is the new, lightweight weapon.

Returning to this tank: it was powered by a six-cylinder Lanchester engine rated at 80hp, coupled to a three-speed epicyclic gearbox and worm differential drive to the cross shafts by the same manufacturer. Williams-Janney gear was not

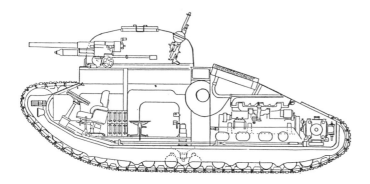

D1 Vickers No 2 tank showing the 3pr mounting and internal arrangements.

abandoned altogether but in this instance a single unit was mounted over the differential. Thus it was still used to control the steering by acting, like a brake, on either output shaft as required to slow down one track or the other. No reports survive on its performance, beyond the fact that it was disposed of in 1927, but there is no reason to suppose that it was any better than the first one. The third model was never even completed as a tank. Instead it was modified during construction to appear ultimately as a tracked carrier for an 18pr field gun, which was loaded aboard over a ramp at the back. In this guise it became a prototype for a family of gun tractors, built for the Royal Artillery, which for some unknown reason the Gunners called Dragons.

The absence of documents on any subject presents the would-be historian with a pretty quandry. It is difficult to tell if they ever existed in the first place or if they have been lost, suppressed, disposed of and if so, why. The situation applies when we come to examine one of the most important British tanks of this era so it must clearly be stated the writer has used conjecture, based on experience, for the following three paragraphs, and could easily be wrong.

This much at least is clear: by the middle of 1922 the War Office found itself in a very awkward situation. The decision to close down the Department of Tank Design was imminent, if it had not already been taken, since nothing it had produced so far was in any sense suitable for issue to the Tank Corps. Yet the attempt to find an alternative, conceived in some haste, had also failed, and it hardly needs repeating that unless something was done, and quickly, the Treasury would win this round hands down, and the development of a new tank be put back by at least a year, with all that implied. It is also reasonably obvious that if a new design was to be prepared in time it would have to be based, as far as possible, on existing technology; this was no time for brave experiments. The available evidence outlined below supports a credible hypothesis and, if it is correct, then it has to be said that where tank design is concerned there are sufficient examples from recent times to show that it can happen.

The basic suggestion is that the new tank was not so much designed as put together from various existing components, probably by the MGO's department in conjunction with Vickers, but that the basic responsibility lay with the former acting under urgent instructions – possibly word of mouth – from the War Office. So where did these components come from? The suspension was basically the same as Vickers had used on their first tank, but since the same system had also

been used, at around the same time, for an artillery Dragon built at the Royal Ordnance Factory (ROF), there is no telling who first conceived it. The engine, an Armstrong Siddeley V8, was specially designed for another Dragon*, built by that company early in 1923, while the transmission, both in terms of layout and operation, was virtually identical to the system employed on the Mark V tank of 1918, brought slightly up to date. Even the turret was little more than a larger version of the type fitted to contemporary Rolls-Royce armoured cars.

It has to be stressed again that, even after years of research, no documentation of any kind has ever been found, either in the Vickers' or War Office archives, to explain how the new tank came to be designed. No letters, memos or reports even hint that a new design is in the pipeline; the tank just appears. Thus one is inclined to the obvious conclusion that they never did exist. That instead the design was literally cobbled together from available components and then attributed to Vickers Ltd since, officially, there was now no tank design staff working for the Government. If this is true, and it is still a considerable 'if', then it was a remarkably fortunate piece of work for this new tank, and its derivatives, kept the RTC going for the best part of 20 years, and even influenced designs overseas.

Another telling factor in their history is that no prototypes, as such, were ever built. The first two were completed in mild steel, instead of armour plate but they were built as part of a production order which saw tanks, as they were completed, being issued direct to operational battalions even while the preliminary trials were being conducted. These tanks have always been known, inside the Army and out, as Vickers Mediums, but the maker's name never formed part of their official title and, indeed, by no means all of them were built by Vickers. Originally they were classified as Tanks, Light Mark I, later as Tanks, Medium Mark I when even lighter machines appeared. Twenty-seven were ordered: 14 came from the ROF at Woolwich, six from Vickers' River Don Works in Sheffield and the final seven from their Elswick plant at Newcastle-upon-Tyne. The official War Office handbook on these machines, in its introduction, says that the new tanks 'were the first . . . to embody the lessons of the Great War', but this is nonsense. Disregarding, for the moment, the mystery of their origins, it is perfectly clear that neither they, nor the experimental machines that preceded them, owed anything whatever to previous concepts of tank warfare as worked out on the Western Front, but everything to the future. The Mediums, as they soon became – and from now on we shall continue to call them – were the first British tanks to enter service with a revolving turret; the first with sprung suspension and the first to employ an air-cooled engine. In this final respect they were also effectively the last, but there were good reasons at the time. They were not only a generation ahead of the lumbering wartime tanks, they established a similar lead over any yet built by a foreign country and gave Britain an advantage it should never have lost. Unfortunately their durability, along with the prevailing climate of financial stringency, kept them and their successors in front line service with the Royal Tank Corps for 15 years, and the last examples

---

*See Ventham and Fletcher. *Moving the Guns: The Mechanisation of the Royal Artillery, 1854–1939*. HMSO, 1990.

were not retired from duty, as training machines, for another two or three years after that.

In the light of what has already been surmised about their origins, and in view of their importance throughout the era under review, we must now take a closer look at these tanks. The first impression is of bulk. The box-shaped hull rising above the tracks, surmounted by a large turret, actually gave a false impression; at 8ft 11ins the tank was only about one foot taller than a First World War Mark IV. At 17ft 6ins the Medium was much shorter than a Mark IV but about the same width, if the latter is measured without its sponsons. The derivation of the suspension has already been described. On the Mark I it consisted of five main bogies on each side with smaller front and rear bogies at the ends, along with return rollers to support the top run of the track. The adjusting, or idler wheel was at the front and the drive sprocket at the back while the tracks consisted of ribbed plates, riveted to inner links. The Armstrong Siddeley engine was located at the front, to the left. The large air-cooled V8 was, for the time, an inspired choice. Its most obvious advantage was the ability to operate in very hot climates without water, exactly what the General Staff had specified, but this could also prove advantageous in very cold regions where water was liable to freeze. Nevertheless there was a price to be paid. Air-cooled engines often have an unreasonable appetite for oil, and the Armstrong Siddeley was no exception, but since it was also confined within an armoured compartment it needed forced air cooling and this was achieved by fitting a large Keith Blackman intake fan which absorbed an inordinate amount of power in the process. Two Claudel Hobson carburettors, one feeding each bank of cylinders, drew fuel from a small header tank in the driver's cab, and this was replenished from two large petrol tanks at the rear. Although these appeared to be within the main hull they were, in fact, sealed off by a bulkhead and designed to drain straight to the ground if perforated. A multiple dry-plate clutch attached to the engine carried the drive, by means of a shaft, to a four-speed and reverse gearbox located, for want of anywhere better, slap in the middle of the fighting compartment floor. Another prop shaft carried the drive to a bevel box at the back, from which sprang a cross-mounted counter shaft. This shaft passed into two-speed epicyclic gearboxes on either side, and ended in pinions that meshed with gears attached to the track drive sprockets. These sprockets were mounted on a dead axle, parallel with and behind the countershaft. The epicyclics served three purposes: pulled halfway back they provided an extra low gear for cross-country driving and pulled all the way back they served as brakes to stop the tank, if only one lever was pulled it braked the relevant track to bring about a steering motion so, although the transmission layout was identical to the wartime Mark V, it did perform a greater range of functions.

Like those earlier tanks the hull of the medium was of riveted plate on frame construction and, apart from the turret, was formed entirely of flat plates of quarter inch homogeneous steel. The rear part, which formed the fighting compartment, was simply a very large box with an access door in the rear and various smaller openings along the sides. The driver occupied a narrow cab just ahead of this box on the right, with a sloping plate ahead of him and a semi-circular cover for his head. The plates on his left, covering the engine, were louvred for

5 A Medium Mark I splashing through the mud on Salisbury Plain. The method of opening the driver's head-cover shows up well and one of the hull machine-guns is also visible. However, this tank is running on the new No 3 link track while the white painted gun and letters CS on the turret reveal that it is masquerading as a Close Support tank during an exercise.

ventilation and hinged. They sloped down almost to trackguard level with an exhaust pipe emerging here to run along the left side track guard ending in a large silencer. The vertical plate that formed the front of the hull between the tracks was fitted with a large door giving access to the engine. The turret, as already explained, was like an enlarged version of the Rolls-Royce armoured car type. Basically a drum about six feet in diameter with a flat top panel and bevelled sides. In terms of armament the Medium Mark I was an odd mixture of old and new features. The main weapon was a 3pr, quick-firing gun of 47mm calibre. With a muzzle velocity of 1,750 feet per second, and the ability to penetrate one inch of armour plate at 500 yards range it was somewhat inferior to the old 6pr of wartime tanks, but a good deal lighter. Elevation and traverse were controlled by geared handwheels which offered a degree of accuracy that had never been possible during the war, especially on the move. Although the handbook speaks of high explosive shells these were never supplied for the tanks, which only carried solid, armour piercing shot. Rounds were stowed in clips around the fighting compartment and beneath the floor. The ability to fire high explosive shells, known as close support work, was not developed in British tanks until the Second World War. Before that time close support was regarded as the facility to fire smoke emitting rounds and, since the 3pr could not do this a 3.7in breech-loading mortar firing a 15lb smoke round was fitted to some tanks. Tanks so equipped were classified as Mark ICS and generally issued to headquarters companies in a battalion. J F C Fuller, in a lecture given in 1924, quotes a General Staff statement to the effect that: 'the Vickers tank . . . is looked upon as a universal machine – that is, one which can be used for all tactical purposes'. This is a rather sweeping claim. For one thing they were far too big, noisy and slow to be much use in the reconnaissance role and their main armament was intended only for dealing with other tanks. Granted machine-guns were provided for use against other targets but, without the ability to fire high explosive as well there are certain circumstances in which such a tank can be impotent. This was not adequately appreciated until 1940, and was not adequately remedied until 1943, yet even Fuller, an outspoken critic of the Vickers tank, never picked up on it at the time.

The secondary armament consisted of two water-cooled Vickers machine-guns fitted in ball mounts on each side of the hull. This really was a throwback to wartime ideas since the need for such heavy flanking fire hardly accorded with modern tactical thinking. Indeed when tanks were advancing in line abreast upon a position they were a distinct liability. The crew of a medium tank consisted of five men: commander, driver, gunner and two machine-gunners; but just in case they did not have enough to do the tank was provided with a tertiary armament of air-cooled Hotchkiss guns, for which three mountings were provided around the sides of the turret, and a fourth in the roof for shooting at aeroplanes. Yet, although a medium tank fairly bristled with weapons the layout was hardly ideal. For instance the only way a commander could bring a machine-gun to bear ahead of his tank was to swing the turret until one of the Hotchkiss guns pointed forwards, but then, of course, his main armament was waving about uselessly to one side or the other.

The air-cooled engine and suspension, suitably amplified by the large hull, made the medium an uncomfortably noisy tank. Inter-crew communication was very difficult and, until something better could be developed the driver was obliged to wear a set of leather reins, like some errant child, which the commander could jerk, left, right or both together if he wished the tank to steer or stop. Since this did not always produce the desired result a well aimed kick was generally preferred, except by the driver! Fully laden for action a Medium Mark I weighed 11 tons, and had a top speed of 15mph. However, it is said that crews soon learned to doctor the engine so that the best recorded speed was in the region of 25mph. Across country the tanks gave a rough ride at any speed, the short travel of the suspension springs, coupled with a lack of shock absorbers, caused the machine to pitch violently or bottom hard on the suspension if the shock was too great. In this connection it is interesting to note a particular stunt laid on by the Gunnery School at Lulworth for the benefit of visiting dignitaries, even as late as 1928. Two tanks, a Mark V★ of wartime vintage and a Vickers Medium, approached a quarry with vertical sides. The medium demonstrated the correct use of ground by selecting an easier route around the side, but the unsprung veteran stole the show by plunging down the face of the quarry, with no apparent ill effects. Besides serving as a means of tripping up the unwary, the gearbox case in the centre of the floor also provided a pedestal upon which the commander could stand to observe through the upper turret hatch. Apart from the driver, who at least had a seat, the rest of the crew worked in supreme discomfort. The commander clung to his turret and the gunner to his gun, both in permanent danger of injuring themselves on any number of projecting metal objects, while, most miserable of all, the two hull maching-gunners had to adopt a sort of half-crouching, half-kneeling position to serve their weapons, and all this on a hard steel floor. Even so, with practice, crews were able to achieve a very high standard of gunnery on the move, which was regarded as the ultimate purpose of the tank in professional circles.

Considering the revolutionary nature of this new tank it seems to have entered service with remarkably little publicity. Even the *Royal Tank Corps Journal* – which commenced publication in 1919 – did not hail its arrival with as much as a line of print, let alone a description. Indeed RTC officers serving in India or the Middle East can be found writing privately to their comrades in Britain to obtain technical details. The first Vickers-built model, the mild steel T15, went to the Tank Testing Section at Farnborough in October 1923 while the Gunnery School was reporting cryptically on the arrival of *David* – otherwise the close support tank T18 – a short while later. The first service unit to receive them was 2nd Battalion, which obtained eight for issue to B Company, and this is probably because they were stationed at Farnborough, close to the Tank Testing Section. One was certainly inspected there by King George V and Queen Mary in the summer of 1924. There is no surer way of discovering faults in a new tank than by placing it in the hands of serving soldiers who use it every day, and quite a few began to show up. Most could be attributed to inexperience while others were poor design features that would have to be remedied. The most dangerous concerned the driver. The armoured cover above his head was hinged, and could be folded back as a complete, D-shaped lid when he drove with his head in the open. At such times it was secured by a notoriously inefficient catch which often failed to work at vital moments. These would normally be when the tank bumped down after crossing an obstacle and it was at these times when a driver might let go of the steering levers and grasp the rim of the opening to steady himself. The effect on his fingers of a heavy metal hatch, suddenly flying forwards need hardly be explained. Although it was provided with an electric starter it was not really man enough for the job, especially in cold weather, so the crew had to resort to a hand-crank. However this could only be operated inside the tank and, being a two-man job, it proved very difficult in a confined space. Other troubles centred on the running gear. There was a marked tendency for bogie rollers to work loose on their spindles and drop off so that, in the early days, it was reckoned an easy matter to trace the course of a medium tank by the trail of discarded wheels. The tracks suffered too, especially at speed on hard ground. Rivet heads were gradually ground down until the sole plate fell off, leaving the tank to limp back to camp on the inner track links, if they held together.

Once production of the Mark I was complete work began on a new model, the Mark IA, of which 31 were built: 14 by the ROF and 17 by Vickers. The most obvious difference lay in the shape of the turret which was given an extra bevelled panel at the rear, into which the anti-aircraft Hotchkiss ball was mounted. The driver's head cover was modified so that only the flat top-plate folded back, while the curved front-plate was split at the middle and hinged to open outwards from the centre, thus saving countless fingers. Less obvious to the naked eye was a small hole in the front hull plate that enabled the crank handle to be inserted and worked from outside, and a pedal operated flap in the floor of the driver's compartment that improved ventilation. A more significant improvement from a combat point of view was the use of slightly thicker armour in some areas, which put the weight up by about a quarter of a ton. The handbook also mentions that more brow

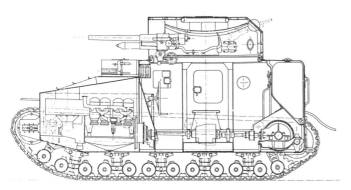

D2 A Medium Mark IA in cross section. Important features, from the front, are the cooling fan; V8 engine; gearbox amidships and final drive at the back.

and chin pads – of leather stuffed with horse hair – were provided, which is another way of saying that on a Mark I some heads were coming to grief against sharp metal projections on the inside. In all other respects the two tanks were exactly the same.

After the tanks had been in service for some time various improvements were introduced that could be applied retrospectively to either mark. These included a new type of track shoe in which each link was formed as a single casting that would not disintergrate on the road. An H-shaped indentation was cast into the sole plate to provide grip on soft ground but, since this soon packed with mud, making the surface smooth again, this was a mixed blessing. The bugbear of roller shedding was also alleviated by a design of bogie that had outside frames. However, it appears that there was no specific programme of improvement. Items were replaced as the need arose so that, in time, it was possible to see tanks with any combination of tracks and bogies, and even when a major change was introduced it did not affect all 58 machines. This took place in 1928, when all the Hotchkiss mountings in the turret were eliminated and a third Vickers gun mounted alongside the main armament, to the right. It was an eminently logical move, both for the reason outlined earlier and because it simplified ammunition stowage – the Hotchkiss taking a different type of ·303in round to the Vickers. Oddly this conversion was only carried out on 13 Mark IA tanks. The old machine-gun apertures were plated over and the Vickers gun mounted on a bracket which elevated with the main armament. Known as a co-axial mounting it remained a standard feature of tank design world-wide for the next 60 years, but in the medium tanks a selector lever was fitted that allowed one weapon or the other to be fired, but not both at the same time. This change upset the equilibrium of the turret, causing it to swing off target when the tank travelled on a slope, so a lead counterweight was added at the rear. This, in turn, increased the weight so the number of turret rollers was doubled to spread the load. On top of the turret the two-piece, flush fitting hatch was replaced by an independently rotating cupola which enabled the commander to survey the battlefield in relative safety. Known, on account of its shape, as the Bishop's Mitre this fitting had sliding vision ports in the front and rear face along with larger hinged flaps at the sides. To increase the commander's comfort a canvas seat was suspended from the cupola by leather slings, although he still had to keep his feet

firmly on the gearbox pedestal to avoid swinging about when the tank was driving cross-country. Tanks so modified were given the designation Mark IA★, in keeping with the old wartime practice of using a star to indicate a major alteration.

Meanwhile the battalions were on the move. Second, as we have seen, was stationed at Farnborough, where it had been since March 1921. Then, in April 1922, the 5th moved to Perham Down on Salisbury Plain while a year later, in March 1923, the 3rd went to Lydd in Kent. Until November 1923 5th Battalion had one company stationed in Germany, at Cologne, but this was then replaced by a company from the 3rd. However no mediums went out to Germany, the companies out there operated wartime Mark Vs. Fourth Battalion was at Worgret Camp, near Wareham, until June 1925 when the War Office lease on the land ran out. They then moved a few miles west to Bovington and settled down with the Depot Battalion until March 1926 when they were sent up to Catterick Camp, near Richmond in Yorkshire.

Between 1924 and 1927 contracts were issued for 100 more mediums, of which Vickers built 37 and the ROF 63. They entered service as the Medium Tank Mark II and, contrary to the popular tendency to lump all of the so-called Vickers Mediums together as a single type, there were marked differences in the new model; as the following description shows. The most significant change – one cannot fairly call it an improvement – concerned the transmission. Although the air-cooled Armstrong Siddeley engine had been widely criticised at first it soon proved itself to such effect that it was specified for the new model, as were the clutch and four-speed gearbox, the changes occured beyond this point. The drive shaft entered a two-speed epicyclic gearbox, operated by a pair of levers in the driver's cab which activated a clutch and brake respectively to provide an emergency low gear. From the epicyclic a flexible coupling carried the drive into a bevel box and thus to the cross-shaft upon which, either side of the bevel box was a Rackham clutch with its attendant brake drum. Invented by an ex-Tank Corps officer, J G Rackham (later of AEC Ltd), it was a complex system that had already been tried on some of the Johnson tanks and certain artillery tractors. Put simply it employed a series of cam-operated rollers which caused the drive to disengage and a brake to be applied, stopping the track on that side. Drive passed from here, via pinions on the countershaft to the drive sprockets in the usual way. Theoretically this system operated like an epicyclic without the complication of gears, but in practice it was a lot more difficult. To start with the driver had four levers to juggle with, rather than two, not including the primary gear stick, but the Rackhams also generated a fair amount of heat when applied for any length of time and the crew were often obliged to squirt them with Pyrene extinguishers to prevent a fire from breaking out. The suspension and tracks were the same as for the Mark I, and subsequently underwent the same changes, but on the Mark II and its derivatives hinged skirting plates were fitted which hung over the suspension and protected the bogie rollers to some extent. A detail modification also carried out on some Mark I series tanks was the change to rubber tyred return rollers, the original ones being of steel.

Visually the suspension skirting plates are a good guide to distinguishing a Mark II from a Mark I, but there is an even better way. From the driver's cab on the earlier models the

*6 Medium Mark II** tanks moving in column. Notice how the driver's head-cover opens in this case, and the tinplate hoods that cover the headlamps from aerial observation. The co-axial Vickers gun and wireless box behind the turret are major identifying features.*

view ahead was poor. The lid of his head cover being level with the upper hull plate of the tank he had to stretch his neck to see where he was going and often, on the public roads, an extra crewman had to cling to the outside of the tank alongside him, in order to assist. On the Mark II the driver's position was raised so that the head cover stood up, just ahead of the turret. It opened in the same way as a Mark IA, but provided the driver with a much better view of the road. This change involved the reshaping of the engine cover plates to meet the new angle of the front panel, and the whole effect was to make the tanks look larger, and bulkier than ever. The turret remained the same but the main armament was improved with the adoption of the 3pr Mark II, which had a slightly longer barrel, higher muzzle velocity and marginally better performance against armour. As in the Mark I series a few tanks were completed with the close support weapon. The weight of a Mark II in service trim was about 14 tons. This is accounted for by the changes already mentioned and a slight increase, by about one third of an inch (8mm), in hull armour thickness.

Improvements to the Mark II mirrored those already described for the Mark IA. That is the deletion of Hotchkiss mountings and the adoption of a co-axial Vickers gun plus the fitting of a Bishop's Mitre cupola, leading to the designation Mark II★. About a year later, in 1931, just over half of the Mark II★ tanks were further improved by the addition of a large steel box to the rear of the turret which housed a type MB wireless set. In this form the tanks were classified Mark II★★. The larger subject of wireless in tanks will be discussed later,

but in two cases it affected the actual design of Mark II tanks and is covered here. The first was a conversion, involving the Royal Ordnance-built Mark II, T198. The turret was given an entirely flat roof and extended rearwards to form a large square bustle for the wireless sets, of which it carried two. Since it did not feature the co-axial gun mount or cupola this modification probably took place before 1930 but this cannot be confirmed. What makes this conversion most curious is the fact that something eminently more suited to the role already existed. In September 1926 a contract had been issued to the ROF for a machine described as a Tank, Medium, for Radio and Wireless – a nice distinction. It was basically a Mark II hull which was enlarged to form a large box – so no turret was fitted – in which was housed communications equipment and staff suitable for a battalion, or even brigade commander. Known throughout the RTC as *Boxcar* it served with the Armoured Force and later Tank Brigade and was clearly very popular. In 1927 four more were ordered to the same description but surviving evidence suggests that these were never built. No doubt financial restrictions were the reason, but whether T198 was designed as a cheaper alternative, or for some other purpose, cannot be ascertained.

In 1928, five years after the first mediums appeared, and even while experimental work was progressing on their replacements, contracts were issued for ten more. The reason given was the raising of a battalion for service in the Middle East; for which, otherwise, there were no tanks to spare, and again various improvements were incorporated. Naturally these tanks were built with the co-axial Vickers gun and cupola as standard but, when the design was being discussed, there was a move by the RTC to have them built with the Mark I style transmission instead of the Rackham clutches. This was vetoed by the design staff and, indeed, a Mark IIA, as this type was known, is almost impossible to distinguish from a Mark II* unless one is able to check the War Department number or Road Fund licence registration plate. However, there is a way; it requires a close inspection of the return rollers. If the spindle passes through the longitudinal girder that supports them, then the tank is a Mark II; if the spindle rests in a bearing bolted to the top of this girder then the tank is a Mark IIA. It is no more and no less than that! The 1930 edition of the handbook also mentions slight modifications to the suspension bogies but, since these are hidden it is no help. As usual a few were issued as close support tanks and some, if not all ten, were later adapted to carry a wireless set in a turret bustle, in which form they became the Mark IIA*. Other details of these tanks will be found in the chapter dealing with developments in the Middle East.

During the period 1930 to 1932 the authorities paid a great deal of attention to the problem of noise in tanks, notably the mediums. They looked at two aspects in particular: the degree of external noise which, as they put it, renders these vehicles conspicuous in military operations, and the internal noise which caused severe physical and mental fatigue to the crew. The causes were readily identified but the remedies appear to have been matters of basic design that could not easily be resolved on existing models. The air-cooled engine, for instance, was a primary source. The type was always noisier than its water-cooled counterpart but the Armstrong Siddeley had a characteristic rattle caused by the auxiliary valve and timing gear while the fan-drive gave off an ear-piercing shriek during acceleration which was amplified by the drum-shaped casing. Progress was being made on silencer design but this would not cure the other problems. Then there was the matter of tracks and suspension. Metal to metal contact between the rollers and tracks was the primary cause. It was alleviated to some extent by fitting rubber tyres to the idler and return rollers but apparently the idea of fitting tyres to the road rollers was never considered, probably on the grounds of wear. A shorter pitch track was investigated, but nothing came of it, and it was discovered that the mudguards reflected the din, but these could not be discarded. When it came to the hull and turret there was general agreement that here was the main problem. On account of its shape the drum-like turret, on top of a hollow box hull was said to create a virtual sound box and, in the long term, it was felt that rectangular turrets would be an improvement. In the meantime investigations were pursued towards improving the existing type. One suggestion involved inserting a soft material between adjoining plates, but this was quashed because, it was explained, a strong, rigid hull depended on tight rivet joints which insulation would destroy. If the material was firm enough to prevent this then it would probably transmit noise just as well as the present joints. The idea of lining the interior of the fighting compartment with cork or asbestos was also discussed. The former was rejected since it had a tendency to absorb petrol and therefore increase the risk of fire, but even asbestos required a good adhesive to hold it in place and investigations by the National Physical Laboratory showed that, the better the adhesive, the more

inflammable it was. A cork-based material called langite was investigated by the Physics Branch of the Military College of Science, and this looked promising for a while until the adhesive problem was raised. Ultimately it was agreed that nothing really effective could be done for the present but, since the problem was also being studied by commercial vehicle producers it was decided to see what developed and no doubt hope that in the meantime crews would become immune.

Before turning to examine later types of medium tank it is now necessary to take a brief look at other modifications carried out on the original types. None of these were mainstream developments, but they form an interesting part of the story whether they served any useful purpose or not. The first dates from 1926 and involves the Mark I tank T15, the first Vickers-built machine. In that year it spent quite a long time back at the factory, and when it emerged it was clear that something drastic had happened. Hanging from each end were pairs of solid tyred spoked wheels, attached to moveable sub-frames. The scheme was as bizarre as it was spectacular and related directly to the problem of track wear already discussed. In May 1923, at the time of the General Strike, two medium tanks, along with some armoured cars, had been stationed at Chelsea Barracks in London. As it turned out the tanks had nothing to do so; by way of a diversion an articulated lorry, normally used for carrying cable drums, was borrowed and fitted with a deck of railway sleepers to form a rudimentary tank transporter. The scheme worked well enough, although it was clear that to be effective a more specialised design was required, and that would be expensive, especially if sufficient transporters were obtained to lift an entire battalion. The Vickers' plan was, in theory, simpler because it made each tank its own transporter, at a fraction of the cost. The idea was that a tank, faced with a long road journey, would hoist itself up onto its wheels in order to travel faster, with less noise and no track wear. When required to deploy for action it would settle back down upon its tracks and proceed across country like any other tank. It was not a new idea, the French had already tried it with limited success and in Britain it became known as the wheel-cum-track principle. However, it was one thing to build a specially designed vehicle, as the French had, and quite another to try and adapt an existing design to accept it; that was asking for trouble. A power take-off from the gearbox operated screw jacks to lower the wheels and so raise the tank until the tracks were free of the ground. Drive to the rear wheels was next selected and the tank moved off, steering on the front wheels from a tiller bar in the cab. Of course, as the tank went up, so did the centre of gravity, and the resulting instability was aggravated by the narrow spacing of each pair of wheels, which was essential if they were to fit between the tracks at each end. Although it is not specified the weight must have increased to at least 12 tons which, when considered along with solid tyres, indifferent brakes and general top heaviness adds up to a terrifying prospect for other road users. After a brief trial the whole idea was abandoned and the tank returned to its original form. While all this was going on the tank was also being used to test an alternative design of driver's visor, a curious form of shutter, not unlike the lid of a domestic bread bin, which may have been kinder on the fingers although it, too, was never seen on any other medium tanks. To complete the story of T15, in 1928 it was again returned to Vickers to be

7 *The experimental wheel-cum-track Mark I perched rather precariously on its wheels. This picture provides a very good view of the suspension system, which here is at full stretch.*

fitted with a new type of suspension employing bell cranks and coil springs. Known as the Japanese type, since it had been developed for a commercial medium tank sold to that country, it appears to have been very effective. It spent some time with a service battalion and was found to produce a very steady gun platform and, as late as 1937, it was loaned to the Vulcan Foundry to help in the development of a similar system for the famous Matilda infantry tank.

In 1926 a Medium Mark II was converted into an experimental bridgelaying, or to be more accurate, bridge-carrying tank. In deference to a War Office instruction that the conversion should not involve any major structural alterations, the designers simply fitted brackets to the tank and hung the parts of the bridge on them. On arrival at an obstacle the crew dismounted and struggled with the heavy girders; first lifting them off the tank, joining them together and then pushing the assembled bridge across the gap. They then climbed back aboard their tank and drove over the girders. It was hardly the true spirit of specialised armour since the most important factor, protection, was denied the crew at the most crucial stage of the operation. It would have been a lot more sensible, and not one whit more dangerous, to bring the bridge components up on a lorry and assemble them while the tank provided covering fire. On a similar theme, and at about the same time, Maj. Martel put up the suggestion that these tanks could be fitted with floats in order to cross water obstacles, but this was rejected. Returning to bridgelayers, a more practical design was produced at Christchurch using a Mark I Dragon as the

basis. This was altered to carry a 30ft girder bridge on its back and launch it by a pulley system from the vehicle. It proved far more effective since the crew could work under cover, but it was not proceeded with either.

Although the diesel, or compression ignition engine, was by no means a new concept in the 1920s, it had made very little impact on the commercial transport industry at that time, except in Germany. However, interest was growing slowly in Switzerland and Britain and the War Office was prepared to examine the idea. The consultant engineer Harry Ricardo, designer of the first purpose-built tank engine in 1917, was called in and started work on the project in 1927. In the meantime the War Office obtained a marine diesel from Beardmores of Glasgow and, for trial purposes, installed it in the hull of an old Mark V** tank held in RAOC stores. Known as their type 6/1 it was a four-cylinder unit rated at 400hp, but it required a separate petrol engine just to start it. Trials soon showed it to be unsatisfactory. Attention then turned again to Ricardo and, when it was ready, his engine was installed in the Mark I tank, T14. Known as the S90 it was a sleeve valve, four-cylinder water-cooled diesel rated at 90hp. The front end had to be heavily modified to accept it. The engine compart-ment roof plates were remodelled and an opening cut in the front to accept a Still type radiator and oil cooler, mounted behind an armoured panel. So much torque was developed by the engine that first gear had to be blanked off to prevent damage, but otherwise the tank performed very well. Following a demonstration at Bovington in February 1930,

8 *The Sixteen Tonner A6E1, here with its main turret reversed. It is shown posed aboard the original Scammell tank transporter.*

T14 travelled back to Farnborough under its own power. The worst problems were always associated with starting, especially in cold conditions, and the voltage was steadily increased to the starter motor from 12v through 18v to 24v in an attempt to cure it. By 1933 this tank had served its purpose; the engine was removed and sent to Bovington for instructional use, while the tank was restored to its original form and subsequently sent to South Africa – where it still survives. Meanwhile, in 1930, orders were placed with Ricardo for two improved S90 diesels for extended trials, with a view to using the type in the new medium tanks being built for service in Egypt: the Mark IIAs. Considering that the Armstrong Siddeley petrol engines were chosen with tropical use in mind, this seems to be an odd move although, of course, the air-cooled V8s were now getting on for eight years old. Development work certainly took a long time, and it was 1933 before they were ready for installation in two more modified Medium Mark Is at ROF Woolwich, but by then it was too late. A 1934 report states that, although tests were continuing the engines were not of a commercial design and, in any case were out of date, so the tanks were mainly being used for suspension trials. A number of commercial firms, notably AEC and Fodens, had been working on diesel engines since 1930, sometimes of new design or adaptions of existing petrol units; and as we shall see some of these were tested in a new generation of tanks.

If a theme can be discerned in medium tank development between the wars then it is basically one of automotive improvement. Suspension systems were developed while engines grew increasingly more powerful and transmission systems so complex that, according to legend, men went mad trying to design them. No such trend could be detected in terms of fighting power, except perhaps for a proliferation of machine-guns, and if armour protection increased it could be measured in millimetres. Riveted construction remained standard and the advantages of cast or welded armour were only studied by foreigners. It followed that while armour got no thicker there was no incentive to develop more powerful guns to defeat it. If one cared to look abroad there were signs that lightweight, inconspicuous anti-tank weapons were under development, but in Britain these were largely regarded as the poor man's weapon and ignored. There was field artillery of course, but the tank that could resist that must be so heavy that it would not move, so mobility was offered as the antidote

instead. While Britain remained the pace setter in tank design it could afford to take this view, but it is a dangerous attitude to adopt forever.

Mainstream tank development in Britain continued with a type that was known, somewhat optimistically, as the Sixteen Tonner. Three prototypes were ordered from Vickers to GS specification A6 and the first two, A6E1 and A6E2, appeared in 1928. A considerable degree of latitude was allowed in preparation of the design although Vickers' suggestion that, in addition to the main turret, three small machine-gun turrets should be carried, was turned down because the War Office required the tanks to have skirting plates over the suspension and both features could not be incorporated within the weight limit. This was set at 15.5 tons – to enable the tanks to cross a standard Army pontoon bridge – but it was never achieved. Design work began on the first two in 1926, with the stated object of producing a machine superior to the Marks I and II in terms of fire power, protection, ease of control and mobility generally; in other words to remedy as many as possible of the basic faults inherent in the hasty original design. The layout was influenced to some extent by the heavy tank Independent, which was undergoing initial tests at this time and, indeed, the effort put into Independent was blamed, to some extent, for the general delay in settling details of the Sixteen Tonners. The chosen power unit was a version of the Armstrong Siddeley V8 uprated to 180hp and the factory bench tests of this engine are interesting since it was the first time that such tests had been conducted with the power unit enclosed in a replica engine compartment. The matter of transmission was only settled after long and complicated discussions involving Maj. W G Wilson, one of the original inventors of the tank and a well known expert on gearboxes. Ultimately, although both tanks employed Wilson's epicyclic steering system they had different gearboxes for evaluation purposes. A6E1 employed a standard Armstrong Siddeley fourspeed crash box, a normal lorry type, while A6E2 had the Swiss Winterthur/SLM type; a constant mesh unit with oil-operated clutches, normally fitted into diesel locomotives and railcars. Both tanks used the Vickers box bogie suspension system as employed on the earlier models but since higher speeds were anticipated, the leading bogie had larger diameter rollers capable of taking the punishment.

The hull was of riveted construction of course, with armour to a maximum thickness of 14mm; which was definitely an improvement on the original mediums, but not much. To say that firepower was improved, however, was a dubious claim. It was increased, but that is not necessarily the same thing. From Independent the Army had apparently learned that weapons should be disposed among as many turrets as possible, but quite what the advantage was, was not explained. As originally conceived by Vickers, as already explained, the tank would have a main gun turret and three smaller ones: two at the front, mounting a machine-gun each, and a third behind the main turret, pointing rearwards and mounting a pair. This last was abandoned when the War Office demanded 6mm armour over the suspension so, as completed, the two tanks mounted a main turret containing a 3pr and co-axial machine-gun, and two small front turrets each with a pair of Vickers guns fitted. Thus the improved firepower amounted to five machine-guns instead of three, plus the fact that at certain angles all five could be brought to bear on a single target. Yet in terms of defeating armour the firepower was not improved at all. The tank carried a crew of six: driver, two machine-gunners, commander, gunner and loader. The last three all occupied the turret although the loader had another duty. There was a theory, current at the time, that a tank commander had quite enough to do, controlling his own tank, without having to keep an eye on the battlefield situation as well. Thus the turret was equipped with two, dome-shaped cupolas, one for the commander, the other for his observer – the loader in his alternative role – but it was an expensive luxury, especially where weight is a consideration. The basic layout of the new tank was a great advance. The fighting compartment at the front was quite separate, a bulkhead cutting it off from the engine and transmission compartment at the rear. It was not a new idea, some wartime tanks such as the Mark VIII and Medium C were the same, as was the ill-fated original Vickers tank and Independent, but it might be taken as yet another example of what a hodge-podge the Vickers Medium was. In order to reduce the risk of fire – at least inside the tank – the petrol was carried in tanks mounted on the track guards, behind armour of course. In due course these began to rust and had to be replaced with expensive stainless steel types. Otherwise the layout of the engine decks was reckoned to be a model of good design, taking into account accessibility and adequate ventilation for an air-cooled engine.

Tests at Farnborough showed the tanks capable of a top speed of 28mph on the roads and 19mph cross-country, but this performance, coupled with the weight, gave the suspension quite a battering. This was mainly evident at the front, so schemes were devised to cure it using different combinations of wheel size and springing arrangements; none of which really cured the problem. The SLM gearbox also gave trouble and there was a suggestion that it should be removed. Yet in 1933, when A6E2 was fitted experimentally with a 180hp Ricardo diesel engine, the SLM system was retained. Due to limited space a new three-speed version was chosen, which appears to have given a much better performance. A6E1 was still fit enough to work with the Tank Brigade in 1936 but A6E2 had ceased running by that time and nothing is heard of either of them after that date.

The third Sixteen Tonner, A6E3, was ordered from Vickers in August 1928, and delivered the following year. It was outwardly identical to the other two except that the machine-

gun turrets only mounted a single weapon each, mainly because two, mounted together in a small turret, were extremely difficult to handle. The Armstrong Siddeley engine was used again but the greatest advance in design was a new and highly sophisticated transmission, known as the Wilson epicyclic cross shaft system. This was a form of compound epicyclic that gave six speeds, but it was possible for the driver to achieve powered turns by selecting a different speed for each track. Furthermore, if he had to change gear during a turn it was possible to do so without upsetting the respective difference in ratios between the tracks. The gears were oil-operated, using the Williams-Janney equipment again, only this time with more success. Despite its complications the tank seemed to work very well indeed. At a demonstration in October 1930 it was said to have outdistanced a number of other machines, including the new light tanks, on a cross-country course and to have negotiated a particularly steep hill on a very low throttle setting. By 1933 Wilson pre-selector gearboxes were becoming common in commercial use, particularly for buses, and improvements in production coupled to general simplication in design, rendered the gearbox obsolete; although Wilson himself referred to it as a bureau of information, notably in connection with the steering of heavy tracked-vehicles, which in time would give Britain a decided lead on its competitors.

Suspension was, however, still the main bugbear of all these tanks, and in 1934 an effort was made to overcome it. Sir John Carden, of Vickers-Armstrong, working in conjunction with Mr Horstmann of Slow Motion Suspension Ltd, worked out the design of a bell crank system for medium tanks, based to some extent on the arrangements recently evolved for a series of light tanks. This was felt, in some quarters, to be something of a leap in the dark and the earlier Vickers Japanese suspension was pointed to as a more suitable type. In 1935 Horstmann had adapted both systems into something suitable and it was fitted to A6E3 for extended trials. Leading and trailing bogies were based on the older Vickers system but the main central portion used a combination of coil springs and bell cranks to produce a suspension with good absorbtion, capable of handling an 18-ton load at 30mph. Double-acting hydraulic shock absorbers were also fitted which could be activated, or switched off, by the driver as conditions demanded, and trials at Lulworth showed the new system to afford a very good gun platform. Various modifications were made over the next few years and by 1937 the system had been selected for a new heavy cruiser tank. However, it was first essential to establish its performance at much higher speeds than the old Armstrong Siddeley engine could manage, so A6E3 was experimentally fitted with the type of engine destined for the new tank. This was a big Thornycroft RY/12 marine unit rated at 500hp. The actual speed achieved is not recorded, but reports show that the suspension stood up very well to the challenge.

In 1930, even while trials were continuing on the prototype Sixteen Tonners, an order was placed for three more. These were to be production machines known as the Medium Mark III. Hopes must have been high at Vickers-Armstrong that this would be the start of a major re-equipment programme since, although experimental work was not exactly carried out at a loss, it was expensive and only justifiable in a commercial sense if it resulted in production orders that could be counted upon to return a reasonable profit. If so they were to be disappointed

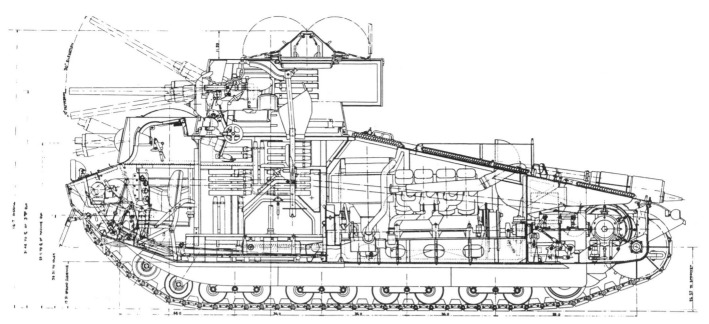

D3 Internal layout of the Medium Mark III.

9 A factory view looking down upon a Medium Mark III tank shows clearly the enlarged turret and Bishop's Mitre cupola.

for three were all the War Office ever ordered, and two of them came from the ROF. This duplication of the prototypes has caused confusion ever since, many writers, assuming that only three tanks were involved in all – their designations having been changed at some stage – have failed to notice the physical differences between them. It is no new mistake, even the Mechanisation Board make it in contemporary reports.

Mechanically, all three tanks resembled A6E1, with the Armstrong Siddeley four-speed sliding gearbox and V8 air-cooled engine; the main difference lay in the central turret. The shape was changed out of all recognition, the 3pr and co-axial Vickers gun shared a new type of mounting and the turret was extended rearwards to incorporate a large wireless bustle. It was quite flat on top, with a Bishop's Mitre cupola, for the role of observer was done away with. The commander now had a pedestal, which rotated with the turret, upon which he could stand to look through his cupola while the gun crew had seats, suspended from the turret ring, for their greater comfort. The two machine-gun turrets, each mounting a single weapon, were set slightly further forwards to alter the centre of gravity, while larger hatches were provided for the driver in the glacis plate to make it easier for him to escape in an emergency. A new type of plate, known as Cemented Tank Armour (CTA) had been developed; it will be described in more detail later, but its chief advantage was that it provided better resistance to small arms fire, for a given thickness, than conventional plate. Thus, 10mm CTA plate used on a Medium Mark III was considered to be equivalent to 14mm ordinary plate on the A6 series, with a considerable saving in weight.

Deliveries began in 1933, the Vickers-built tank arriving first; but gunnery trials at Lulworth revealed that it was no improvement on A6. On rough ground the suspension bottomed heavily, making accurate shooting difficult on the move. All three tanks served with Ist Tank Brigade in 1934, two of them being equipped with extra wireless sets and rail aerials around the turrets for the command role. The brigade commander, P C S Hobart, used T907 – the Vickers example – as his personal control vehicle throughout the exercises on Salisbury Plain. One of the ROF tanks was so badly damaged by fire that it was judged to be beyond economic repair and was handed over to the RAOC as a hulk for use in salvage, or what we would now call recovery trials. The subject of tank recovery* was creating a lot of interest at this time, and one suggestion was that surviving Mark V and Medium C tanks from the wartime era should be modified for this purpose. Following trials at Farnborough it was agreed that they were really too old and slow, even for this humble purpose, and the scheme was dropped. Another idea was to build a special, turretless version of the Medium Mark III for the task but expense killed that, and the concept of the armoured recovery vehicle went into abeyance until the next war created an urgent demand for it.

There is no doubt that the Sixteen Tonners were expensive, but as we shall shortly see, attempts to cut costs in tank design did not produce anything better. In fact there is now little doubt that, with these machines, British tank design reached a high point that it never really regained until 1945. They were virtually copied by the Germans with the *Neubaufahrzeug* of 1934 and certainly influenced Russian and Japanese thinking on tank design; however, their unit costs were more than the British Treasury was prepared to contemplate in peacetime so they fell by the wayside. Yet despite their imperfections it is interesting to find, in the late thirties, many RTC officers often referring to them when good tank design was being discussed. On these grounds alone it is a great pity that none of them survived.

In 1928 the War Office announced that it would be building two prototype medium tanks to concepts worked out by the Superintendent of Design. The stated aim was to produce a tank that was faster, longer and lower than the current Medium Mark II, and the project was given the GS specification A7. Design and construction spanned four years, so it has generally been assumed that the A7 programme was initiated as a cheaper successor to the A6, in fact it seems to have been a case of

parallel development. Both machines were sometimes referred to as the 10.5-ton Medium Tanks, at least until they were completed. It was then discovered that they weighed closer to 14 tons. Improved protection was also claimed, although this was restricted to an ability to resist armour piercing small arms fire down to point-blank range with a maximum plate thickness of 14mm, which was hardly a dramatic improvement. The tanks were built by the ROF and, as might be expected, were outwardly identical. Hulls were long and low and rather on the narrow side, with the usual arrangement of a forward fighting compartment separated by a bulkhead from a rear engine and transmission section. Possibly on account of earlier comments about noise the interiors were lined with langite, a patent cork-based insulating material, and the turrets were rectangular in plan, rather than round. A similar type, on a smaller scale, would soon appear on some light tanks. The side panels sloped gently inwards from the base to a flat top plate surmounted by an independently rotating cupola for the commander. The turret held a crew of three, all of whom were seated and able to turn with it. The rear end was extended to provide space for a wireless set while a simplified co-axial mounting for a 3pr and Vickers machine-gun was located at the front. The driver sat at the front, naturally, but for some strange reason he was seated on the left, and to make matters worse his view to the right was totally obscured by a large steel box housing the hull machine-gun. It appears to be an ill-considered layout for a tank which would do most of its running in a country where people drive on the left-hand side of the road and there seems to be no good reason for choosing it; at least none is given. There were no side access hatches in the hull, although this had been one of the better features of the A6 type. Instead what appears to be an incredibly stupid scheme was devised which placed the only hatch in the front. It was a large, double-flap arrangement located directly below the machine-gun mounting. From a purely structural point of view it has to be questioned since the nose plate of a tank has a lot of bearing on the rigidity of the hull, so a large opening here, covered by two moving panels held in place by hinges and a catch, is not going to help. The vulnerability factor also has to

10 The Royal Ordnance designed Medium Tank A7E1 photographed at MWEE. The crazy front hull hatch can be seen, but notice also the turret shape and large cupola.

*See Baxter. *Breakdown: A History of Recovery Vehicles in the British Army.* HMSO, 1989.

be taken into account and, at such a vital area, a single solid plate must be regarded as essential. However, these considerations appear to be of relative unimportance when the crew is considered. In an emergency, especially when under fire, one or two might escape through the turret hatch or cupola, but the natural route would be out through the hull where the crew are entitled to expect some cover, but not in the A7: here the men must crawl through a hatch to find themselves in front of their tank, precisely where the enemy is most likely to be.

So much for the similarities without. Internally the main thing the two tanks had in common was a 120hp version of the air-cooled Armstrong Siddeley V8. In respect of transmission and suspension they were quite different. This was a deliberate move to test different systems, but the main automotive components were interchangeable so that a tank which was off the road for any reason could be used as a source of spare parts if the other one broke down too. A7E1 used a regular Armstrong Siddeley four-speed sliding gearbox with emergency low, coupled to a Wilson epicyclic steering system; making it in that respect the more conventional of the two. However, it had the more elaborate suspension. This consisted of trailing bogie rollers, linked in sets of four by short leaf springs mounted overhead. There were thus, in effect, two of these compensated units on each side. The stated object was to provide a steady gun platform. A contemporary report explained that if the tank attempted to cross an obstacle five inches high the compensating effect meant that each end of the hull only rose about half an inch. Since the springs themselves only gave a very modest deflection it is clear that it was the relative movement within a compensated bogie that really did the work. In passing it is worth noting that before this system was adopted, advice was sought from Slow Motion Suspension Ltd of Bath. Horstmann himself then proposed a series of independent rollers on bell cranks, connected to a series of rods that passed across the floor of the tank and were anchored in brackets on the far side. Springing was achieved by a twisting motion in the rod imparted by the action of the bell crank, but it was rejected at the design stage as unsuitable. This might well have been one of the most short-sighted decisions on tank design ever made by British tank designers, since this torsion bar system, as it is called, was used extensively by the Germans throughout the war, and subsequently by the Americans and others with considerable success.

The suspension system chosen for A7E2 had originally been planned for both tanks. It employed the same number of rollers but in this case each set, on its trailing arm, worked against a vertical volute spring, independently of the others. Again the deflection was not great and, in order to avoid metal to metal contact on rough ground rubber bump pads, of the type used on railway rolling stock, were inserted above the springs to increase absorption. This tank was to be fitted with a six-speed Wilson epicyclic gearbox in conjunction with Rackham steering clutches on the cross shafts, but when the two tanks were delivered, late in 1931, the Wilson unit was not ready, so to begin with this tank also had the simpler sliding type. The Wilson system was delivered and fitted ready for trials in March 1932.

Both tanks suffered badly from engine trouble and at one stage, when they were out of action the better parts of the two

engines were combined and fitted into A7E2, only to fail again shortly afterwards. Trials were conducted at Farnborough, Bovington and Lulworth, where both tanks were better as gun platforms than the Vickers types had been, although the compensated type was judged the best from this point of view. All the same there was concern about its vulnerability since, it was argued, only one part needed to sustain damage to seriously affect the rest. The A7E2 might give a rougher ride across country at speed, but at least it could spare a bogie or two without being totally disabled. By 1934 the springs on A7E1 were in such a bad state that all further work on it was abandoned. At the same time A7E2 was fitted with longer volute springs that increased absorption by one inch, and in 1935 Luvax shock absorbers were added and the rubber bump stops removed. Following what was otherwise a successful trial run along a course studded with railway sleepers, at speeds of up to 24mph, it was discovered that the suspension had received such a hammering that all units were badly damaged. Repairs were undertaken, but to no real purpose since both machines were written off shortly afterwards.

11 A7E3 viewed from the same angle as A7E1 to show the new style front hatch. The pattern of access panels covering the suspension also show up well but the most important feature, from a design point of view, is the roller type mantlet for the 3pr and Vickers gun. Compare this with the earlier model.

In 1934 the Superintendent of Design was instructed to begin work on an improved model of the A7 series, which left the ROF, as A7E3, late in 1936. Although similar in outline to its sisters the new tank was wider, and easily identified by the mass of small, triangular inspection panels bolted to the skirting plates. It was felt by this time that the Armstrong Siddeley engines were getting a bit long in the tooth, and in any case thoughts were turning towards the use of a diesel engine once again, since these were now common in commercial haulage. The only drawback was that no manufacturer had felt the need to develop such an engine big or powerful enough for a tank, and there was no incentive from the War Office. Certainly no funds could be found to encourage a designer such as Ricardo to develop one, so a pair of production units were chosen instead. This could well be regarded as another short-sighted step. The Armstrong Siddeley V8, for all its vices, had served the RTC well for more than ten years, yet in all that time nothing had been designed to replace it, with the result that another serious limitation was imposed upon British tank designers, which lasted well into the war years. Thus the engines chosen for A7E3 were AEC types, developed for London buses. Each was a 7·7 litre, six-cylinder, water-cooled diesel which, fortuitously in this case, came in two types. One fitted the conventional, front-engined AEC Regent while the other was developed for an experimental mid-engined bus, the Q type. This engine was designed to rotate in the opposite direction to the Regent so the two could be installed, side by side in the tank, without having to alter the action of either gearbox. These gearboxes were Wilson four-speed pre-selectors, again of the type used in the buses, although there was one minor change. As used by London Transport the engine and gearbox worked through a Daimler fluid flywheel, but this was found not to operate so well in an enclosed space so the tank had flywheels with flexible spring couplings instead. In their report for 1934 the Mechanisation Board explained that this was the first occasion when a standard commercial engine and transmission had been employed in a medium tank, but it would not have been stretching a point to remind them that the Medium A Whippet, of 1917, had also used two bus engines and gearboxes in its day. At that time the whole twin-engine concept had come in for a lot of criticism from Tank Corps Central Workshops who complained that it took twice as long to service a tank with two engines. Such ignorance of historical precedent, and consequent rediscovery of problems that ought to be well known, is a recurring human failing that affects engineers, especially tank engineers, as it does everyone else. Also, it should be noted, the demise of the Armstrong Siddeley, long overdue as it was, brought to an end the reign of the air-cooled engine in British tanks, so A7E3 also mounted two large radiators, one for cooling water and the other for oil, which were located beneath louvred panels on the sloping rear engine deck.

A7E3 employed a suspension system similar to A7E2; that is, independent pairs of trailing rollers, although in this case stronger hellical springs were used. Reports claim that this gave the tank an exceptionally smooth ride, although it was stated elsewhere that it reached full absorption at 15mph, whereas the tank was quite capable of doing 25mph. However, since the new tank weighed a little over 18 tons this was hardly surprising. The curious left-hand-drive arrangement remained, but there was talk, at the design stage, of fitting a small machine-gun turret at the front. By the time the design was finalised this had been changed to a form of gimbal mounting in a fixed structure, which swept a 100° arc at the front. The main entry or escape point remained in the same place, beneath this machine-gun. The square double hatch was replaced by a single round manhole, hinged at the bottom; which if nothing else was not likely to weaken the front hull plate quite so much; even so it must have been an awkward thing to close from inside. Turret and cupola followed the design adopted for the other A7s although provision was made to fit the new No 9 wireless set, and there was a change in the design of the gun mounting. The 3pr and co-axial Vickers guns protruded through a roller shaped mantlet which was claimed to be virtually splash proof, and it certainly seems to have been a more effective way of sealing the aperture.

The engines and suspension required some modifications following initial trials but, generally speaking, the tank performed very well and the vacuum assisted gear change was particularly popular. Steering was based on the system employed in A6E3 but, inevitably, armour thickness remained at 14mm. The transmission allowed one engine to start its neighbour and, should one of them fail, it was possible to drive the tank at reduced speed on the other. Gunnery trials were successful too, and it was beginning to look as if, after all this time, the British Army might be getting a really acceptable medium tank, in fact it was already too late. Ideas on tank warfare underwent some fundamental changes in the late thirties, largely as a result of the recent Tank Brigade exercises, so other uses had to be found for A7E3. Early in 1939 the turret was ballasted to equal the weight of that proposed for the new A12 Infantry Tank, which resulted in further gunnery trials at Lulworth. When these ended the turret was removed and the hull sent over to Christchurch where it was employed by the Experimental Bridging Establishment, mainly as a test vehicle on new types of military bridges.

With the demise of A7E3 the whole medium tank concept passed into history, and it only remains to examine one other that might have been. This was the Medium A8, which only existed as a wooden mock-up. When this was inspected, late in 1933, it resulted in an order for one tank, A8E1, being placed with Vickers-Armstrong. The tank would have carried an A7 type turret on a hull that also featured left-hand-drive and an auxiliary machine-gun turret at the front. The matter of suspension was never settled although the box bogie system applied to A6E3 was seen as a starting point, but it might well have been revised in view of the success of the Horstmann system applied to A6E3 in 1935. Power would be provided by two Rolls-Royce Phantom petrol engines mounted side by side but arranged to drive forwards into a train of spur gears. The centre gear then drove the input shaft of the gearbox, which was located between the engines. Wilson designed a new six-speed gearbox for this tank which acted through bevel gears on the cross shaft. Steering epicyclics would then be used, of a novel pattern which gave different steering characteristics in high or low range. The fate of this interesting design can be summed up in two entries from the Mechanisation Board reports:

1935: There is nothing further to report. Delivery of the vehicle is anticipated in 1936.
1936: There is nothing further to report.

2 Testing the Tanks

In July 1921 the Director of Artillery wrote to the GOC Aldershot Command, informing him that a Tank Testing Section (TTS) was to be established at Pinehurst Barracks, Farnborough, for the purpose of testing and reporting on new tanks, mostly those being produced by the Department of Tank Design and Experiment at Charlton Park. It was formed, on a temporary basis, in September with an establishment of four officers and 28 men, drawn from 2nd Battalion Tank Corps, which was already at Farnborough, and the Tank Corps Centre at Bovington. The first commanding officer was Capt. H M Hordern MC, RA and one of his engineer officers was Lt. D M F Sheryer from Bovington. One Crossley tender was provided for transport, but covered accommodation for the tanks, and even tools to work on them seems to have been a bit of a problem. At first the TTS was treated as a section of 2nd Battalion, even after it had been officially approved in April 1922. Tanks began arriving almost at once, the first six coming from Charlton Park; by December the original Vickers tank was there and, before long, all sorts of other vehicles: wheeled and tracked tractors and some of the early half-tracks were being examined. By March 1923 the TTS had achieved a degree of autonomy and even acquired some old hangars from the RAMC, but their tools were limited to the equipment carried in an old wartime workshop lorry. However, when Johnson's department closed down Lt. Oddy was sent up to Charlton Park to help himself to what they had left behind; other items were obtained from the Tank Corps workshops at Bovington.

All the same it was not the business of the TTS to modify tanks; all they needed tools for was to keep them running during trials, or pull them to bits to see how they had survived. Any major modifications had to be carried out by the manufacturers, so some vehicles seem to have spent most of their time travelling back and forth between Farnborough and their makers until everything was put right. At the same time both Hordern and Sheryer in particular spent a lot of their time at the tank factories – mostly Vickers – undertaking acceptance trials of new vehicles before they were released to the service. This work soon reached such proportions that the TTS undertook to train inspectors for the Chief Inspector of Armaments and, in order to fulfil this task they are reported as having misappropriated a hangar belonging to the RAF. As the work of evaluation developed a series of test tracks gradually appeared on War Department land in the Farnborough area, including the test slope on Miles Hill and a two mile sand circuit in Long Valley. For road running there were two favoured routes: one of about 40 miles took vehicles out through Rushmoor and back via Hindhead and Haselmere to the Godalming by-pass; then over the Hog's Back and home. The longer 100 mile course ran via Basingstoke to Stockbridge; then west almost to Salisbury and back, either by the same route or through Andover and Micheldever. Later a course was used in South Wales, south of Abergavenny on the B4246, over what was known as the Mountain Course. More locally there was the ominously named Pirbright Triangle, chosen because it included a considerable range of road surfaces which tested track wear. Since there was also an obvious need to work in conjunction with Bovington and the Gunnery School at Lulworth, road-runs were also organised in that direction. Lulworth had been selected as the site for the Gunnery School largely because it was close to Bovington and also because it provided a suitable location, in the crowded south of England, where tanks could fire live ammunition without endangering the population. The camp, to the east of the famous Cove, provided firing platforms on a hillside facing, across a valley, the sheer side of Bindon Hill which absorbed most of the ammunition; any overs landing harmlessly in the sea. The TTS was also responsible for supplying staff and sample vehicles for events like the Wool Trials of 1925 and 1927 which were held on the Bovington ranges; however, these events were only loosely connected with tank development. At this time all AFV development was carried out under the overall control of the Mechanical Warfare Board but, from January 1925 onwards, more specifically by the Tank and Tracked Transport Technical Committee under Col. S C Peck, with Hordern as a member. Its purpose was to advise on design in conjunction with Farnborough so the TTS was obliged to change its title, now being known as the Tank and Tracked Transport Experimental Establishment!

In January 1928 this euphonius, if cumbersome, title was changed again, to the Mechanical Warfare Experimental Establishment, MWEE (but known to all and sundry as 'MeeWee'). This was not just another piece of clerical juggling, it foreshadowed a widening of responsibility, for in April of that year the Royal Army Service Corps Training College lost its responsibility for testing wheeled military vehicles and this task became another MWEE function. From now on they would test everything, from tanks to motorcycles, and even trailers, before declaring them fit for service, or otherwise. In that same April Lt-Col. A W Richardson replaced Hordern as CO, the latter having already had his term of office extended once. These changes were further enhanced by an increase in establishment – to 171 by September – and the division of the organisation into five separate departments: including technical and driving wings, administration and workshops. By 1933 a branch was operating in Egypt, under the cover title of Z Section, 3rd Battalion RTC; since the War Office refused to sanction an official branch there. Then in 1934 the title changed again, to the Mechanisation Experimental Establishment (MEE) for sadly the delightful twenties word *mechanicalisation* had fallen into disuse by this time. Such was the authority and experience of the establishment by this time that it was carrying out tests on behalf of the RAF (on transport vehicles), the Oversea Development Corporation and even, in an advisory capacity, the Royal National Lifeboat Institution (on beach-launching tractors). A strong and useful bond also developed between MEE and the National Physical Laboratory at Teddington, and of course with industry. This 1934 change of title was the last before the war.

permanently attached to the hull and it was the tracks that moved up and down, on external guide rails, as required. Powered by the inevitable Armstrong Siddeley V8 engine at the front, this strange machine was built of 8mm plate and mounted two turrets. The large central one was designed to mount a pair of machine-guns (although no weapons were ever fitted), with a smaller turret intended to take a single machine-gun stepped down behind it. The driver sat alongside the engine at the front and there were two huge access doors at the

12 The wheel-cum-track machine D3E1 posing on its tracks. The front wheels are obvious, but the rear ones are hidden in recesses just ahead of the drive sprockets. Notice too the positions of the two turrets.

Most of the records kept by MWEE survive, and form the basis for much of what information we have on military vehicles of this period, especially some of the rare experimental ones. Most of the armoured vehicles, whether tested by MWEE or not, fall quite comfortably into categories covered by other chapters, but one or two are so difficult to classify that it might be more logical to study them here; the more so since they spent almost their entire lives in the hands of MWEE or one of its out-stations. Two in particular were the wheel-cum-track armoured cars D3E1 and D3E2 which, despite their titles, can hardly be regarded as armoured cars, although they were certainly not tanks. Both arrived at Farnborough from the Vickers' works at Sheffield in May 1928. The purpose of the wheel-cum-track principle has already been explained in connection with the modified medium tank but that machine was a diabolical improvisation, being basically a tracked vehicle capable of being converted to run on wheels when required. With D3E1 Vickers (or Vickers-Armstrong as it was by then) turned this idea on its head. On this machine the wheels were

back. The tracks were of a narrow cast pattern, deeply indented at the centre, while the track frames contained eight paired rollers on each side; although signs of springing cannot be detected. The wheels were 36in diameter discs running on narrow, semi-solid tyres. The front axle, which was undriven and carried the steering wheels, was attached to the front of the hull, suspended from a transverse spring, while the rear, or driving wheels, were located in recessed arches near the back, almost hidden by the track frames.

Mechanically the thing was a nightmare. The engine drove through a conventional four-speed gearbox – although it was difficult to find such a box with suitable ratios for both wheeled and tracked running – and then into a transfer box that gave three options. One was to the differential axle that operated the rear wheels; another went to a bevel box and from there, via braked epicyclics, to the rear mounted track sprockets which were the only part of this system that did not move; while the third activated the track elevating mechanism. On wheels the vehicle seems to have been quite stable, if very low to the

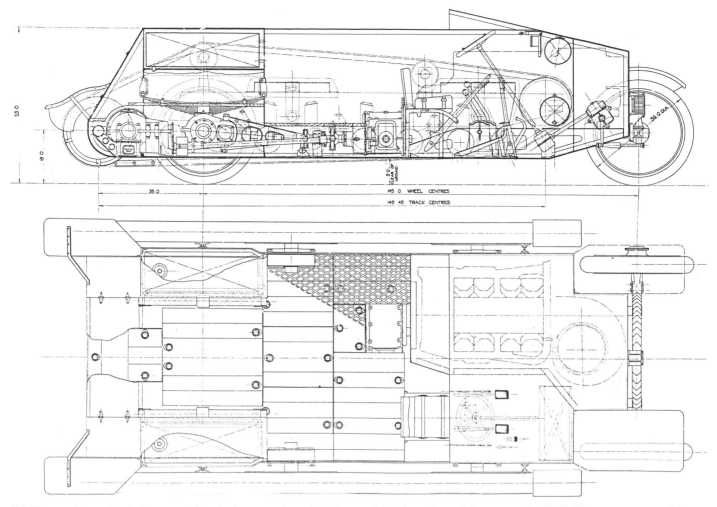

D4 The complex mechanical layout of the wheel-cum-track machines is revealed in these views of the unturreted D3E2. The exact purpose of this vehicle has never been established.

ground and probably hard riding, but on tracks it was even rougher. The short track base and lack of suspension would inevitably create a pitching motion that must have been very uncomfortable across country. Speeds of 13mph on tracks, and 30mph on wheels were recorded by MWEE but, to judge from the number of times the vehicles went back to Sheffield, the design problems were never solved. Since it had turrets the basic role of D3E1 is quite clear, but D3E2 remains a puzzle. Behind the engine and driver's position it was totally devoid of superstructure, nothing more than open well, closed off by a pair of hinged flaps at the back. No clue survives as to what it may have been intended for; an infantry carrier perhaps, or a supply vehicle? Even an artillery tractor or transporter would not be impossible, but it was still classified as an armoured car. Both vehicles were out of commission by 1933 without ever being issued to service units, although a delegation from the Portuguese Army came to inspect them at one point. D3E2 went for scrap while D3E1 was passed to the RTC Schools at Bovington as an instructional example (of how not to do it?). By some quirk of fate it survived, minus its engine, and now rests in a corner of the Tank Museum, oddest of oddities from this most fascinating period of tank development.

Among the major duties of MWEE was the task of providing vehicles for official demonstrations. They came in many forms:

as instructional affairs for serving personnel or politicians; as glorified sales and educational shows like one staged for a visiting party from the Spanish Army in 1928; or extra special events laid on for such dignitaries as Earl Haig (20 June 1927) and the King and Queen (17 May 1928). Historically the most important of all took place at Camberley on 13 November 1926, ostensibly for the visiting Dominion Premiers who were attending the Imperial Conference in London. With them came the Secretary of State for War, Sir Lamming Worthington-Evans, Mr Amery, the Colonial Secretary and Winston Churchill, now Chancellor of the Exchequer. As they travelled down from London on that Saturday any of them might have been forgiven for thinking that someone wanted them dead with pneumonia, for it was a fearful day for standing around in the open, with a cold wind and driving rain, but the Army put on a superb show, as it invariably does. It covered the entire gamut of military mechanisation including transport, artillery and tanks, with horse-drawn guns and wartime machines preceding the latest types to drive the point of progress home. A section of medium tanks charged the crowd in line abreast, with guns firing and aircraft swooping beneath the low cloud cover, until at the last minute the tanks swung through 90° into line ahead, just in front of the stands. A battery of the new Birch guns, which were self-propelled 18prs based on medium

13 The Dominion Premiers' demonstration at Camberley in November 1926. The Independent thunders by escorted by a bevy of tankettes.

tank components showed off their capabilities, as did a selection of prototype tankettes which attracted a good deal of attention from the press.

However, the star of the show was so top secret that, after it had completed its run, it was parked in a special enclosure which the press were told to keep away from. The Tannoy announcer 'knew they would understand,' which says something about Fleet Street in 1926. This tank was the famous Independent, which was so new that it had only arrived at Farnborough from Vickers' Sheffield works about four weeks earlier. Press photographers were allowed to take pictures of it as it drove by, and to emphasise the effect of size it was accompanied by a swarm of tankettes. The official handbook for the show described it as the 'latest type of Heavy Tank', giving its weight as 29 tons and its speed as 18mph, reduced to 10mph cross-country. In fact in terms of weight and overall length – around 25ft – the Independent was little different from the 1918 Mark V which had led the parade, but it gave the impression of being a lot bigger. This was partly on account of the length relative to height, but it was enhanced by the cluster of five turrets at the front, giving it the appearance of a battleship on land which, in a sense, it was supposed to be.

The Independent is another of those machines which deserves to be studied in isolation. It hardly compares with anything else being built at the time and there is something in the story of its conception which, in a sense, sets a pattern for British tank development that is often repeated. In December 1922 the General Staff drew up outline specifications for a heavy tank which was to have low ground pressure, low speed, low silhouette but a good trench crossing ability of nine feet. They required an armament of one 3pr and two machine-guns, but specified that the highest point should be the driver's head cover – which effectively ruled out a turret – with the top run of the tracks forming a straight line. They asked for a rear engine configuration and suggested a horizontally opposed type, while the gun was to be mounted in the nose, and the machine-guns in sponsons at each side. This is clearly a reversion to wartime ideology – remember this is only 1922 – and may well be due to a slight attack of nerves in Whitehall lest the newly adopted creed of mobility might be false after all. Exactly the same thing occured in 1940, and led to the appearance of another huge white elephant called TOG. The specifications in both cases were more suited to the Ypres Salient in 1917 than to any of Fuller's ideas on armoured warfare.

Sir George Buckham of Vickers selected a team to work on a set of drawings but, at the same time, had an alternative scheme laid out which differed dramatically from the original concept. Vickers' motives for this are not easy to discern; it can hardly be confidence borne of experience since they had only designed two tanks up to this point. Yet clearly they considered their own scheme to be better than the official one. Further to this it is worth noting that the Vickers' design featured a dome-shaped turret – like their first two tanks – which might be taken as more evidence for the Mark I Medium design having been foisted upon them. Both sets of drawings were completed in March 1923, and submitted to the War Office. Presumably a good deal of thought was given to the choice, for it was a further 30 months before a contract was placed. By this time the attack of nerves must have passed off, because it was the Vickers' design that was chosen, in preference to the General Staff one. The point to note here is that the turretless tank had been specified for a particular reason, if perhaps a mistaken one, while no prior requirement can be ascertained for the design as chosen. Had Vickers talked the General Staff round, or had they changed their own minds? Vickers were experienced in engineering but they were not supposed to be arbiters of tactical doctrine; the General Staff were supposed to know what they wanted in that respect, yet, when faced with the choice, they picked, or were sold, something different. According to the Mechanical Warfare Board, writing in 1924,

14 Independent nearing completion at the Vickers factory. Four of the five turrets are visible, as is the driver's hood at the front.

the tank was designed for independent action or with cavalry, it was to carry 13mm armour, have a top speed of 20mph and be transportable by rail, and have five turrets. This smacks a bit of retrospective specification writing, but it is the nearest any official body ever got to producing one.

The contract was placed with Vickers on 15 September 1926; ten years to the day since the Battle of Flers had ushered in the age of tank warfare, but the decision to build had clearly been made before then because the order for the engine was placed in August. Following an evaluation of alternatives the choice settled upon an air-cooled Armstrong Siddeley V12 rated at 350hp, which was developed from the 90hp V8 used in the medium tanks. A small 10hp starting engine was installed to the right of the main one but this was later replaced by an Aeromarine inertia starting device, manufactured in the United States and fitted to Greyhound buses. The main engine was coupled to a Swiss-designed gearbox by Winterthur, an oil-operated synchromesh type which required no clutch, while the final drive consisted of compound epicyclics inside the track sprockets. Dominating the front end was the main turret, mounting a 3pr gun, and clustered around it like satellites were the four machine-gun turrets, the rear left-side one of which had a modified mounting that allowed it to elevate sufficiently to shoot at aircraft. The driver sat in a central cab at the nose, sandwiched between the two forward turrets. Armour around the crew compartment was 28mm with between 8mm and 13mm elsewhere. The main turret featured a commander's cupola at the left and an extractor fan beneath a cowl on the right. It has been claimed that the cupola was fitted with a device (and it would have been a very complicated one) which showed the commander at a glance which way each of the five turrets was pointing at any time, but there is no sign of it in the tank, or in the original records. Each of the small turrets does have a graduated scale with a moving pointer on its internal rim, and there is an interesting arrangement in the main turret – shaft-driven off the turret ring – which would show the commander which direction his turret was pointing in relation to the tank, but that is all. Officers of the RTC were invited to inspect the design and offer comments of their own, but the only one known to be adopted concerned the side access hatches to the fighting compartment. These, it was said, should be so shaped that a standard military stretcher would pass through with a casualty laid upon it; not the kind of thing that bespeaks great confidence in the design as a whole.

When it was completed the tank put up some impressive runs of up to 20mph; 13mph faster than the original GS specification and 5mph faster than the official top speed of a medium. But it could only manage an eight foot trench. Fuel consumption was just over one mile per gallon but, with a total petrol capacity of 180 gallons this was not a serious limitation, it was the oil consumption that upset all the calculations. The big air-cooled engine was getting through oil at the rate of 4.5 gallons per hour, yet the heat levels were still so great that manifolds burnt out at an alarming rate. The suspension was of the Vickers box bogie type, suitably strengthened to bear a weight of 29 tons, which was about five tons over the original specification. Vickers had hoped to keep the weight down by building the tank without armoured skirting plates over the suspension, but the authorities would not hear of this. Normally tanks with a long stretch of track in contact with the

ground are difficult to steer, and this only improves as the tanks get wider. Independent was less than nine feet wide, to enable it to travel by rail, yet the steering is never criticised. This may have been due to the hydraulically operated, servo-assisted epicyclics which were activated by a steering wheel for large radius turns, while lever operated clutch and brake steering was used for tighter turns.

The tank was tested at Farnborough for about 12 months. While it was there the General Staff initiated a scheme which later became an important feature of British tank nomenclature. This involved awarding each specification issued by the General Staff with a number; prefixed A for tanks, B for tractors and carriers, D for armoured cars, etc. Independent was retrospectively awarded GS specification A1, and being the first of its type was known as A1E1. Had further prototypes been built they would be A1E2 and so on. It also carried the War Department number T1020 but for some reason – possibly because it never ran on public roads – it was not issued with a road licence number. MWEE gave it their number 66 when it arrived there for tests. When they began many minor faults showed up, apart from the ability to drink oil, mostly involving the rubber tyred road rollers and brakes. The former were replaced by steel rimmed rollers, like the medium tanks, while the Ferodo company, after extensive experimental work, perfected a brake lining material which, in the end, might be seen as one of the few really positive results of the Independent's story. In the short term, though, these new brake linings were nearly, and quite literally, the undoing of the tank because the testing establishment noted that the stress set up by the brakes was actually starting to peel the track frames away from the hull at the rear.

Somewhat belatedly, some might think, W G Wilson was called in to advise on the transmission. After an inspection of the original design he declared it, 'quite impossible, and doomed to failure'. On his expert advice Independent was rebuilt in 1928, at least at the rear end. Simple two-speed epicyclics were mounted inboard of the drive sprockets, to which they were connected by Oldham flexible couplings. This allowed a new type of spoked, self-cleaning sprocket to be used, with an external bearing for extra support and a sort of dead axle, containing a duct for lubricating oil placed across the rear of the hull to increase rigidity. In this rebuilt form the tank weighed 31.5 tons. Trials continued, with a break in 1930 while the engine was again investigated for its oil consuming tendencies, until 1935. It is said to have covered only 630 miles on its tracks – although these were replaced at one stage – for a total cost in excess of £150,000 (the engine alone cost over £27,000). In all that time the War Office was never able to state categorically whether they regarded it as the prototype of a new kind of heavy tank, or an experimental test machine. By 1935, however, it was clearly out of date, and probably worn out so it passed into retirement at Bovington Camp, where it still survives as an impressive museum piece. Before closing this examination it is worth pointing out that, for all its size and cost, the Independent actually disposed less firepower than a Medium Mark I as originally built. Both shared the 3pr as a primary weapon, but the Mark I carried five machine-guns to Independent's four; and even a rebuilt medium carried three Vickers guns, with a crew of five to the heavy tank's eight.

3 Armoured Cars

If it was action one was looking for between the wars, then service with the armoured cars was well worth considering. There can scarcely have been a month in that 20 year period when they were not on active duty in some part of the world, ostensibly keeping the peace in some remote corner. Indeed their war never really ended, for trouble in India and the Middle East continued without a break, taking no account of any Armistice that the major belligerent powers might have signed.

The real problem was equipment, for the wartime survivors would not last forever, and there were no new designs in the pipeline. Twin-turreted Austins of 17th Battalion were still operating in Ireland while others, along with an ageing fleet of Rolls-Royce, not yet affiliated to the Tank Corps, tried to keep the lid on recurring trouble spots in Iraq, Persia, Palestine and Egypt, under Machine Gun Corps control. New cars were urgently needed, but very few firms in Britain showed any enthusiasm for building them. Relief that the war was over,

and a burgeoning demand from a car-starved civil market, combined to make such warlike trade unattractive. The immediate solution was an unsatisfactory one borne of urgency and desperation. The War Office released 100 Peerless lorry chassis which they persuaded the Austin Motor Company to equip with armoured bodies. The Peerless was a 5-ton, chain-driven truck manufactured in the United States. It was, to coin an appropriate phrase, built like a tank, and had proved its worth as a transport vehicle with the British Army on nearly every front during the war; it required a special effort to damage a Peerless, although it was slow, heavy and mercilessly uncomfortable, with its solid rubber tyres. Austins adapted the twin-turreted armoured body, which they had built for their own cars to fit the Peerless, but even then a generous amount of spare chassis was left sticking out at the back, which the armour did not cover. The result was a stately, rather imposing vehicle weighing some six tons, which swayed alarmingly on the road and promptly got bogged down if it left it. Each turret

15 A Peerless armoured car in Yeomanry service, which seems to have got itself into some sort of trouble. Whatever these big cars may have lacked in style they made up for in robustness, being virtually indestructible.

mounted one Hotchkiss machine-gun and the four-man crew included one who could take up a rearwards facing driving positions if it was required to extricate the car from a situation where it might have difficulty turning around. The cars entered service in 1920, and some went immediately to Dublin, where 17th Battalion exchanged them for their old Austins which finally went for scrap. Fortunately their work here was mainly confined to the roads, patrolling or escorting convoys, for their limitations would soon have become obvious if they ever tried to move across country. When the Irish Free State was created in 1922 a few Peerless were among a batch of armoured cars handed over to the new Irish Army, while the rest returned to Britain. These again saw service during the 1926 General Strike, when two improvised companies from Bovington went up to London. Working out of Chelsea Barracks they spent most of their time escorting essential food convoys from the London Docks, which again suited their penchant for running on good roads. When the Territorial Army was reformed after the war it included eight Yeomanry Armoured Car Companies which came under RTC control when the Machine Gun Corps was disbanded, and they usually took a complement of Peerless cars with them on annual summer camp. This must have imposed a far greater strain on the young men concerned than ever it did on those tough old vehicles, so that some were still on the strength when the Second World War broke out. These were either issued to unlucky Home Guard units or packed off to RAF airfields to frighten away German paratroops.

17 A Peerless lorry armoured for service in Ireland. The fact that it began life as an anti-aircraft gun truck is obvious from the screw-down jacks beneath the chassis.

18 An improvised armoured Model T Ford photographed at Bovington Camp.

16 A protected Crossley tender in Northern Ireland.

Strikes in Britain and the Troubles in Ireland after the Great War led to the adoption of various emergency measures. The troops in Ireland took to armouring their lorries with odd panels of plate and wire mesh covers to keep bricks and bottles out. Even smaller vehicles such as Crossley tenders were treated in this way, and in order to regularise the situation the War Office designed a standard body to fit the Crossley chassis, and a larger one for the Peerless. In the latter case the chassis were those of erstwhile anti-aircraft vehicles, fitted with high-sided steel bodies and wire mesh roofs for both cab and body. However, by the time these were ready the situation had changed, so the brunt of this work was borne by another type. This was the Lancia IZ, a popular 30cwt used extensively by British forces as a light truck during the war. It featured a

covered cab in its armoured form, with a rear-entrance box body, sometimes covered by a gabled wire roof. Normally, however, these vehicles were open at the top and fitted with a pedestal mounted Lewis gun. Once again a number were handed over to the new administration on the formation of the Free State while the remainder passed to the RAF for service in the Middle East. The workshops at Bovington produced what were known as fighting lorries on the Ford Model T one-ton chassis. Two are known from photographs, both differing in detail, but they consist of simple covered bodies with a small machine-gun turret, probably taken from a redundant Austin armoured car, at the back.

Without doubt the best armoured car of the First World War had been the Rolls-Royce, which first appeared in 1914. Making due allowance for casualties, the majority were still in service at the Armistice, some in Ireland but mainly in the Middle East, and there is evidence to suggest that a few more, with enlarged turrets, were supplied in 1919, probably on existing service chassis. Thus, when it came to choosing a new model for the post-war Army there seemed no good reason for changing the design, except in detail, and it is said that the War Office consulted the original Admiralty drawings when they ordered the new model from Woolwich. The 1920 pattern Rolls-Royce Mark I armoured car was, if anything, an even better looking vehicle than its wartime predecessor. Still using the superb 40/50hp chassis, it now came with more shapely front mudguards and Michelin disc wheels, doubled at the rear. The outline was unmistakably the same, although the turret was taller and the radiator doors provided with ventilation panels. Armour was 9mm thick, and the total weight of the car in fighting trim was 4·5 tons. Officially a crew of four was carried, at a top speed of 45mph, but the latter was often exceeded and the crew invariably limited to three. A Vickers ·303in water-cooled maching-gun, fitted in a fork-mounting occupied the turret which was manually traversed. Overall length of a car was 16ft 7ins, and wooden ditch crossing beams, just over eight feet long were carried. Originally these were mounted vertically at the sides, but later on they were arranged to lay horizontally, in brackets beneath the running boards. The first cars went immediately to Ireland, serving with 5th Armoured Car Company which had been formed from surviving elements of the old 17th Battalion.

19 The prototype 1924 Pattern Rolls-Royce armoured car, the only one to feature this extended body.

In 1923 a new body design was drawn up, and a prototype built, probably on one of the spare Rolls-Royce instructional chassis which had been ordered with the original cars. Still unmistakably a Rolls-Royce it was fitted with a longer armoured body that reached all the way to the back of the chassis instead of the open platform with wooden side-lockers used hitherto. A new style of turret was fitted, without the prominent side bevels and surmounted by an oval cupola set crosswise. This turret had a slight slope towards the front and a short, steeper one at the back and the machine-gun was now fitted into a splash proof ball mounting. Because the bonnet was longer the spare wheels were located further forwards, instead of on the body sides, and this left room for a door to be fitted on the near side of the body. In March 1925 the car left Bovington with a crew that included Col. George Lindsay, then Chief Instructor at the RTC Central Schools, and toured South Wales. It was photographed in Pontypridd where one of Lindsay's brothers was serving as Chief Constable of Glamorgan and the paper reported that it was there for trials in the Rhondda Valley and surrounding mountains which were supposed to represent conditions on the North West Frontier of India. Not that the armoured car was designed with India in

mind, it was in fact to be the prototype of a new model for the home army, the Rolls-Royce 1924 Pattern, Mark I.

Twenty four were ordered, but when they appeared it could be seen that some changes had taken place in the design, presumably to reduce the weight. The covered rear body section was replaced once again by the open style in wood, with side lockers and a hinged tail gate. Armour was reduced to 6mm thickness all over and a side door was added on the driver's side, but the new style turret was retained. As far as Rolls-Royce was concerned the 40/50hp Silver Ghost chassis went out of production in 1924, to be replaced by the Phantom, and it is interesting to note that late production 40/50hp chassis for private use featured servo-assisted brakes by this time. Yet to judge from the vehicle handbook there was no difference between the two armoured car models in this respect, so the chassis may have been built to a common standard especially to War Office requirements. In that same year some of the 1920 cars were modified to bring them closer to 1924 Pattern standard. This included a ball mounting for the Vickers gun (which was also applied to some otherwise unmodified 1920 cars), an oval cupola fitted longitudinally on the flat top of the original turret, and splash rails arranged chevron fashion along the top of the bonnet to deflect shot away from the driver's visor. In this form cars were given the designation, 1920 Pattern, Mark IA.

In 1929 both Bentley and Rolls-Royce were experimenting with evaporatively-cooled engines, and the Army took an interest. In such a system the water remains at a permanent state of boiling which, it was claimed, reduced the loss of coolant through leakage, although the engine naturally ran much hotter. Its greatest advantage was said to be at higher altitudes, which was not necessarily of much use to the British Army, but since it might have other possibilities a trial was organised. One of the 1920 Pattern cars was fitted with an evaporatively-cooled Rolls-Royce Phantom I engine supplied by the company, and tests were conducted by MWEE. They

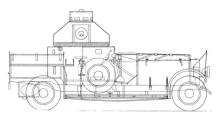

D5 Rolls-Royce 1920 Pattern Mark IA armoured car showing the turret cupola.

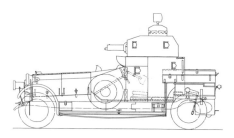

D6 The 1924 Pattern Rolls-Royce.

resulted in damage to the rear axle, caused it was reckoned, by the extra power delivered with this engine, so the entire experiment ceased there and then. Like their wartime predecessors the new Rolls-Royces gave remarkable service all over the world for many years, although the majority were in the Middle East. With the advent of the light tank in the early thirties RTC interest in armoured cars declined rapidly, but some passed to the newly mechanised cavalry while others were passed on to the Yeomanry to supplement the supply of Peerless armoured cars. A Yeomanry regiment would have three Rolls-Royces on its permanent establishment, along with a six-wheeled lorry, sometimes partly armoured as well, to represent a fourth. For annual summer camp the regiment would be supplied from a pool of 13 reserve vehicles held at Woolwich, which would pass from one regiment to another, like some travelling circus, until the training season was over. Thus each regiment was allowed to function with a full complement of armoured cars for one week every year, although it was hard on the cars, travelling so far afield and in the hands of a succession of inexperienced drivers. Yet the Rolls-Royces survived, the majority for long enough to see active service in the early years of the Second World War, a remarkable tribute to their quality.

By 1927 thoughts on armoured car development in Britain had started to crystallize. It was generally agreed that the four-wheeled type with just one driven axle (4×2) had reached the limit of its potential, and that in any case the time had come to waive the ruling that armoured cars should not exceed five tons overall weight. There was also a school of thought which believed that two turrets were better than one, even on armoured cars. Whether this new thinking resulted from developments elsewhere, or was simply a coincidence, cannot be ascertained, but it came at an opportune moment, for at this very time a revolution was taking place in the design of military transport within the British Army. A new type of six-wheeled lorry chassis had been designed which came close to combining the cross-country performance of the half-track with the roadability of the lightweight four-wheelers then in service. This new type, built to War Office Subsidy Scheme requirements by a variety of manufacturers, featured a patent rear bogie assembly designed by the RASC. It was a 6×4; this is a six-wheeled chassis driven on all four rear wheels, and it was this assembly that gave the vehicles such a good cross-country performance. It first appeared on vehicles in the 30cwt class and was later expanded to include 3-tonners, but its potential was not lost upon armoured car designers; yet, as is often the case, they immediately went right over the top. A research committee working for the Chief of the Imperial General Staff (CIGS) laid down a series of specifications, some of which seemed to be totally incompatible, that included the need to carry two maching-guns and a crew of at least four, along with a good cross-country performance, but capable of at least 45mph on the roads for short periods. Yet all this had to be achieved using a commercially available chassis within a weight limit as close to five tons as possible. The sensible solution might have been to commission one firm, already engaged in six-wheel lorry production, to create such a vehicle and indeed at this very time Maj. Martel – inventor of the Tankette who we shall encounter in a later chapter – had made such a suggestion. He proposed using the Morris subsidy

chassis, narrowed and shortened to suit, as the basis for an armoured scouting machine, but this was rejected. Instead the War Office approached a manufacturer who did not build commercial vehicles at all, but quality motor cars. The object being to come up with a really high-grade chassis, ideal for armoured cars but too good for a lorry. Yet the firm concerned, the Lanchester Motor Co of Brimingham – part of the BSA group – had no more experience of the work than supplying chassis during the war which were equipped as armoured cars by the Admiralty. What they knew about six-wheelers, or modern armoured cars for that matter, is difficult to imagine.

20 The first six-wheeled Lanchester armoured car photographed before the hull machine-gun position was fitted alongside the driver.

An order for two prototypes was placed in July 1927, and they were ready for testing by March 1928, under the GS specification numbers D1E1 and D1E2. In the meantime it had been decided that in future armoured cars should mount an anti-tank weapon, which immediately casts doubt upon their intended role. This is not the place to go too deeply into the whys and wherefores of armoured warfare but it is, perhaps, worth saying something about the work of armoured cars. Although it is an over simplification this might be twofold: for internal security situations, where the use of tanks might appear heavy handed; or as long-range reconnaissance in conventional warfare. In the former case protection is of far greater value than firepower, for obvious reasons, and since such operations are normally conducted in urban areas, manoeuvrability is a prime consideration. For reconnaissance a car needs to be swift, silent and inconspicuous. Again manoeuvrability helps, as does a good cross-country performance, but firepower should be kept to a minimum for the simple reason that the object of reconnaissance is to gather and report information. It is not normally the task of such units to fight for it, especially against enemy tanks, but if you give a crew the means of doing this the chances are they will, to the detriment of their proper duty. The fact that in this case the weapon selected was the ·5in version of the water-cooled Vickers machine-gun, which could only penetrate the thinnest armour at relatively short ranges does not alter the principle.

The two cars were of slightly different design. Both used the same long six-wheeled chassis, powered by a 38hp, six-cylinder

21 A Mark I Lanchester, fitted here with overall tracks at the back, seen during trials at Bovington.

engine, driving through the usual Lanchester three-speed epicyclic gearbox with a further two-speed auxiliary box and worm drive rear axles. D1E1 carried ·303 and ·5 Vickers guns co-axially mounted in a large turret with another ·303 weapon in the hull, to the left of the driver. D1E2 had a similar turret, mounting a single ·303, with another in the hull. Both cars had turret cupolas and open rear platforms like the Rolls-Royce. Trials at MWEE and Lulworth, followed by short spells with the newly mechanised 11th Hussars revealed a host of faults, mostly of a detail nature. The cars were cramped inside despite their size, and the long bonnet made forward visibility for the drivers very difficult while driving in reverse was almost impossible. Indeed D1E1 had been fitted with a rear steering wheel in an attempt to solve this. The chassis proved insufficiently rigid for cross-country work and hardly strong enough to cope with the modest weight of 5·5 tons. A third chassis, intended for instructional purposes, was given the designation D1E3 but it was never handled by MWEE. Undeterred by this catalogue of faults the War Office, over the next four years, ordered 35 of these cars, with certain changes in design to overcome most of the problems encountered with the prototypes. These included deeper, stiffer chassis members in which a cylindrical fuel tank was fitted crosswise at the rear to increase rigidity, and better brakes. The driver's position was moved forward and, to improve his view of the road the engine was canted slightly from the vertical so that the shape of the bonnet could be improved. For all that these cars were nearly 20ft long and over 9ft high, and with 9mm armour, weighed 7·5 tons fully equipped with a four man crew. They

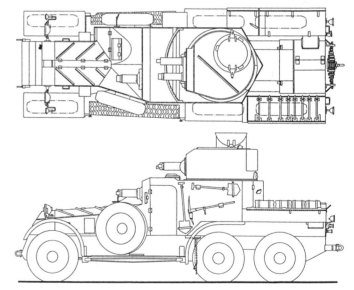

D7 The Mark II version of the Lanchester, showing the Bishop's Mitre cupola.

were divided into four groups. The Mark I had three machine-guns, like D1E1, but a roomier turret with a drum-shaped cupola. The Mark IA was identical except that the hull machine-gun position was eliminated to create space for a wireless set, which was of far more value to a reconnaissance machine, if that was to be their role. The Mark II, which was ordered in 1929, was basically similar but only had single wheels on each rear axle; it is most readily identified by the Bishop's Mitre type cupola. The Mark IIA was the wireless-equipped version of this type.

Once the initial problems had been overcome the Lanchesters certainly proved to be reliable cars, powerful and smooth to drive despite an alarming tendency to heel over on corners due to the excessive top weight. The rear driving arrangement was dropped in 1934, it took far too long to set up in an emergency and it proved very difficult for the two drivers to co-ordinate their operations. In any case when driving backwards the rear door had to be left open, increasing vulnerability. Other changes included improvements to the gear selecting mechanism and a device which caused the wireless aerial to drop down whenever the turret swung in its direction, to prevent it from being shot away by an over zealous gunner. There was talk, at one stage, of sending some Lanchesters out to India but the furthest they got at this time was the Middle East. However Still tube radiators were fitted to many of the cars for use in hot climates, instead of the usual honeycomb type. Lanchesters served with both of the original mechanised cavalry regiments, 11th Hussars and 12th Lancers. The latter operated them in Egypt and Britain, and even took 12 out to the Saarland in 1935 as part of an international force charged with supervising a plebiscite which decided that the region should be incorporated into Germany, having been administered since 1919 by the League of Nations. As late as 1942 a few cars were serving with the Argyll and Sutherland Highlanders in Malaya, where they were finally captured by the Japanese. The Lanchester Company is believed to have offered designs for both six and eight-wheel-drive armoured cars in the thirties, both of which were rejected.

Although Martel's suggestion for the Morris chassis was ignored the type was considered for a lighter type of armoured car in 1929. Of all the six-wheelers operated by the British Army the 30cwt Morris-Commercial D type was far and away the most popular, so in the interests of standardisation, if nothing else, it made sense to utilise it for an armoured car. However, calculations revealed that the Morris chassis was simply too light for this kind of work, so attention switched to a rival design, the Crossley BGV2. Two prototypes were built to GS specification D2E1 and D2E2, with hulls by the ROF, to drawings prepared by the Superintendent of Design. It was agreed that the second car would not be built until the first one had been tested, so that any major faults would not be duplicated. D2E1 was completed in 1929, and the initial trial reports explain that it was a three-man car, armed only with ·303 machine-guns. In other words, despite their original requirements for a crew of four and an anti-tank gun the War Office had already modified the specifications in two fundamental respects in the interests of economy. The car had a high, square bonnet that restricted the driver's view of the road, and a tall narrow hull surmounted by a small, round turret carrying one Vickers machine-gun; the other weapon was mounted to the left of the driver. A pair of ditch-crossing boards was carried on the right side of the hull and special wrap-around-tracks, that fitted over the rear tyres were also supplied. When fitted, these converted the car into a sort of rudimentary half-track for crossing very soft ground. The usual catalogue of minor faults, inseperable from prototypes, soon manifested themselves and, in February 1931 the Crossley

went out to Egypt, complete with a new gearbox and stronger axles. Reports from Britain suggest that it handled well, especially on narrow winding roads, compared with the bigger Lanchesters; but under test by Z Section MWEE in Egypt it was found to be much worse over desert terrain. This may well suggest a case of horses for courses. The Lanchester was clearly

22 Another entrant in the same trials was the original Crossley six-wheeler D2E1. It also has tracks fitted but they have not prevented it from getting well and truly bogged down. The rectangular object fitted to the side is an unditching plank which it is soon going to need.

22A The same Crossley when later fitted with an anti-aircraft mounting in place of the turret.

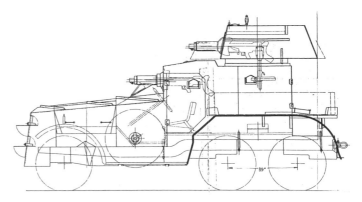

D8 Armour profile of the Crossley armoured car.

far too big for European conditions, particularly in built up areas, but size could be an advantage in desert conditions, as the Germans discovered with their big eight-wheelers during the war.

The second Crossley, D2E2, appeared in 1931. The basic layout was similar, but the bonnet had been improved to give the driver a better view so that the car looked more like a small Lanchester in this respect. The turret was said to be 'improved' although it looks much the same, and bullet-proof rivets were used in the construction of the body. It was planned to send the car to India, so it went over the North Wales test course, but once again it never went there. A scheme had also been announced to fit the cars with wireless sets and, after rejecting locations within the hull D2E2 was fitted with one of the rectangular-shaped turrets from a Light Tank Mark II, which was designed to take a set at the back. Meanwhile, D2E1, on its return from Egypt, underwent an even more drastic modification. The problems of protecting vehicles from attack by low-flying aircraft came up for consideration in the early thirties, but something more mobile than the old anti-aircraft lorries was needed, something that could open fire without first having to stabilise itself with jacks and might even be able to fire on the move. An open type of turret was developed, mounting two ·5 Vickers machine-guns fed from large ammunition drums, and this was fitted to the car's turret ring, while the hull weapon was retained. It looked impressive, and was also tested on a light tank, but nothing more was done at the time. In due course five production cars were built as the Crossley Mark I, almost identical to D2E2 with the light tank turret. They weighed just under six tons and this was clearly a

problem since they normally ran without spare wheels or unditching boards fitted. They spent most of their time in Egypt, and will be mentioned again in the relevant chapter.

In addition to the mainstream development of six-wheel armoured cars represented by Lanchester and Crossley, there were some interesting protypes evaluated by MWEE which never progressed beyond that stage. One was offered by Scammell Lorries of Watford. It arrived at MWEE in June 1928, and was soon fitted with a mock-up of the proposed armoured body in wood. Scammel had, in fact, built a scale model armoured car about a year earlier, of a very unusual design that featured a low frontal driving position and rear, horizontally mounted radial engine, but it was not proceeded with. The trial car used a version of Scammell's highly successful Pioneer lorry chassis which first appeared in 1927, and considering how popular this chassis later became with the British Army it is strange to see how long it took them to appreciate its qualities at first. For a 6×4 type it had a remarkable cross-country performance which was achieved by two patent features. One was the front axle, which was pivoted at the centre giving a great deal of lateral flexibility. The other was the final drive and rear bogie. A single heavy duty differential axle was located across the chassis in the usual way, but each half-shaft ended in an enclosed gearcase which was free to pivot quite dramatically around the point where the half shaft entered it. Stub axles on each end of the gear casing carried the four driven wheels so that these, too, had a high degree of flexibility on a fore and aft line. Thus the vehicle could cross very uneven terrain without losing ground contact on all six wheels. In order to adapt it for armoured car work the

23 The large and handsome Scammell armoured car at MWEE. In this light the fact that most of it is made of wood shows up clearly.

front end of the chassis was dropped about eight inches but otherwise it was equipped with the regular Scammel 40hp engine driving through a five-speed gearbox.

As already mentioned, thoughts on armoured car design in the late twenties turned towards the idea of fitting two turrets, probably to give a car more flexible firepower in urban situations. It was not a new idea, the Russians in particular have favoured it during the war and many British armoured cars built for the Tsar's Government were so equipped. Two turrets were fitted to the wheel-cum-track vehicle D2E1 in 1928, and the Scammell, being a contemporary, was similarly equipped. The master turret, in the centre, mounted two machine-guns and was virtually a copy of the type fitted to the Lanchester prototype D1E1. The second turret was a smaller affair, with only one machine-gun, mounted behind the main one and lower down, but still with a good arc of fire covering well over 180°. Despite being over 21 feet long the Scammell gives the impression of being a well-balanced design which ought to have had a good cross-country performance. But after tests covering over 3,000 miles it was considered unsuitable as an armoured car and was tested instead as an anti-aircraft gun tractor. In the summer of 1929 it was handed over to the RAOC, who removed the wooden body and turned it into a breakdown lorry. In this guise it lasted, in military service, until 1944, when it was passed on to the Ministry of Works in Sheffield.

If a six-wheeled vehicle which drove on the two back axles had a good cross-country performance then it followed that one which drove on all three axles would be even better. Yet the type was in its infancy, at least in Britain, between the wars and only one major manufacturer was seriously involved in six-wheel-drive (6×6) construction. This was the FWD Company of Slough, who had already built half-track and 6×6 tractors for the Army and commercial customers, when they, too, entered the armoured car field. It seems probable that this, like the Scammell, was a speculative design but early in 1928 a chassis was tested by MWEE. Unlike their usual products this

version had the engine – a four-cylinder unit rated at 42hp – at the back driving a three-speed gearbox and two-speed auxiliary to the three differentials. No mock-up body was ever fitted and no designs can be traced to discover what a completed FWD armoured car might have looked like, but one very interesting feature is the driver's position. It was well to the front, and so low that the seat appeared to be directly above the front axle, so that the driver's legs would actually have been below chassis level. The engine, on the other hand, was surprisingly high, and located directly above the rear bogie, with the radiator behind it. Fuel tanks were located above the engine so one has to imagine a car with its turret at the front, firing over the driver's head, but possibly unable to traverse all the way to the rear. On the test chassis a large wooden box was located ahead of the engine containing four tons of ballast to simulate the weight of armour. The vehicle was tested for about two years at Farnborough and ended its days as an exhibit at the RTC Schools, Bovington, although the reasons why it was rejected are not known.

It might perhaps, be surprising to learn that the earliest suggestions for what amounted to a Royal Armoured Corps, date from just after the Great War. Such an organisation would have been dominated by mechanised cavalry regiments and could even have eclipsed the Tank Corps. In the event there was so much resistance from cavalry circles that it did not happen. If tradition and sentiment played a part it must be admitted that there was a good deal of reactionary stubborness on the part of many senior cavalry offices who simply could not stomach the idea of change. Nevertheless, it was inevitable, and the first steps were taken in 1928 when the two most junior non-amalgamated regiments, the 11th Hussars in Britain and 12th Lancers in Egypt, sent their horses back to the remount depots and took over Rolls-Royce armoured cars instead. Over the next few years many other regiments got involved in mechanisation in a small way, but in 1936 the nettle was finally grasped, and all the remaining cavalry regiments were warned to prepare. Even then mechanisation could not take place over

24 The six-wheel drive FWD armoured car chassis, fitted here with non-skid chains. Notice the very low driver's position, the big ballast box amidships and the rear engine layout.

25 Two 1920 Pattern Rolls-Royce of 5th ACC in Shanghai. Their Top Hats are readily visible and it is just possible to make out the front bumper on the rearmost car; both local additions.

night, there simply was not enough equipment to supply them all, and even when the Royal Armoured Corps was established, in April 1939, there were still at least two horsed cavalry regiments waiting for the change.

At the same time there was a polarisation of roles; generally speaking the RTC was being equipped with slower, heavier machines for infantry support while the cavalry retained its traditional mobility with armoured cars, light tanks and ultimately cruisers. Thus, apart from the Yeomanry armoured car regiments, and the companies in India, the RTC lost most of its armoured car companies by the late twenties, and by 1933 they had all gone. They had all been remarkable in their way, often of very strange antecedents but always adventurous and independent, especially when operating far from home. Yet one stands out, and its story might well be recorded. In 1918 the Tank Corps had but one armoured car battalion, the 17th*, which, after the Armistice went on peace-keeping duties in Ireland following a short spell in Germany. In May 1920 the battalion was disbanded, but the personnel were mostly transferred to the newly formed 5th Armoured Car Company, which was the first to be equipped with Rolls-Royces as they came into service. By February 1923 the 5th was in Belfast, and the following month it moved over to Scarborough, its place in Ireland being taken by 12th ACC.

*See Fletcher, *War Cars*.

In 1927 civil war was raging in China. Chiang Kai-shek's Cantonese Revolutionary Army was moving southwards, pushing the Chinese Northern Army ahead of it and, before long, the International Settlement, basically a trading enclave at Shanghai, was under threat. The British responded by sending troops from India along with mechanised artillery and a RTC unit from home; this last was the 5th Armoured Car Company. They took with them a full complement of 16 Rolls-Royces, eight of which were shipped aboard the SS *Karmala*, leaving the Royal Albert Dock on 29 January 1927. On the same day the remaining eight travelled to Birkenhead and embarked aboard the SS *Bellerophon*. There was an interesting contrast in loading techniques. Aboard the *Karmala* sections 1 and 2 had been stowed below in such a way that access to them was possible throughout the voyage. Batteries were kept topped up and the engines turned over every so often, so that when they arrived in Shanghai on 9 March the eight cars were ready to go into action from the moment they landed, had that been necessary. The *Bellerophon*, on the other hand, was badly loaded. The cars were placed around the sides of the hold with two large workshop lorries in the centre, and then a few tons of fodder was dumped on top for good measure. Nobody could get anywhere near them during the voyage, and when they arrived at Shanghai, on 22 March, the cars were not only hard to start, due to damp magnetos, dirty carburettors and stiff pistons, they were half full of straw as well; and the trouble was they were needed at once. The Revolutionary Army was just outside the city and infiltrators, in sinister black uniforms, were creating incidents and keeping everyone tense. The worst incident, as far as the armoured cars were concerned, took place late on 21 March. Two armoured cars were patrolling a narrow street; approaching a corner where barricades were set up, Lt. T P Newman, in the leading car, passed through the first barricade when two machine-guns opened up from a building on the corner, at point-blank range. Shots penetrated the front visor, wounding three of the crew, but Newman answered the fire as did Sgt. Tomlinson, commanding the second car, leaving Newman and his driver to reverse it out of danger. Behind him Tomlinson had by now silenced one of the machine-guns while a policeman in the vicinity had extinguished the nearest streetlamp with his revolver, since it was proving more useful to the rebel gunners than the armoured car crews. Newman dismounted from his car twice, and each time was hit in the wrist of the same arm, the wounds being no more than an inch apart. The first time was during the evacuation of his crew, the second when his armoured car got caught up in the barricade. However, Tomlinson had anticipated this and roped his car up to Newman's and towed it out of action. In all 93 hits were counted on the leading car, and carefully picked out in chalk for the cameras, but the task of repairing it was more than the RTC fitters could manage so the New Engineering Company in Shanghai undertook the work.

In addition to the British a French contingent arrived, with some White armoured cars and Renault light tanks, while the US Marine Corps brought along a few of their little six-ton tanks, which were virtually copies of the Renault design. However, the Americans went a stage further and started to armour their transport, mostly five-ton trucks of wartime vintage. Some had a few rudimentary panels of armour stuck around the cab and body while others were given a much more thorough treatment, turning them into effective mobile strongpoints. This appears to have given the British a similar idea. A Morris 30cwt lorry was obtained, and plans drawn up to fit it with armour to the design of Capt. Lawson of the 5th ACC. Quotes were obtained from various local engineering firms but all proved too expensive, so the scheme was dropped. Yet some lessons were learnt about the armoured cars, and they were sent, a few at a time, to the New Engineering Company for modification. First a front bumper was fitted, to prevent accidents with crowds during a riot, and a sort of hinged, armoured hood, called a Top Hat, was fitted over the turret hatch as an armoured cupola for the commander. At least one car had a ball mounting for a Hotchkiss gun installed within the small hatch at the rear of the turret. A dismounted Hotchkiss was always carried as secondary armament by these cars, but this allowed it to be mounted ready for action if required. Sections 3 and 4 worked frantically, all through the night, to get their cars ready, but it was 25 March before this was completed, and by then the immediate danger had passed. By December 1928 the threat had virtually ended and early in January 1929 5th ACC prepared for the voyage home, and disbandment.

In the event this plan was changed at the last minute, and in February the Company disembarked in Egypt, where they joined 3rd ACC for operations in the Western Desert. In due course they were both gradually converted into independent Light Tank Companies, their cars going to 12th Royal Lancers. In 1933 these two RTC companies became the nucleus of the newly formed 6th Battalion, RTC. Thus was the heritage of one famous tank battalion, first raised in 1917, preserved right through until 1960 when, as the 6th Royal Tank Regiment, it amalgamated with the 3rd RTR which survives to this day.

4 Tankettes

The word tankette sounds as flippant as the flapper, as dated as the Charleston; two adjectives that might well be applied to the machines themselves. It was coined to describe a sort of baby tank. At least that was the initial idea but, as with so many others, events conspired to turn it into something quite different in time. The concept can be traced back to the Renault FT17, two-man light tank used in large numbers by the French Army during the last year of the war. Col. Henry Karslake was one who saw the potential of such machines, both for reconnaissance and to form a skirmishing screen for the medium tanks during a general action. Among those with whom Karslake discussed his idea was Lt.-Col. Giffard le Q Martel, a Sapper who had served with the Tank Corps during the war. Martel, however, took the idea a stage further and imagined a really small one-man machine, armed with a machine-gun, which would work with the infantry during an attack, giving them the immediate fire support they needed at this crucial moment. Naturally there were those who poured scorn on the idea, claiming it was yet another device for subordinating the entire Army to the tank idea. Martel therefore settled upon a more tangible means of getting his idea across; he decided to build a full-size working model of the thing he had in mind, and offer it to the War Office as a going concern.

In addition to being a professional engineer, Martel was a gifted amateur mechanic. He was living at Camberley, on a posting to the Staff College at this time, and in the garden of his house had built an ingenious workshop on a turntable, which could be revolved to take best advantage of the available sunlight; it was here that he started to build his little tank. He obtained an old Maxwell car, removed the body and transferred the engine to the rear of the chassis, which now became the front of his machine. In an effort to keep the cost down Martel selected a half-track configuration, since this provided a simple solution to the steering problem. Thus the rearranged chassis had short track units at the front and the car's original steering axle and wheels at the back. Obviously it was beyond Martel's resources to make the tracks and suspension units, so in this he enlisted the help of an old Tank Corps colleague, Philip Johnson of Medium D fame, now running Roadless Traction Ltd in Hounslow. They supplied a fairly crude set of tracks, road rollers and drive sprocket, the other pair of car wheels serving as idlers. The body, built of wood, featured a louvred grill at the front, covering the radiator; sloping engine compartment and an open cockpit amidships for the driver. It was completed in the summer of 1925 and demonstrated privately by the designer before being handed over to MWEE for official trials in December. Tactical thought on the employment of such machines was limited to Martel's own ideas at first, and were simple enough for anyone to understand. A number of the little vehicles would be issued to each infantry battalion, and during an advance would move forward with the troops, firing machine-guns as they went to keep enemy heads down, and escorting the infantry right up to the enemy line. But this kind of logic has a habit of getting carried away with itself and before long Martel was considering a more revolutionary idea. This, he argued, was a mechanical age, yet the infantry were almost alone, compared with other employed people, in that they still walked to their work. Instead of providing each battalion with what amounted to a mechanised machine-gun company he now suggested that every man – or pair of men – should have a vehicle to travel in. Working on the round figure of 1,000 men to a battalion he proposed halving that number, and placing the men, in pairs, in two-man versions of his machine. They would then be more mobile, better protected and capable of delivering vastly increased firepower. The cost of 250 tankettes, taken over a period of about four years, would be more than offset by the saving in manpower. Except for specialised operations in mountainous country or forests, for which conventional battalions might be retained, the day of the foot soldier would be over. Martel had the sense not to promote such far reaching ideas too widely at first, they had a tendency to frighten people off. For the present he was content to have his little machine accepted, and it was.

In 1926 the War Office ordered four pilot models from Morris Motors: two one-man machines like the prototype and another pair with wider cockpits to take two men. There was a general feeling that one man would have enough to do just driving his machine, without having to load his gun, look for targets and fire it at the same time. There was also a morale factor to be taken into account if each man was to be shut up in

26 Martel peers over the top of his own wooden wonder, the home-made tankette that started a fashion in cheap armoured fighting vehicles.

27 *The Morris-Martel one-man No 2 machine seen at the time of the 1927 Wool Trials.*

his own tiny tank. Martel was not convinced; he argued that
the pilot of a single-seat fighter aircraft did all these tasks alone
as, in a sense, did the mounted cavalryman, but he did not
press the point. The four machines appeared in two batches;
each of a one, and two-man machine. All were powered by the
Morris 15.9hp engine driving through a four-speed gearbox
and two-speed epicyclic auxiliary. They had an effective top
speed of 30mph, although the steering wheels tended to take
charge at anything over 12mph, making the vehicles unstable,
and very dangerous to handle. The weapon carried was a
stripped version of the Lewis gun, air-cooled like the infantry
weapon but lighter since the barrel jacket was removed. In the
one-man machines it was mounted and fired through a slot
alongside the driver's visor, but the two-man machines had
extra mountings so that the gunner could fire to the side or rear
as necessary. The first two pilot models had disc drive
sprockets, like the prototype, but on the second pair they were
replaced by a new, spoked pattern which was less prone to clog
up with mud, and there were other detail improvements to the
cooling arrangements and crew compartment. Early trials
showed a tendency for the tracks to come off, but this was
cured by Roadless Traction – who supplied them. However,
the steering troubles still remained. It was thought that the
problem was due to the pressure exerted by the rear wheels,
lifting the tracks and pitching the centre of gravity forwards, so
the two-man No 1 machine was modified to take a small single
tail wheel, at the end of a very low slung beam extending from
the chassis. This does not appear to have made much
difference, although it was agreed that the two-man type was

28 *A glimpse into the original Tank Museum at Bovington. The nearest
exhibit is the Morris-Martel two-man prototype fitted with the single-
wheel tail assembly.*

easier to handle than the single seaters and, following trials of
the second of these at MWEE an order was placed for eight
production models, subject to certain improvements being
made.

Martel's original project received quite a lot of publicity;
partly because of his novel approach in building a home-made
tank, but also because it appealed to the influential military
journalist and pundit, Capt. Sir Basil Liddell Hart, thus
encouraging another, even more gifted engineer to enter the
field. This was Sir John Carden, a wartime Army Service Corps

officer who, it might be said, thought small in a big way. In 1912 Carden designed a tiny motor car, which entered production in 1922. Known as the Carden Cyclecar it was representative of a type which became extremely popular in the years following the Great War. An unkind critic might say that a cyclecar was little more than a child's pedalcar with a small engine. The type was cheap, and simple to the point of crudity, but it appealed to a generation that wanted to take to the roads but could not afford a full-size motor vehicle and did not mind getting wet. Carden was also interested in aviation and built the Flying Flea, a sort of cyclecar of the air, powered by a Ford engine; however, in 1925 he was involved with another ex-officer, Capt. Vivian Loyd, in a garage business in west London. During the war Carden commanded a unit based at Avonmouth Docks, unloading Holt Caterpillar tractors from the United States, preparing them for military service and then shipping them to the front, so he already had some experience of tracklaying vehicles. Given his interest in mechanical miniatures it is not surprising that his latest idea was a very small tank, which was demonstrated for the first time on a patch of ground in a Kensington mews.

No photograph of this machine has yet been traced, but it was described in a lecture given by Maj-Gen. S C Peck, who witnessed that first demonstration. It arrived on the back of a Ford truck, which had to be tipped up in order to get the machine off. The impression given is of a Model T Ford engine, gearbox and driving axle fitted with tracks. There is no suggestion of a body and Gen. Peck even goes so far as to say that there was no suspension of any sort, nor any rollers for the tracks to run around; however, some sort of skid rail must have been provided for support. The track itself was nothing more than industrial conveyor chain which, in appearance, resembled oversize bicycle chain, and must be assumed to have run around a sprocket at one end of the frame and a roller at the other. Some sources claim that the driver adopted a prone position, but whether face downwards or otherwise is not clear. Peck says that he sat on the axle casing, with a leg each side of the engine, which could mean that the engine was in front of the driver, or that he was crouched in the saddle like a racing motorcyclist with his legs behind him, it is impossible to tell. Either way he was very close to the engine because Peck thought he would be well advised to wear asbestos trousers! Steering was by foot pedals, acting on brakes, while the gear change was effected by a short joystick, the opposite of the normal Ford technique. On grass or soft ground it ran quite well, but on a hard surface its progress reminded Peck of an antelope, so it must have moved in leaps and bounds. A weight of 7cwts is given, and a track life estimated at 20 miles, which was not very promising.

Clearly those who saw it were sufficiently impressed by its potential, for an improved example was delivered to MWEE in March 1926. It was probably the first model rebuilt, and in this case the engine and radiator were definitely at the rear: for the drive passed to front sprockets, while the driver sat upright. The track was still conveyor chain, but now with a flat steel plate riveted to each link. This passed beneath a series of lightly sprung rollers in the frames, so that speeds of 20mph were achieved, while a track life of 80 miles was estimated, which was an improvement. At this time the machine must still have been entirely open, for MWEE records show that mudguards

29 The original Carden-Loyd machine after the body had been fitted. Notice in particular the crude tracks.

were fitted in April, and a body at the end of June. The body was little more than an open-topped box, with a cover at the back over the engine. Other recorded details speak of handlebar steering controls, a weight of 16cwt and the ability to cross a four foot wide trench. It was returned to the makers in August 1926, but by that time the firm, Carden-Loyd Tractors Ltd, had supplied two more test vehicles. These were basically the same shape as the first machine, but slightly longer in the track frames, and fitted with a small turret at the front. This was an odd design: open at the rear to accommodate the driver's head and shoulders, but narrowing towards the front with a mounting for a light machine-gun. Obviously, since he also had to drive, the arc of fire available from the turret was minimal, but it was capable of being swung through a full circle and, in some views, is seen facing aft so that the driver had a better chance to see where he was going. The presence of a turret confirms that in these two vehicles the tankette concept was very much alive; however, they appear to have been used primarily to test various forms of track and suspension. The former gradualy evolved into a single piece phosphor bronze casting for each link, and as such may be seen as the forerunner of a highly successful range of hard-wearing tracks developed by Carden-Loyd and Vickers over the next ten years; the suspension on the other hand just got confusing. From photographs one can identify two main types. The first involved tiny rollers – up to ten per side – and associated coil springs of varying lengths, though rarely bigger than one would expect to find on a bed frame. These were forever being changed, either from one type to another, or from one machine to the other, or even from one side of a machine to the other, so

nation which he would now be expected to feed without its help? Morris-Commercial, in conjunction with Roadless Traction, had also produced some experimental half-track tractors for the British Army which were not unlike the Morris-Martel in some respects, except that they were the other way around, with the wheels at the front. Martel suggested that these could be fitted with wood, and/or canvas imitation tank bodies, presumably for training, and both sorts were tried on the prototype vehicle. Whether the next stage would have been an armoured version is not clear, for this idea also went by the

33 *A Carden-Loyd Mark V wheel-cum-track carrier,* Caliban *of 3rd Battalion RTC at Lydd. The gunner, for some reason, is sitting on the rear mudguard. Notice the chain drive from the front track sprocket to the wheel.*

32 *A rear view of the one-man Crossley-Martel tankette with its radiator doors open.*

board in a short time. Yet in the meantime Martel had found a firm prepared to continue work on his tankettes. This was Crossley Motors Ltd of Manchester, who took as a starting point their 15 cwt half-track vehicle using the French Kégresse system. It was a clumsy design in many respects; a one-man machine again which had much more in common with the Morris type, at least in terms of height, than the Carden-Loyds which Martel had hoped to emulate. As a fighting machine it might be better than the Morris, because the crew compartment was at the front, over the tracks, but this meant that the engine was rear mounted above the steering wheels, which thus moved the weight away from the tracks where it could do most good. The vehicle was said to be more comfortable to ride in than the Morris version, and much easier to steer. Comfort would have been enhanced by the rubber Kégresse tracks, but they had a nasty habit of throwing dust back at the engine, so that it was worn out by the time the vehicle had done 1,000 miles. A second was fitted by MWEE – who had received the vehicle for evaluation in March 1927 – but they reported in October that the suspension was overloaded, so the trial was terminated. They also remarked that the new vehicle had only half the trench crossing capability of a Morris-Martel. Although it was not obvious at the time, the Crossley-Martel marked the end of the tankette concept as originally perceived, almost before it had begun.

Shortly after it had been converted to wheel-cum-track configuration, the two-man Carden-Loyd machine was further

modified to mount a water-cooled Vickers machine-gun. This seemingly unimportant change actually signified a great deal, for this weapon was hardly compatible with the original tankette idea. It was designed to fire at long range along fixed lines, rather than at close range from a moving vehicle which would be pitching violently on its short tracks and spraying fire in all directions, except perhaps where it was needed most. It was one thing to place such weapons in the relatively stable medium tanks, but quite another to expect it to be of any use in a close-quarters machine like the Carden-Loyd. When the eight production machines, based on the two-man wheel-cum-track, appeared, they also carried tripods for the machine-guns, so clearly they were now seen as weapons carriers: delivering the gun to a fire point on the battlefield where it could be set up and fired in the usual way, and only used from the machine in an emergency. Following their debut with the Mechanised Force the new carriers, now styled Carden-Loyd Mark V (although Mark numbers had never been applied to the various prototypes) were attached to 2nd Battalion, King's Royal Rifle Corps, as part of an experimental machine-gun company in May 1928. The *KRRC Journal* said of them, 'a Carden-Loyd Mark V knows not when it will return to its garage, for he breaketh down in out-of-the-way places'. A photograph taken at the time reveals that the wheel-cum-track feature was proving more trouble than it was worth, for the carriers are seen in every stage of transition from full wheel-cum-tracks, through those that only retain a vestige of the equipment, to some running on tracks only. The need for this inefficient system was already being questioned; for one thing the latest tracks were wearing even better than had been expected while the road-speed on tracks was quite respectable enough, without the need to change over to wheels very often. In any case the wheels, hanging from the sides of the vehicle, tended to suffer damage from unintentional contact with undergrowth, trees and gate posts. Two of the carriers were further modified into section leaders' vehicles with improved protection for the gunner, who reverted to using a stripped Lewis gun. In due course most, if not all of them, were modified to Mark VI standard, the next stage in Carden-Loyd development.

With the tankette concept now history the Carden-Loyd company had the field to themselves, and large orders for carriers were anticipated from the War Office. This potential business was more than such a small company could hope to handle on their own, so, in March 1928 they were taken over by the huge Vickers-Armstrong concern, although they continued to trade as Carden-Loyd Tractors Ltd. They were still completing old contracts until August, but a new order for 35 machines was completed by December. Vickers acquired more than the business for both Vivian Loyd and Sir John Carden joined the parent firm and, in the latter they gained an employee who would prove to be one of the most gifted tank designers of the period. In the meantime production went ahead on a series of new models which were, in effect, the Mark V type with the wheel attachments deleted. There was also a move to widen the scope of the product by offering various attachments to suit it to a variety of roles. One of the first was a smoke producer. This, in its original form, carried smoke generating equipment which used chlorosulphonic acid under pressure, which issued as a cloud from a pipe projecting at the back. A later version had a sort of dispenser mounted on the front deck, through which smoke-emitting flame tubes could be dropped, which lay on the ground making smoke while the vehicle moved on.

A few days after the first of these smoke carriers arrived at MWEE – in July 1927 – another machine appeared which was, in fact, the original one-man machine completely rebuilt. Indeed there was nothing of the first machine visible in the newcomer which, to all intents and purposes, was another in the two-man Mark VI series. However, as things turned out, it proved to be a very significant milestone in Carden-Loyd development. Its first declared purpose was as a carrier for the larger ·5in Vickers machine-gun, and in this form it weighed something over one ton. Early trials revealed that this was too great a weight for the original two-speed gearbox to cope with, so a secondary two-speed transfer box was interposed between the existing transmission and driving axle, giving a range of four speeds overall. Following tests with a mounted ·5in machine-gun, a series of tiny return rollers were added to the track supporting skid, although they were never employed on future examples so they probably made very little difference to its performance. Towards the end of 1928 towing gear was fitted and the carrier was tested as a tractor for the 3·7in mountain howitzer, which was carried on a small tracked trailer. With the auxiliary gearbox there was certainly sufficient power, and probably even a bit too much, for the extra torque delivered through the new transmission proved too strong for

the existing Ford driving axle – it was calculated at three times the original design limit – and tended to twist it out of shape. The carrier was then fitted with a heavy-duty driving axle of the type manufactured for Ford 1-ton trucks, which could easily cope with the extra stress. It was thus agreed that in future all carriers built for the tractor role should have this type of axle, while those intended as machine-gun carriers would retain the original pattern. In the end, however, common sense prevailed and all future carriers left the factory with the new axle, irrespective of their intended roles.

In this form one has the definitive Carden-Loyd Carrier which, on account of its importance, should be examined in greater detail. The hull was a six-sided box formed of bullet proof plate from 4mm up to 8mm thick in places, and roughly resembled a boot in shape. The open section at the rear housed the crew of two: driver on the left and gunner on the right; while the enclosed 'toe' contained the transmission. The radiator was at the back and two doors in the rear panel could be opened to improve air-flow. Ahead of the radiator, and between the crew, was a Ford T 20·5hp four-cylinder engine coupled directly to the Ford epicyclic two-speed and reverse gearbox. Ahead of this again was the two-speed auxiliary box, connected to the driving axle at the front. Sprockets on the ends of this axle engaged the short pitch track, which by now was being produced in malleable cast-iron, which had an

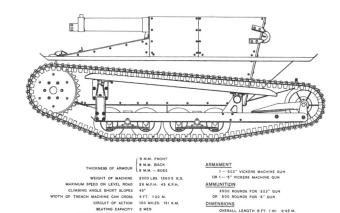

CARDEN-LOYD TRACTORS

D9 Outline and data for the Carden-Loyd Mark VI.

34 The true prototype, the Carden-Loyd ·5in machine-gun carrier rebuilt from the original one-man machine. In this view it still has the old Ford T driving axle fitted.

35 An early example of a Carden-Loyd Mark VI doing a balancing act. No machine-gun is fitted although the mounting can be seen, and like most early models this one lacks the side stowage bins.

average roadlife of 2,200 miles. Unlike the Mark V – which as already explained had no suspension as such, but rollers anchored directly to the frames – the Mark VI had very short leaf springs connecting each pair of rollers, mounted just below the frames. A wood and metal skid served in place of return rollers to support the top run of the track and small, adjustable idlers were fitted at the back on each side. Resting on the front of the hull, at the right, was a mounting for the Vickers gun while the tripod was carried, folded, at the left. Light metal track guards ran along both sides, and most carriers had two open topped stowage bins, capable of holding spare ammunition boxes, fitted outside the hull at the back. The controls included a tiller bar for steering, which activated clutches and brakes working on the sprockets, and a hand throttle. As in the Ford T car the primary gear-box was worked by foot pedals; an extra lever, offset to the right, was also operated by the driver's foot to select an auxiliary gear. Since both gearboxes were operating in series only three speeds were nominally available; the lowest – the fourth – being regarded as an emergency low gear for crossing difficult obstacles. A fully equipped carrier weighed 26cwt and had a top speed of 28mph, which could be dangerous at times due to the phenomenon known as reverse steering. This happened if the driver failed to apply the steering brake firmly enough when the carrier was going downhill. The track would be declutched and then start to over run the driven track, causing the vehicle to slew the opposite way to that intended. Skilled drivers would use this situation to their advantage, and avoid unnecessary braking, but it was always risky. On one occasion when 3rd Battalion

was moving from Lydd to Lulworth by road there were a number of such incidents, usually in hilly towns, and invariably involving shop windows. Some 300 carriers were built for the British Army, production being shared between Vickers-Carden-Loyd Ltd, and the ROF. The problem was what to do with them.

Clearly as they stood they were best suited to infantry use; carrying forward machine-guns to suitable fire points and then waiting in the wings until they were ready to move again. However, they were never employed in this role on a very large scale. When they were issued to infantry battalions it was only in very modest numbers to provide some experience of handling tracked vehicles. It was still the RTC that made the greatest use of them, either as substitute light tanks on annual exercises, or as inconspicuous reconnaissance vehicles to operate with the medium tanks. In the former role they were little more than tokens while, in the latter, their inability to carry a wireless set – except in a clumsy trailer – made them of very dubious value. Only one attempt was made to improve combat effectiveness and this came back, in a sense, to the original concept as devised by Martel. One vehicle was converted into what was called an 'Infighter'. According to a contemporary report this was a word 'newly coined and designates a machine that is capable of pushing its way forward in the fight and covering with its machine-gun from a forward position the advance of the infantry'. The vehicle concerned was one of the original eight Mark V carriers – now brought up to Mark VI standard but refered to by MWEE as Mark V★ – which was further altered by the addition of a raised screen of

36 The one and only Infighter, showing the raised-hull front and machine-gun shield. Rebuilt from a Mark V, this vehicle has undergone a change of driving axle, indicated by the curved cover on the nose.

frontal armour covering both crew members, with an aperture for a Vickers gun which was also fitted with a shield. All this extra metal put the weight up by 3cwt, reduced the speed by 4mph and more or less ruined its cross-country performance. The newly coined word didn't last long enough to get into the Oxford English Dictionary, or anywhere else for that matter.

Even so the idea that Carden-Loyd carriers might prove suitable for other roles inspired everyone to have a go, and before long MWEE was being asked to test a whole range of conversions that usually ended in tears. One had a 3in mortar mounted on the front, complete with baseplate, although the main barrel tube was stowed across the back. Although it is sometimes suggested that the mortar could be fired from the carrier the stubby barrel would have left the range dangerously short, and the normal practice would surely have been to dismount it. Then the main tube could be added and the weapon used in the normal way. In any case a second carrier, towing an ammunition trailer, would be essential to transport the rest of the crew. Another version of the mortar carrier was advertised with the weapon stowed across the hull front and space for extra ammunition provided where the machine-gun would normally be, but this may not have been supplied to the British Army. Trials of a prototype carrier towing a small artillery piece on a tracked, transporter trailer, has already been mentioned; further developments along these lines are covered in another title*. Yet trailers had to be considered if the tiny carriers were to fulfill other tasks and Vickers-Carden-Loyd produced a number of experimental examples, all on four-wheeled running gear which could be fitted with tracks if required. One, a sort of gable-topped box, was intended for use by a Forward Observation Officer (FOO) controlling the guns of an artillery battery. Presumably the idea was to equip it with a wireless set which the FOO could use to call down a barrage. One of the strangest was a small four-seater in which the crew sat back to back. The idea may have been to use it for the movement of dismounted cavalry troopers, but trials revealed that the carrier vehicle was simply not powerful enough to handle such a trailer at sufficient speed to keep pace with mounted cavalry, so the idea was dropped. Even so these contraptions were seen on exercises with four quite senior officers aboard having great difficulty maintaining their composure and dignity in their obvious discomfort. It is one thing to follow manœuvres in a staff car, but quite another to be dragged around backwards in what was virtually an unsprung trailer with ones backside only inches from the ground. The same trailer was also used in conjunction with a light anti-tank gun which also ran on tracks. This was a ·8in (20mm) weapon developed by Oerlikon, which was hailed at the time as a serious antidote to the tank. A standard Carden-Loyd Mark VI hauled the crew trailer and the little gun behind it, and despite its low silhouette the impression given is of vulnerability, both to enemy fire and rough ground which would have seriously handicapped the entire ensemble.

Not surprisingly, many of these attempts to make the Carden-Loyd do things it was never designed to do gave rise to complaints that it was underpowered. At the same time it was becoming obvious that, with the Ford T engine on the verge of becoming obsolete, something was needed to replace it. Among those considered was the Austin 12hp and a Coventry Climax 20hp, but all were rejected on the grounds that the machine

would have to be drastically redesigned in the process. Thus, faced with a continuing commitment to the Ford engine the War Office consulted Harry Ricardo, who had produced the engine for the Mark V tank in 1918. He now ran a small company devoted to engine research at Shoreham-by-Sea and had recently completed a major project for Shell on fuel performance. His solution to this problem was to fit Specialloid aluminium pistons and a turbulent head, which raised the effective horsepower from 22·5 to 26. Unfortunately it also raised the working temperature, leading to a situation where the engine required more frequent servicing, so following trials the scheme was dropped.

Clearly there was now little alternative but to redesign the entire machine, having first selected a new engine. This was settled in favour of an air-cooled Armstrong Siddeley four-cylinder type, rated at 25hp; a seemingly odd choice despite its possible compatibility with the old medium tank engine, since it was not a standard commercial type. Since the hull had to be redesigned to take the new engine the opportunity was grasped to increase the height, and thus provide better protection for the crew, at the expense of visibility. In taking this step the designers were moving away yet again from the current concept. It was a lot more difficult for the crew to dismount quickly, and even harder for them to get the machine-gun out. It follows that this design was reverting, in a sense, to the fighting vehicle idea; not the one-man tankette as such, and not just a weapons carrier either. This must be seen as a reflection of their actual use, if not the intended one, since the main user, the RTC, employed them as substitute light tanks, even though it was almost impossible for them to fire on the move with any accuracy at all. Naturally the weight increased, and partially offset the advantage of a more powerful engine, which in turn required heavier duty tracks. These ran around a revised suspension which featured return rollers instead of a skid, and an idler raised to the same level as the drive sprocket and attached directly to the body. Two prototypes were built, one of which went out to Egypt for trials while the other stayed at MWEE. Complaints were received from both places about the heat and fumes which built up in the more enclosed hull, and the noise; problems typically associated with an air-cooled

37 The number B11E1 identifies this as the first Carden-Loyd Mark VIA, with its higher-sided fighting compartment.

*Moving the Guns.

engine. The first two were remedied to some extent in four production models of what became known as the Carden-Loyd Mark VIA when they appeared in 1931, but the noise level remained high and the suspension caused excessive pitching across country. Thus the next batch of ten, ordered from the ROF, had the idler lowered again, and other faults remedied that came to light during trials with the Mark VIA models. Classified as Mark VIB they were similar to the previous six except for the track configuration, which is not always obvious, and are best identified by the enlarged exhaust silencer at the back. Even so crews still complained about the noise although they agreed that heat and fumes were less of a problem. Five of these vehicles remained in Britain while the rest went out to Egypt, and reports suggest that the ride was improved and the engine delivered sufficient power to cope with the increase in weight without any trouble. By 1935 all 16 had been withdrawn due to faulty transmissions, which made them dangerous fellow travellers on the road.

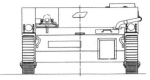
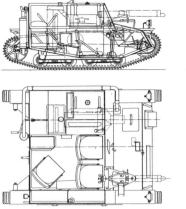
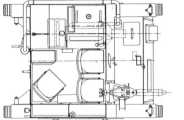

D10 B11E10, the three-man Carden-Loyd, showing the internal arrangements.

38 This is a Carden-Loyd Mark VIB, in this case complete with Vickers machine-gun and shield. Notice the lowered position of the rear idler compared with B11E1.

Early in 1931 an ordinary Mark VI carrier arrived at MWEE showing signs of modification. This concerned the suspension system which had a pair of return rollers on each side, rubber tyred idlers and wide tracks. MWEE reported that noise levels were reduced although the carrier was slower and much harder to steer. This may have been part of a general scheme to improve the machines, or a trial for another new model which appeared in 1933. This was the larger three-man carrier B11E10, which a contemporary report describes as being constructed 'on lines somewhat similar to the Mark VIA', which was odd because it does not look like the Mark VIA at all. It appears more like an enlarged Mark VI with a slightly wider hull, squared off at the back. The power unit was a four-cylinder Ford Model A type rated at 24hp. It was mounted offset to left, so that the driver now sat in the centre, with the machine-gunner to his right and the extra man tucked away in the corner behind him. The question was, what was this extra man for? One report speaks of the three-man carrier as being a steadier gun platform, but by the time it appeared light tanks were available in large numbers, and they were not only better gun platforms, they were better in many other respects too. The crew were well protected from the engine, which was fully enclosed, and by having the exhaust pipe

39 The three-man Carden-Loyd, viewed from the back.

emerge from the front of the hull and pass along the side to end in a silencer pointing vertically downwards at the back. This arrangement was apparently chosen to prevent trailer drawn passengers from being gassed. The engine was coupled to a four-speed gearbox and lever steering was employed. Delivery of the prototype was delayed, and even the preliminary trials revealed that it was not going to be a success. Words like heavy – it weighed 2 tons 6cwt – and bulky appear in the report, which also claims that the engine was overloaded, so no more of this type were built.

The Model A Ford engine was more effective in a pair of carriers which arrived at MWEE some six months before B11E10. Outwardly they were similar to the Mark VIA type, with the obvious difference that a four-piece hinged roof was fitted over the fighting compartment, which effectively sealed the two crew members in with the engine when closed. Tests in North Wales in 1932 showed that the performance was much improved over all other models, especially on hills, and the Still-pattern radiator improved cooling, although what it was like inside with the roof closed and the engine running is not recorded. Among the adverse comments a higher fuel consumption was noted along with greater brake wear, but worse than these was the severe pitching, due no doubt to a return to the earlier track configuration of the Mark VIA. The new model was classified as Mark VI*, and a report published at the end of 1932 spoke of the greater tractive effort available, claiming that the results of trials were very promising. In fact they were far more successful on the export market – as we shall see – but at home they represented the last of the line.

Thus production of Carden-Loyd Carriers for the British Army effectively ceased in 1932, and the first to be phased out of service were the last to be built: the various experimental types. This still left a substantial number of the basic Mark VI type in service, getting a bit long in the tooth and considered underpowered with their Model T engines, yet there was clearly not a great deal wrong with the balance of the original design, even if its purpose was still a bit vague. Over the next few years they were still to be seen on military exercises in various parts of the country, with infantry and RTC battalions, serving in a variety of roles. In 1933 eight of them were serving with 7th Infantry Brigade as tractors for 3·7in howitzers, while by 1934 they had been supplied to a number of formations as anti-tank gun tractors and mortar carriers. We have already seen that they were made adaptable to these tasks but it was now made clear that they were only being used to familiarise the infantry with the operation of tracked vehicles, pending the delivery of something more suitable. They were only serving as substitutes with the RTC as well, although here the situation was somewhat more ludicrous. During the Tank Brigade exercises on Salisbury Plain they performed as representative

light tanks, until adequate numbers of the real thing had been delivered. However 4th Royal Tanks had just been reorganised as an Army Tank Battalion which would be equipped with infantry tanks. Now an infantry tank, by definition, is supposed to support the infantry, and to that end was designed to be capable of absorbing heavy punishment while leading an attack on prepared defences. The only trouble was that no such tank existed in 1934, and to use these diminutive carriers, even as token infantry tanks, was a travesty.

Of course the problem of moving machine-guns about still remained, and while the Carden-Loyds were being misused the infantry had to look elsewhere. In 1934 the Vickers-Carden-Loyd company had introduced a tiny little one-man tracked tractor as a supply carrier. Since it was neither armoured, nor a fighting vehicle in the strict sense it can only be spared a passing mention here. As the Light Utility Tractor it was accepted by the War Office as first-line supply transport for infantry battalions, in which role it hauled a small, two-wheeled trailer. There were also two narrow panniers on either side of the driver which held more supplies, and some infantry battalions found that with a bit of a squeeze they could get a Vickers machine-gun in one pannier, and a very uncomfortable gunner in the other. The Mechanisation Board commented favourably on the practice, but the tractors were soon replaced

40 A vehicle full of character, the armoured Burford-Kégresse machine-gun carrier B11E5. With the gun mounting removed it could also function as an armoured personnel carrier, but notice there is no connection between the driving cab and rear compartment.

by a new type of platoon truck which took over this role to some extent, although by that time a new type of carrier had appeared upon the scene, which will be discussed in a later chapter.

While Carden-Loyds represent the mainstream of machine-gun carrier development it was by no means the only one. Various unarmoured vehicles carried such weapons, mainly for anti-aircraft defence, but special light six-wheeled lorries were also developed which were capable of carrying two machine-gun detachments each. At the very bottom end of the scale was the bizarre Auto-Culto machine which was nothing more than a two-wheeled, motorised contraption of the type used in gardens and allotments to cut grass or turn the soil. A tiny, single-cylinder engine powered the wheels but the thing was controlled by a man, in this case a soldier, walking along behind. Exactly where the machine gun fitted is not obvious but the contraption was seriously tested by MWEE for this purpose before it mercifully vanished in 1928.

At about the same time another armoured machine-gun carrier was being evaluated under the designation B11E5. It was based on the 30cwt Burford-Kégresse half-track chassis with an armoured body fitted by Vickers at Erith. This was a high-sided arrangement, open at the top and fitted in the rear portion with a substantial frame upon which was mounted a Scarf ring capable of taking one, or two Vickers machine-guns. Although classified as a machine-gun carrier the vehicle was clearly designed with anti-aircraft use in mind since; even when firing horizontally the weapons were well above ground level. The exact number built is not known, but it would not have been very many. Two, operated by the Cheshire Regiment, served as part of the experimental machine-gun company raised in 1928. There is some evidence to suggest that they were also tested as armoured personnel carriers, which would have suited them well and foreshadowed the development of armoured half-tracks by the US Army and Germany during the Second World War.

Finally we return to where we started, with Giffard Martel. In 1935 this officer returned from a spell of duty in India and, surveying the current scene, he observed how his original tankette concept had been lost sight of over the years. He was still firmly of the opinion that small armoured machine-gun carriers, acting in direct support of the infantry, were a viable, indeed an essential, proposition. Convinced as ever that there was nothing to beat a practical example he again set about building a working prototype, only this time he kept it simple in the interests of speedy production, if not economy. The result was a very shallow steel box, aptly nicknamed the 'Mechanical Coffin', which ran on chain-link tracks like the original Carden-Loyd machine, and was probably driven by an electric motor. The crew, which consisted of one man, lay face down inside the box and closed the lid above him; the whole thing in this form being no more than 20 inches high. The idea was that he would then advance with the infantry, peering

41 Martel's Mechanical Coffin supported on its tricycle undercarriage while its demonstrator tries to look dignified.

through a slot in the front, until he reached a suitable firing point close to the enemy lines. Here he halted, raised the lid to form a frontal shield, shipped a light machine-gun – represented by a double-barreled shotgun – and opened fire. In Martel's view sufficient of the things – at least 16 operating with each rifle company – could bring a devastating volume of fire to bear at very close range with the minimum of risk to the operators. Martel seems to have been aware that the project, as presented, would be treated in a somewhat light-hearted manner by his peers and superiors, and he was prepared to go along with the joke. In the long run this may not have helped his case, which was further weakened when he demonstrated how he proposed the machine should travel during the approach march. On rough country it would still move on its tracks, but the controls would be adjusted so that the driver sat upright, looking for all the world like a fully clothed man travelling in a small bathtub on tracks. It may have looked silly, but it was a lot more comfortable than lying flat on one's face, especially with the lid shut. In order to keep pace with mechanised columns on the road he experimented with a wheeled undercarriage. It was not a wheel-cum-track system as such, because it was not permanently attached to the vehicle. Instead a pair of wire spoked bicycle wheels were fitted at the back and driven off the sprockets, while a single wheel of similar size was mounted, in cycle type forks complete with handlebars, at the front. It is hardly necessary to add that the scheme did not impress the War Office, although it is worth noting that in both France and the United States machines of a roughly similar type were tested, albeit with no more success, and that a variation of the idea surfaced again during the Second World War in the form of Praying Mantis.

5 Light Tanks

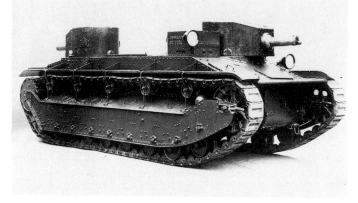

42 Carrier MG No 1, alias the three-man light tank A3E1. This front three-quarter view emphasises the odd layout of this strange design.

The family of Vickers' designed light tanks that dominated the second half of our period stemmed directly from the Carden-Loyd carrier, and therefore by definition from the Renault FT17. Of course what we know as the Vickers Mediums were classified as light tanks when they first appeared, so the term is a very loose one, and it was also applied to a strange machine that was built by the ROF in 1926. Referred to variously as the Three Man Light Tank or Machine Gun Carrier No 1, it appeared at the Dominion Premiers' demonstration of that year and is described in the souvenir booklet as an economical machine using a commercial engine and the simplest type of cast steel tracks that could be produced. It was designed to be inconspicuous, being a little over six feet high, but one questions whether a tank that only carried three men and two machine-guns needed to be 17ft 9ins long! The hull was a long, rectangular box, sloping slightly at each end and supported on conventional track frames, the skirting plates of which prevent us from seeing the suspension. Since this is not recorded anywhere else one can only guess at a system of coil springs and rollers as the most likely. The engine, a four cylinder AEC unit rated at 52bhp, was located in the centre of the hull, driving through a four-speed gearbox with auxiliary reduction to Rackham steering clutches and rear track sprockets. The total weight is given as 6 tons 14cwt with armour plate to a maximum half inch thickness and a top speed of 16mph. The driver sat at the front, on the right with his head inside an armoured cube providing vision to the right and straight ahead. His view to the left was totally obscured by a small turret, mounting a Vickers machine-gun which would have an arc of fire covering about 270°. An identical turret at the rear had a wider arc of fire since it was not adjacent to any other structure. The rear gunner appears to have been completely isolated; if he

was able to crawl down a passage to the front it is not recorded and seems unlikely. Presumably there was enough room for the front gunner to duck down and talk to the driver but the official method of communication was by Larnygaphone. This was a sort of throat microphone which was supposed to eliminate all extraneous sounds but probably distorted the human voice to an unearthly croak at the same time. This peculiar tank spent some three months at MWEE in the spring of 1926 but, apart from its brief appearance at Camberley in November, little more is known about it, and nobody saw fit to record the reasons that lay behind the design. From a tactical point of view it would seem to be completely useless, either as a machine-gun carrier or light tank.

Two years passed before anything more was done to develop a true light tank, and this was as a direct attempt to improve upon the Carden-Loyd carrier. Indeed the prototype was listed as the Carden-Loyd Mark VII in MWEE records, although this was qualified by the explanation that it was an experimental light tank. It was amazingly low, measuring just over four feet in height, yet it incorporated a fully revolving turret and quite a large engine – the six-cylinder Meadows type EOC. It weighed a mere 2 tons 7cwt in its unladen state. The suspension clearly derived from the Carden-Loyd Mark VI, with an outside girder supporting the springs, but its obvious difference was in the size of the road wheels, which were something more than just rollers. The driver sat in the front of a shallow hull with the gunner behind him in the lowest of turrets, which even had bevelled panels like a Rolls-Royce armoured car. Trials at MWEE showed that the driver's position was just too low, he was both cribbed and cramped, and the turret was so small that the gunner could neither load nor handle the Vickers machine-

43 The first of the true light tanks, A4E1, with its tiny turret dominated by the machine-gun. Notice how the suspension has derived from the old Carden-Loyd system.

gun properly. Performance on the road seems to have been quite good; the little tank ran down from Farnborough to Bovington on one occasion in very good time. Since it did not have a speedometer of its own the tank was paced all the way by a Jowett staff car which reported speeds of up to 45mph. Across country it was a different matter. An ordinary four-speed car-type gearbox simply did not provide the power needed to climb slopes, and the lack of an emergency low gear was criticised. So too were the steering and the tracks which came off far too frequently, while the armour, especially at the sides and back, was so thin that the hull distorted. Even so the little vehicle – which was the prototype for one of the largest families of tanks ever produced in Britain – had one overriding quality in the opinion of the War Office and Government, it was extremely cheap.

Later in that year, 1928, the War Office placed a contract with Vickers-Carden-Loyd covering four more machines designated Light Tank Mark I. They were delivered to MWEE in October 1929, three being identical while the fourth was quite different. All shared the same type of hull, stepped down at the front with a raised fighting compartment and sloping rear plate. Once again the Meadows engine was chosen, but this time coupled to a two-speed primary and two-speed auxiliary gearbox incorporating reverse. Drive was to the front sprockets with clutch and brake steering in the usual Carden-Loyd tradition. The suspension was improved: four large spoked wheels were fitted on each side, joined in pairs by short leaf springs, while the idler was of a similar pattern and adjustable for tension by an ingenious ratchet device that soon became

standard for most Vickers-Armstrong light tracked vehicles. Three of the tanks carried a small, round turret mounting the usual Vickers water-cooled machine-gun, while the driver was accommodated beneath a sliding headcover, which was still described as cramped. The overall height was up by about one foot on the prototype. Armour was increased to 14mm and the weight went up to about 3·5 tons, but the speed was still a respectable 32mph. The fourth tank had no turret but instead carried a pair of ·5in heavy machine-guns in an open mounting fitted to the turret ring, which was clearly designed with anti-aircraft use in mind. The mounting appears to be identical to that fitted on a Crossley armoured car and described earlier. The short, stiff leaf springs gave a very harsh ride across country, and one of the tanks was later modified by Vickers, working in conjunction with Horstmann of Bath, to a system that employed horizontal coil springs linking each pair of wheels. This, on the other hand, gave rise to excessive pitching and, in a crude effort to improve this, interconnected struts were fitted between the bogies and hull to give a damping effect. Known as the controlled scissors suspension it has all the hallmarks of a stopgap solution. Individual vehicles were issued to RTC units for evaluation, but none of these tanks entered service.

Although the mainstream of light tank development progressed in a logical way from one mark to the next, some unusual examples appeared from time to time; usually from manufacturers other than Vickers. However, the first was built by Vickers to a War Office contract dated October 1929, and it arrived at MWEE sometime in the following year. It was a

44 A Light Tank Mark I, seen here at MWEE sitting on a special bogie transporter trailer also supplied by Vickers-Armstrong.

45 *The anti-aircraft version of the Light Tank Mark I viewed from the rear.*

three-man light tank, armed with a pair of machine-guns mounted side by side in a turret described as being of the Lanchester type, and this so dominated the hull as to give the tank a surprisingly bulky appearance. The hull was both wider and higher than the two-man types, and a Mechanisation Board report claims that it was more heavily armoured; however, MWEE records give a figure of 9mm, and this is borne out by the weight, which was about 4·5 tons. Nevertheless, the suspension gives every impression of having been designed for a much heavier machine. The tracks ran around conventional Vickers sprockets, idlers and return rollers, but in place of the

large spoked wheels this tank had eight very small rollers on each side, linked in pairs by short leaf springs. These in turn were attached to the ends of very substantial half-moon shaped castings which pivoted on cross tubes running through the hull. Deflection would have been very limited, yet the tank had a top road speed of 28mph, reduced to 18mph across country. Trials soon revealed that the suspension was not suitable, and a new design was evolved which was described as being of the Horstmann type. However, it differed from the normal pattern in that each wheel was attached to a separate arm and sprung vertically on a coil spring which bore against the return roller bracket. No picture of it in this form has yet been traced, but the description of the suspension suggests that, in principle at least, it had something in common with the American Christie system. The tank had been fitted with the more powerful Meadows EPC engine when built, but trials in 1931, following the change in suspension, suggested that something even more powerful was required, so a type ESC rated at 100hp was chosen instead, along with a Meadows type nine gearbox. Clearly the suspension had not been much of a success either, for when last reported upon in 1932, the tank was at the Royal Arsenal awaiting the new automotive parts and another suspension of the Horstmann type suggested by Slow Motion Suspensions Ltd.

Returning to the development of two-man light tanks we now come to five examples built under the designation Mark IA, which appeared in 1930. Changes from the Mark I design mostly concerned the hull, which was higher, with sloping

46 *Another curiosity, the three-man light tank A5E1 showing the unusual suspension system which adds to the general effect of bulkiness.*

47 *A camouflage painted Light Tank Mark IA. This one was being used to test a Ricardo diesel engine.*

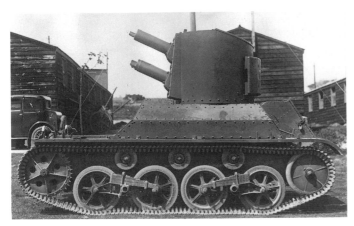

48 *Photographed at Lulworth where it went for gunnery trials the double-gun turreted Mark IA was yet another oddity.*

sides; no doubt to provide more room for the crew. It brought the overall height up to 6ft 2 ins; but with only 9mm armour the weight remained at just over four tons. As built the tanks all used the same Meadows engine, two–plus–two gearbox and leaf spring suspension, while four of them carried the same turret as the Mark I. By 1931 at least four of the tanks had been reworked to take the Horstmann suspension. Two then went out to Egypt, two more went for user trials to 5th Battalion RTC at Perham Down while the fifth remained at MWEE. This last tank had another odd turret design, much taller than the normal type and mounting two-machine guns vertically, one above the other. The lower gun was a ·5, the upper a ·303 and they appear to have been linked to synchronise elevation. The reason for this curious arrangement can only have been to fit a pair of guns into such a small turret, and the emphasis on elevation suggests a ground and anti-aircraft capability. In 1934 two of the conventional tanks were fitted with four-cylinder diesel engines – the Ricardo type S65 – linked to Dorman four-speed gearboxes, but the trials do not appear to have revealed any particular advantages. The period of experiment in light tank design culminating in the Mark IA suggested that a suitable stage had been reached for production to begin, and in December 1930 orders were placed for 16 light tanks of the IA type: 12 from Vickers-Armstrong and four from Royal Ordnance. These first appeared, as the Light Tank Mark II, in 1931.

The transition from experimental to service machines involves a good deal more than simply supplying them to units on a full-time basis. A service tank has to be designed with operational use in mind so it has to be stowed, both internally and out, with the various things that a crew will need to keep them in action and simply let them live in the field for a period of time. These items, and the fittings that hold them, add materially to the weight. During the period under consideration many tanks were also being equipped with wireless sets and, in the case of the light tanks this not only meant even more weight, but a larger turret to contain the set and more batteries.

Fortunately this stage in tank design coincided with a new development in protection, probably the first to reach production status since the original tanks were designed. The new material was known as Cemented Tank Armour, or CTA plate, and it was developed by the English Steel Corporation, a Vickers-Armstrong subsidiary based in Sheffield. It is more commonly known as case, or face hardened armour – a type of plate that was reckoned to have ballistic qualities about 20 per cent better than the homogeneous armour normally used for tanks. The two terms later came to mean something slightly different when more advanced techniques were developed but, in the early days, both described a system known to metallurgists as carburising. Hardness of armour depends on the carbon content of a piece of plate, but if steel with a low carbon content is used it can be hardened, on one surface only, by heating it over a long period in contact with a carbonaceous material such as charcoal. The result is that armour of, say, 11mm thickness, given the CTA treatment, will match the bullet-resistant properties of homogeneous plate 15mm thick. The saving of weight is, therefore, quite considerable, although the process is time-consuming and expensive for a variety of reasons. In the first place any plate needing to be face hardened has to be rolled, cut exactly to shape and then drilled as required before undergoing the treatment; otherwise it is impossible to work. The process takes a long time and the treatment seriously distorts the plate, which has to be flattened out afterwards. This is turn can result in damage, mostly by cracking, so a certain amount of plate in each batch may have to be discarded. Finally such plate does not take a weld easily, and if this is done from the back where the material is softer, it tends to reduce the effective hardness of the face where heat is applied. However since weight was an even more vital factor in these light tanks it was used on all models up to Mark VI.

Outwardly the new tanks were similar to the Mark IA, except for the shape of the turret. The Horstmann coil spring suspension was chosen at the outset, along with a new and more powerful version of the Meadows engine, the type EPC. Urgency prevented the development of a new gearbox in time, although it was appreciated that one was needed. For the present, then, the tanks would be provided with a two-speed and reverse sliding gearbox, coupled to an epicycle dual ratio box. A new, lighter type of cross shaft was introduced for the driving axle along with final planetary reduction gears just inboard of the sprockets. Speeds of 35mph were reached on test, but there were problems with the clutch, and the tiller bar steering system was unpopular. The turret developed at the ROF was, however, quite new, although it would soon be copied in a larger scale on the A7. It was rectangular, with sloping sides, with enough room at the back to accommodate a No 1 wireless set. The machine-gun mounting was also new, to a pattern worked out by the Superintendent of Design, and featured a Vickers gun with rotary drum feed that took up less space inside, while spent cartridges were expelled outside at the front, into a canvas bag to prevent them jamming in the turret ring.

49 A factory shot of a partially completed Light Tank Mark II showing the engine installed and the Horstmann suspension. The rear idlers are among the things which have yet to be fitted.

By 1931 the War Office had come to the conclusion that 22 light tanks would be required for each of three mixed RTC Battalions, so orders were placed for a further 50. Twenty-nine would come from the ROF under the designation Light Tank Mark IIA, and the remaining 21 from Vickers as the Mark IIB. The main difference between the two concerned their petrol capacity: the Mark IIA having two fuel tanks where the IIB had one, although of overall greater capacity. Both differed from the original Mark II in having an adjustable ventilation flap on the hull front and protected air inlet louvres along both sides of the turret top.

Since the introduction of the Light Mark II further investigations had taken place into the matter of transmissions, with the result that the 50 improved models were delivered with five-speed pre-selector gearboxes designed by Maj.

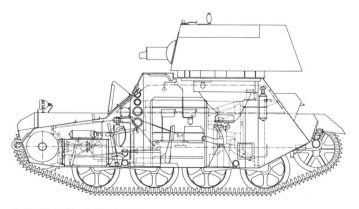

D11 Light Tank Mark IIA.

Wilson and manufactured by Armstrong Siddeley Motors. By 1934 the 16 original machines had also been converted to this system. At about the same time a decision had been reached to replace the Meadows engines with a Rolls-Royce type, the six-cylinder 20/25hp model, and this was undertaken on all 66 tanks between 1932 and 1935. Official records are very vague on this subject and never actually explain why it was done. No strong criticism is ever made against the Meadows unit, and the Rolls-Royce engine had to be extensively modified, not just to match up to the Wilson gearbox but also in respect of oil-cooling and other details. Other improvements involved the replacement of the steering tiller by levers and the addition of a footbrake. As they became available the new tanks were issued, on a limited scale, as company commander's tanks, for which purpose a signal flag box was attached to the turret plus a megaphone for shouting at medium tanks with. As more were delivered they began to replace the Carden-Loyd carriers in the light tank companies of mixed battalions and, ultimately, to form the main strength of the new 1st (Light) Battalion RTC when that was permanently established following the Tank Brigade exercises. Operating in the reconnaissance role the light tanks were given a hard time, especially on cross-country operations, where their speed was exploited regardless of possible damage or crew comfort. This resulted in cracking of the upper hull plates around the turret ring and weakening of the suspension. Wear on the bearings caused the coil springs, which were only on the outer face of each bogie, to twist the road wheels out of alignment, and this in turn caused the springs to bend in the middle and lose their resilience. On most Mark II series tanks they were gradually replaced by a new double spring system devised by Vickers, which will be described in more detail later. As they were gradually replaced in Britain by newer models, the Mark IIs mostly went out to Egypt, where they were fitted with drinking-water tanks and sandguards covering the top run of the tracks. Some were still there, serving as training machines, as late as 1940.

As might be expected various experiments were carried out on these tanks over the years, of which the following were of some importance. One was a conversion kit, designed by Nicholas Straussler, which gave the tank an amphibious capability. Col. Sir Frederick Pile was the moving force behind the project and tests were conducted under the supervision of the Royal Engineers. A trials vehicle was made waterproof, up to hull level, by using close pitch rivets at the main joints, and Straussler provided a pair of collapsible mahogany floats with rubberised seams, that attached to the suspension on each side. These proved capable of supporting the 4·5 ton-tank on an even keel in the water. Modifications were applied to raise the exhaust pipe and fit a bracket at the rear to take an outboard motor. An Elto was first used, later replaced by a 40hp Johnson, which gave the tank a top speed of about three knots and also provided for steering in the water. Initial tests were carried out in the Royal Arsenal canal, and later in the sea off Spithead, in conjunction with one of the prototype Royal Marine landing craft. Two tanks were converted and the system seems to have worked perfectly well, but it was not adopted for service use at this time. Various experiments were carried out with different transmission systems, the most promising of which seems to have been a five-speed sliding gearbox by Vickers-Armstrong which, in top gear, raised the

50 *The Light Tank Mark II adapted for flotation using collapsible pontoons. Points worth noting are the close pitch rivets, raised exhaust pipe and sealant smeared around the driver's visor. One crew member has to squat uncomfortably at the back to operate the outboard motor.*

maximum speed to 36·5 mph. Wilson tried a modified version of his cross drive epicyclic system, as used on A6E3, but this was found to be unsuitable for light tanks. The Freeborn fully automatic transmission appears to have worked perfectly well when it was fitted in 1936, yet it, too, was never adopted. The Goodrich company provided a set of reinforced rubber tracks which were fitted to one tank, but again never adopted, while Vickers modified another experimentally, to be driven by radio control.

In 1932 orders were placed with the ROF for nine two-man light tanks of an improved design, subsequently raised to 42, of which 17 were to be built by Vickers-Armstrong. The main object was to both simplify, and improve upon the Mark II design; the new model being taken into service as the Light Mark III. The Rolls-Royce engine and Wilson transmission were adopted as standard from the start, as was the new Vickers double spring suspension. This used the same type of road wheels, connected in pairs by an articulated cast bracket which acted on a pair of angled coil springs. This system was not only more flexible, it was better balanced and a good deal stronger to absorb the kind of hammering these little tanks were subjected to in service. The hull design was simplified to ease production and accessibility for maintenance, and ventilation was improved by increasing the number of louvred panels around the engine compartment. In an effort to save weight the frames, to which the hull plates were riveted, were made from duralium, but this was later changed to a magnesium alloy. The turret was enlarged so that the tank

51 *A prototype for the Light Tank Mark III, with 'unarmoured' warning triangles on the turret. Vickers double spring suspension can be seen and the distinctive silencer for the Rolls-Royce engine.*

could mount either the ·303in or ·5in Vickers gun as required, but two turrets, of slightly different pattern can be identified. Both featured an enlarged hatch for the commander. The Superintendent of Design came up with another new type of armour that was fitted to one tank but it soon showed signs of fracturing and was replaced by the CTA type. One tank went up to Yorkshire in 1935 for snow trials. These were carried out by 4th Battalion at Catterick and involved various types of spudded track, toothed idler wheels and assorted snow

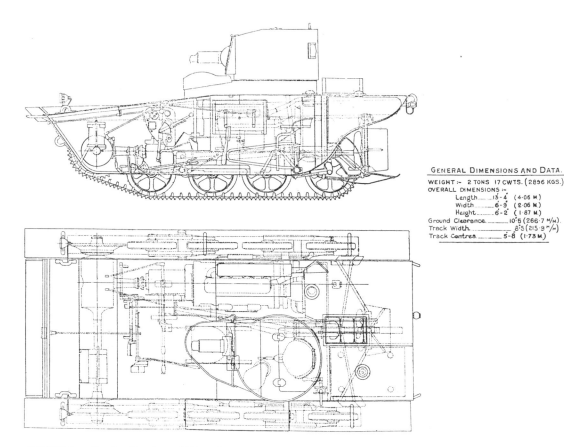

GENERAL DIMENSIONS AND DATA.
WEIGHT :- 2 TONS 17 CWTS. (2896 KGS.)
OVERALL DIMENSIONS :-
Length........13·4 (4·06 M)
Width........6·9 (2·06 M)
Height........6·2 (1·87 M)
Ground Clearance........10·5 (266·7 M/M).
Track Width........8·5 (215·9 M/M)
Track Centres........5·8 (1·73 M)

D12 Vickers-Carden-Loyd amphibious light tank.

ploughs, all of which only served to show that the tank was perfectly satisfactory in these conditions just as it was; a fact Vickers had discovered in 1934 when they tested a commercial light tank in the snows of the Gurnigel Pass in Switzerland. In any case the snow in Yorkshire melted after a couple of days, and the tale was repeated when the tests resumed in January 1936.

Here again we can interrupt the main theme of light tank development to examine two machines purchased more or less off the shelf from Vickers-Armstrong in 1932. They were production models of a light, amphibious tank, the prototype of which had been demonstrated on the Thames near Chertsey in April 1931. The two built for the War Office were classified as A4E11 and A4E12, being identical in most respects to the commercial model, which is described in greater detail in a later chapter. Trials revealed that the designers had cut too many corners in order to save weight. To obtain flotation without the use of additional floats the weight had to be kept down to 2·75 tons, which meant that the armour was too thin for safety, while the hull structure, lacking a strong frame, was liable to distort when stressed. Speed on land was remarkable but in the water it did not come up to expectations, and in sea trials off Shoeburyness it displayed a tendency to dip its nose in

the water and try to behave like a submarine. Although the tanks remained on the experimental list for some years they were never adopted as service types by the British Army.

In 1932 Vickers-Armstrong built two new light tanks for tests at MWEE with a view to their being adopted by the Army in India. Clearly Sir John Carden knew they were good because, in a memo to head office, he suggests that once the War Office sees them it will place orders too; and so it turned out. Known as A4E19 and A4E20 they differed only in the type of turret fitted. The former had a small, six-sided affair of the type favoured in India, which also mounted an experimental Vickers air-cooled machine-gun; a further pointer to tropical service. The second mounted what became known as the No 3 pattern, which was shorter but similar in shape to the type fitted on the Light Tank Mark III. However, it was in the shape of the hull that the new tanks could most easily be distinguished from earlier models. In the never-ending struggle to save weight, Vickers' design team made the tank shorter by about two feet and wider by about eight inches, yet about the same height as previous models. The hull was also sharply undercut at the rear, while the front plate sloped at a similar angle from the nose, in one continuous run, to the top. Since the sides were vertical this gave the tank a curious backward

52 *The shorter track base and revised hull layout of the Light Tank Mark IV are evident from this photograph of a prototype. This tank, however, is fitted with a non-standard turret and air-cooled machine-gun.*

leaning parallelogram profile, and from many angles it was an ugly machine, looking squat and unbalanced. The track was shorter too, this being achieved by eliminating the separate idler wheel. Two Vickers double spring bogies were used on each side, but the rearmost wheel of each rear bogie was made adjustable to do the work of an idler; no return roller was fitted either.

It seems that the Rolls-Royce engines fitted to light tanks operating in the desert had shown signs of excessive wear so the new tanks reverted to the Meadows type, in this case the 100bhp EST. It was direct coupled to a Vickers five-speed sliding gear box. As in earlier designs the engine was mounted on the right side of the vehicle, possibly in order to place the exhaust pipe away from the kerb side. Previous tanks, being longer, still had the driver seated roughly in the centre, but the new tank was so short that he was placed alongside the engine and, consequently well over to the left. The turret, likewise was offset, adding to the generally unbalanced effect of the whole design. The first prototype was built in 7mm plate, but when the War Office took an interest the second had to be completed in 9mm plate and then given additional ballast to represent the weight of a tank with 11mm of armour, which was specified for the production models. Deliveries commenced in 1935; the Vickers-Armstrong tanks were finished first and some were issued to units in time for the summer training season. Those from the ROF were delayed; it was well into 1936 before they were all in service and by that time the requirement for light tanks had changed and they were already out of date. Reports from Lulworth claim that the Mark IV was a much better gun platform than the previous types, although photographs of them in service show that they pitched violently on rough ground, due no doubt to the short track base, and the commander was obliged to hang on tight if he was not to be catapulted straight out of the turret. In most other respects the design was considered to be excellent. With a laden weight of 4 tons 6cwt it was lighter than the Mark III and its top speed of 36mph was greater than any, up to and including the Mark VI,

53 *A production Light Tank Mark IV in company with two Mediums during anti-gas training. The commander is hanging on to the hand grips on top of the turret which were absolutely essential in these machines.*

with the single exception of the original Carden-Loyd Mark VII. It is, perhaps, worth reminding ourselves at this point that by 1936, no less than seven different types, and sub-types of light tank had been designed and built, five of which had gone into service. The pace of development was, in fact, so rapid that Marks III and IV were virtually contemporaries, and this compares very favourably with the time taken over the mediums. Obviously, being smaller, there were fewer problems to contend with and many parts were common to the various mdoels, but it still represents a considerable achievement. Even so, it has to be set against the pace of progress in tactical thinking which was running faster still. This can easily be illustrated by reference to the next light tank, the Mark V, which actually began to enter service before the Mark IV.

This development can be traced to an article written by two RTC officers which, as an eye-catcher they entitled 'The Two-and-a-Half-Man Light Tank'. The point they hoped to make was that there was simply too much for two men to do, driving and operating a light tank in action. Experience gained on exercises showed clearly that, while the driver's job was clear cut and relatively straightforward, the commander was over-burdened with tasks. In addition to the basic job of loading and firing the machine-gun, and clearing stoppages when they occurred, this over-worked soul had to operate the wireless, read a map, direct his driver and conform to the movements of the rest of his troop, while trying to keep an eye on the general battlefield situation. The result was that, on exercises, commanders often chose to sit on top of their turrets, with their legs dangling down inside. They simply reached down through the hatch to fire the machine-gun, without bothering to get inside and sight it properly, in order not to lose touch with what was going on around them; clearly this was unrealistic. So, come to that, was the idea of two-and-a-half men, so the next step had to be the three-man light tank, in which the third crew member was the tank commander, who need not touch the gun.

Two pilot models were ordered from Vickers in 1932 under the GS specifications L3E1 and L3E2, and they were delivered for trials early in the following year. The first one, built with plate on an 11mm basis, featured a hull design that was similar to the Mark IV but somewhat longer. This was essential since the larger, two-man turret was almost as wide as the hull and, therefore, had to be situated behind the engine. With a bigger turret the opportunity was taken to increase the firepower so that this, and all the three-man tanks that evolved from it, carried two machine-guns in a new dual mounting. The guns being water-cooled Vickers ·5in and ·303in weapons arranged co-axially. While this might be seen as adding to the gunner's duties, and thus offsetting the advantage, it was not so in practice since each gun would be used separately, and for a different purpose. The ·303 remained basically an anti-personnel weapon while the bigger ·5 was available for use against enemy light tanks and similar targets. The turret of L3E1 was D-shaped in plan form, with the flat portion at the back, and mounted a Bishop's Mitre type of cupola in the centre, which must have made things difficult for the poor gunner, working around the legs of his commander. On L3E2 the turret was altered to a more streamlined shape at the rear, yet still providing sufficient room for a wireless set, but now

with a drum-shaped cupola offset to the right. This tank was built to a 14mm armour standard, which was specified for the production model – to be known as the Light Tank Mark V – although the 22 tanks built to this order by Vickers-Armstrong were actually completed in 11mm plate.

54 L3E2, the second prototype for the three-man Light Tank Mark V, showing the final turret shape. The picture was taken at MEE, but the purpose of the girder and strut attached to the suspension is not known.

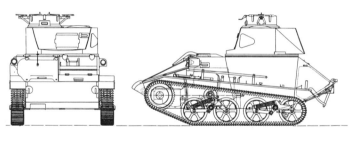

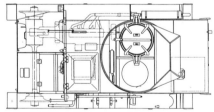

D13 Maker's drawings of the Light Tank Mark V, without armament.

In addition to its basic shape the Mark V shared other features with the Mark IV, notably the Meadows EST engine and Vickers five-speed sliding gearbox. The suspension layout was also the same, except for the addition of a single return roller built into the bracket of the leading bogie. The first nine tanks were hurriedly completed by the summer of 1934 in order that they could be issued to the Tank Brigade in August for troop evaluation. When these were completed in October, six of the tanks went back to Elswick works for final completion while the other three were retained for trials. One went down to Lulworth for firing trials, another went to the Royal Arsenal to be shot at, so that the Chief Inspector of Armaments could determine its immunity to small arms fire, especially in the region of the front, right-hand side of the hull where an air-ingress louvre and the radiator were located. The third tank was sent down to the RTC Centre at Bovington to assist with the preparation of a driver's handbook.

By 1935 all the tanks were in service, mostly with the newly mechanised cavalry regiments but, like the Mark IV version they were never issued to units serving abroad except for the odd example sent to Egypt for desert trials. Experimental variants were few, if one excludes the scissors bridgelayer conversion of L3E1 and some prototype anti-aircraft tanks which are detailed in another volume*. L3E2 was adapted to test another Straussler flotation device and a simple trench crossing attachment. Indeed this latter item was so simple that when Vickers asked Sir John Carden to design an alternative which would free them of the need to buy out Straussler's patent he said it couldn't be done. One of the production Light Mark Vs was used for a series of experiments in suspension layout, mainly with a view to extending the track base and improving the ride.

Modern Formations, a War Office sponsored booklet published in 1931, stated that in light tanks, speed was of greater importance than firepower. It defined the tanks' roles as reconnaissance, co-operation with medium tanks, operating in conjunction with armoured cars and screening transport columns on the move. By the time the Light Mark V appeared it was evident that views on firepower had changed to some extent, although the reason for this was never spelled out, and then in 1936 an order was placed for a light tank in which the need for protection seemed to dominate. For the first time since light tanks had been developed Vickers-Armstrong played no part in the scheme, the design work being in the hands of the Superintendent of Design's office, and construction of the prototype by Royal Ordnance at Woolwich. It was given the designation L4E1, its main features being an increase in armour thickness to a 14mm standard – which placed it on a par with contemporary developments in cruiser tanks – and the fact that this armour was extended to cover the suspension. It seems reasonable to assume, although it is not stated, that this was connected with the move in 1934 to

convert 4th Battalion RTC into an experimental infantry support battalion – a step confirmed shortly afterwards by its being renamed 4th (Army) Tank Battalion. However, in *The Business of Tanks** Brig. MacLeod Ross implies that it was conceived as a rival to the Light Mark V because that tank was such a poor design. Having criticised Vickers for designing tanks around 'as large an engine as British industry had in production at the moment', he goes on to explain that his team, after examining an AEC engine, chose the Meadows – which Vickers had been using for years. He complains about the weight of the Light Mark V, which was lighter than L4E1, and rounds off by explaining how Woolwich, in conjunction with the Royal Aircraft Esablishment, introduced magnesium alloy extrusions and castings, despite the fact that they had been used on the Light Mark III. According to the Mechanisation Board the object of L4E1 was to produce a tank with 'superior fighting performance coupled with better protection and . . . to enhance the vehicle performance while maintaining the gross weight within the lowest limits possible', which sounds like the tank designer's ideal anyway. Since fighting performance could best be improved by an increase in firepower over the Light Mark V, this was certainly not achieved, as the tank mounted the same co-axial armament as the Vickers tank; that is unless one considers the mounting of two smoke grenade projectors on the turret as an improvement. Protection clearly was improved, but at a cost in maximum speed, which was 4mph slower than a Light Mark V.

The tone adopted by MacLeod Ross points to an unfortunate period of infighting between Vickers and the Staff at Woolwich and a suggestion of jealousy. The implication being that the General Staff had effectively handed over its responsibilities for the initiation of tank design to Carden and the people at Vickers, while ignoring the home-grown skills sitting idly by in the Design Department. Whether there is some truth in this or not it has to be admitted that none of the designs produced at Woolwich Arsenal during this period ever reached the mass production stage, except in respect of relative details such as weapons mountings or light tank turrets. Thus L4E1 remained another one-off. It was delivered to MWEE in July 1937, and a report explained that it had been built using the same structural techniques that had been developed for the A7 medium tanks. That is, a longitudinal box-girder frame with plates riveted to it, although how this is supposed to have differed from the Vickers' method is not clear. It resulted in a roomy fighting compartment which even featured a rear escape door for the crew – itself a vast improvement on the A7 arrangement. The tank was about one foot longer than a Light Mark V but the suspension, which is also claimed by MacLeod Ross as an innovation, looks remarkably like the Vickers double spring type with the addition of a separate rear idler, and this was claimed to give a much better ride on rough ground. The engine chosen originally was the Meadows ESTR but, since this was continually blowing head gaskets on trial, it was replaced by the less powerful ESTL unit, which further reduced the speed. What MacLeod Ross fails to mention is that the tank had a Vickers five-speed sliding gearbox, driving the

55 *A stretched Light Mark V with an extra bogie unit added and the drive sprocket moved forward and linked by chain to the original final drive.*

The Great Tank Scandal.

*Macleod Ross. *The Business of Tanks*. Arthur Stockwell Ltd, 1976.

56 *The ROF's attempt to build a three-man light tank, the L4E1. It looks untidy, over-protected and over-weight, even down to having disc, instead of spoked road wheels.*

front sprockets and typical light tank pattern tracks, so that mechanically, and indeed in most other respects except for armour thickness and arrangement, L4E1 was little different from the Vickers three-man tanks, despite attempts to make it seem revolutionary. It received consistently good reports from the Mechanisation Board, yet it was abandoned in 1938 and must ultimately be counted a failure.

The Light Mark V was also given extremely favourable reports by the staff of MWEE and it was proving itself in service, largely in the hands of novice drivers in newly mechanised cavalry regiments. Within its limitations it fulfilled most of the GS requirements except for the recently agreed 14mm armour standard, and this was rectified in the new Light Tank Mark VI, which was ordered from Vickers-Armstrong in the summer of 1935. The first, from a batch of 51, was delivered to what was now the Mechanisation Experimental Establishment (MEE) in January 1936, and the most obvious visual difference from the Light Mark V was the turret, which was enlarged at the rear to house the new No 9 wireless set. In fact the turret featured other improvements for better ventilation and to keep the rain out, while air-flow to the radiator was increased by fitting two armoured intakes over the engine cover plate. According to a Mechanisation Board report these were only intended for use on tanks destined to see service in the Middle East. The increase in weight was offset by the use of magnesium alloy for such automotive components as the engine crankcase, gearbox and clutch housings, although in all other respects these units were identical to those used on the

earlier model. Vickers built another 20 in 1936 but, a shadow of things to come, ten more were ordered from the North British Locomotive Co in Glasgow at the same time. Trials at MEE revealed various minor faults, some of which were apparently due to Vickers making unauthorised changes to components, notably in connection with cooling. An improvement in performance was achieved by fitting twin Solex carburettors, and a standard Borg and Beck clutch replaced the special one developed by the makers.

57 *T1719 was a Light Tank Mark VI built by the North British Locomotive Co. It is seen here on a training exercise during the war with an Army Tank Brigade.*

Later in 1936 an improved model, the Mark VIA, was ready for delivery from Vickers and the ROF. The main changes concerned the suspension. Stronger, wider bogie wheels were fitted and the front bogie assembly moved about five inches further forwards to improve the ride. The return roller, which had been mounted on this bogie in the Marks V and VI was repositioned further back, attached directly to the hull side, and other modifications were carried out on the rearmost bogie/idler wheels. The round style of commander's cupola fitted to the earlier three-man tank was replaced by an octagonal pattern of the type fitted to L4E1. Something over 200 Light Mark VIA tanks were built, but further orders placed late in 1936 specified certain other improvements and yet another change of designation.

The Light Tank Mark VIB may be described as the definitive three-man light tank from the Vickers-Carden-Loyd stable. Most of the changes were of a minor nature connected with the engine and improved splash protection of the driver's hatch, but the two most obvious to an observer were, a change to only one cooling louvre on the engine cover plate and a reversion to the round type of commander's cupola. By now, of course, rearmament was getting into its stride and an increasing number of firms took small orders to gain experience of tank production. These included the Vulcan Foundry, Fowlers of Leeds, Armstrong-Whitworth and Ruston Hornsby, in addition to those already recorded. Total production ran to something approaching 1,000, but this figure includes about

200 tanks ultimately completed as the Mark VIC. This resulted from a War Office policy decision to replace the water-cooled Vickers machine-guns by air-cooled Besas in all future armoured fighting vehicles. In the light tanks this meant that the ·303 Vickers was replaced by a 7·92mm Besa, and the ·5 by a long 15mm Besa, a weapon that proved to be almost as temperamental as its predecessor had been. Also, for some reason, this last version had no turret cupola at all, just another flush fitting two-piece hatch. The only pre-war modification of any note was carried out on a Ruston Hornsby built light tank, T1667, which had its turret replaced by a larger, open-topped pattern, mounting a 2pr anti-tank gun. It was the Mark II version of a similar conversion – recorded later – to a Vickers carrier, and it appears in every way to have been a most promising experiment. Tested at Lulworth and by the 9th Lancers at Tidworth, it was found that the larger turret did not unduly overload the suspension and, had it gone into production, there is every reason to believe that it would have resulted in an effective, and highly mobile anti-tank vehicle along the lines of what later became known as a tank destroyer, since the 2pr was quite capable of penetrating the armour of any combat vehicle that the Germans could field in the early years of the Second World War. There is always an argument, and a perfectly sound one, for not providing reconnaissance machines with heavy weapons. The reasoning is that the crew of a recce vehicle should only be armed sufficiently to defend themselves in an emergency. If they are given heavier weapons

58 The 2pr armed, tank-destroyer version of the Light Mark VI showing the large, open-topped turret. Even so it does not look an unbalanced design and might have proved very useful if put into production.

59 The experimental little Alvis Straussler light tank having its tracks fitted. The designer Nicholas Straussler is the figure in the suit and cap.

the odds are that they will try to use them, instead of getting on with the proper business of scouting, and reporting what they have seen. This makes good sense, so long as those who direct them understand their limitations. When they are misused, as occurred with the Divisional Cavalry Regiments of the British Expeditionary Force in 1940, then the result is disaster, and one wonders what the men of those regiments would have given for a few 2pr armed light tanks when they tried to stem the German advance through Belgium in that fateful summer.

One last light tank deserves to be examined before this chapter is closed. It arrived at MEE in July 1936, from the Alvis Co works in Coventry. It was in fact a commercial design, built for export, but since one was supplied to a War Department contract it can justifiably be discussed here. Its designer, Nicholas Straussler, has already been mentioned in these pages. He was a naturalised Briton, Hungarian by birth, and a gifted engineer with wide ranging interests in transportation and an original approach to most technical problems. He had already produced a number of designs for armoured cars and light tanks which had been built by Manfred Weiss of Budapest, but when he came to Great Britain in the early thirties he teamed up with the Alvis Company. Aware that they already had a perfectly satisfactory light tank in the Mark VI, the authorities laid down some very stringent requirements, mostly in respect of performance, that the little tank was unable to meet. Even so it was a novel design. The

hull contained a pair of six-cylinder Alvis engines, each of which drove the front and rear sprockets on one side of the tank, through French-designed Cotal electro-magnetic gearboxes and two-speed transfer boxes via constant velocity universal jonts. The suspension consisted of two bogies per side, which operated on quarter elliptical leaf springs, much as the original Vickers light tanks had done, and they proved to be just as harsh across country. In order to prove the automotive features the tank was delivered to MEE without a turret, although the specifications called for a three-man tank, with 14mm armour and a performance at least ten per cent better than the Light Mark VI. Steering was controlled by adjusting the respective engine speeds, supplemented by pedal-operated brakes as required. Speeds on the road were up to the 35mph required, but the sensitive throttle controls made steering highly dangerous and a malfunction in either engine could cause the tank to be thrown clear across the road before the driver had time to react. Across country the tank regularly shed its tracks and finished up splitting its road rollers, but attempts by the makers failed to improve things and the tank was duly returned as unsuitable. There is some evidence to suggest that the Straussler tank could run on its wheels if the tracks were removed, although this is not mentioned in the official report. It was photographed later with a turret, undergoing what must have been private trials, but there is no evidence that any were ever sold.

6 The Armoured Force

The study of armoured fighting vehicles, purely as mechanical objects, from the technical point of view, while interesting and valid enough in itself, is only half the story. Their reliability as machines, the accuracy of their guns and other capabilities such as hill climbing or trench crossing, are only of value if they contribute towards their effectiveness in combat. Further, one might add that the effort put into developing them could all be counted as worthless if, when the time came to put it to the test, the techniques of handling them in battle did not match up to what they were capable of. If one ignores Fuller's tactical thinking, which invariably ran far ahead of mechanical feasibility, the impression usually given is that mechanical developments in the 1920s took place in a tactical vacuum; it has already been shown how some types, notably the little tankettes and the big Independent, developed in ways that had never been imagined when they were designed. The ultimate test of machinery and tactics, the one that really matters, is battle itself, but even this has to be practised if success is expected when the final lines are drawn.

The traditional military answer to this problem is the mock battle, or exercise, which attempts, as closely as possible, to recreate the conditions of active service without the attendant dangers. If it can be confined to a military training area then it can be made very realistic indeed, but as mechanisation increased the area over which a battle might be fought, then more space is required and the army finds itself impinging upon the civilian population. This imposes many restrictions on the movement of troops, and the exercise becomes proportionally less realistic, although with careful planning a good deal can still be learnt. Among the exercises staged in the years between the wars, one of the most important was the Experimental Mechanised Force of 1927, but before we look at this in detail, some earlier events are worth recording. It will be recalled that as early as 1921 the MGO had recommended the formation of an experimental brigade, to try out various theories for a new age of tank warfare. The problem was that these theories were generally held by people whom mainstream military thinking regarded as dangerous radicals, so the chances of anything revolutionary happening at once were very slim. It is hardly necessary to stress the point that, with a major war so recently over, most senior officers would inevitably think in terms of that war whenever an exercise was planned; the mental effort required to think along new lines being more than they could manage. Under the circumstances this was quite understandable, but it was unfortunate that none of those officers who had served with the tanks, or thought deeply about their possibilities, had yet reached positions of influence within the Army.

Tanks were used during the 1922 manoeuvres, but they were all of the wartime type and in any case the exercise was on such a small scale that it passed off almost without notice. Much the same was true of the 1923 training season when, for instance, A Coy, 2nd Battalion, worked with the Guards Brigade, but was still operating Medium C tanks. B Coy, on the other hand, had already taken delivery of its first Vickers Mediums, but their part in the operations was not appreciably different. Fuller, in a lecture on the 'Mechanicalisation of Modern Armies', given in 1924, quotes a number of comments received from participating officers, of which the following is typical:

The outstanding feature . . . was that these Vickers tanks were used in the same way as the old Mark Vs were used in the war . . . Time and again one pointed out that a wide movement round a flank and an attack in reverse would not only be likely to bring about the desired result, but would also, perhaps, bring it about in a decisive manner. Such proposals, however, were not accepted because movements of this sort could not be said to be in close co-operation with the infantry. And it is apparently almost as much as a good reputation is worth to employ tanks on what may be called independent stunts.

In 1924 the 2nd Battalion was scheduled to take part in a divisional exercise in the New Forest, but an outbreak of foot and mouth disease caused this to be cancelled. The exercise was transferred to another part of Hampshire, around Alton, where cultivated land made the use of tanks impossible, so horse-drawn limbers were used instead. From the tank training point of view there was patently nothing more ridiculous than cantering around on a horse-drawn wagon plastered with labels indicating that it was meant to be a tank! In any case, practising tactics at company, or even battalion, level was hardly calculated to give anyone much experience in handling large tank formations. Thus a great deal was expected of a large scale exercise announced for 1925. The *Daily Express* called it 'the Greatest Mimic War since 1913', and explained that some 40,000 men would take part, over an area that included Wiltshire, Berkshire, Hampshire and Dorset. The Eastern Force, known as Mercia, was basically an infantry army supported by one brigade of cavalry and 2nd Battalion RTC. The Western Force – Wessex – was stronger in cavalry and armour, having both 5th Battalion RTC and the 5th ACC on its strength. Both sides could also count on air support from Army Co-operation squadrons of the RAF; however, the War Office informed the press, the main object was to try out the new medium tanks under simulated battle conditions. Most newspapers latched on to the importance that the Army attached to wireless and to smoke screens laid by tanks, while some, at least, were aware of the significance that was posed by motorised infantry columns. A number of preliminary skirmishes were reported. One, recorded as the Battle of Chitterne, involved two infantry brigades of which the 9th was commanded by Sir Hugh Elles, wartime commander of the

Tank Corps. His force, supported by 5th Battalion, managed to entice the enemy brigade into a trap which he then sprang by launching his tanks from the cover of a wood, roundly defeating the opposition. For a man who is generally supposed to have lost faith in the efficacy of armour this appears to have been an imaginative stroke that has been missed by his critics. The main exercise, a three day event starting on 23 September, was something of a disappointment. Torrential rain was the main culprit, it made movement off the road a difficult business, even for tanks, while low cloud hampered aerial reconnaissance. In any case the two forces were obliged to start operations with too little space separating them, so opportunities for wide-ranging manoeuvres proved impossible. It therefore became a matter of confrontation at marching pace – almost a reversion to Great War conditions – and very little was learnt. Writing in the *Morning Post* Field Marshal Sir William Robertson could see very little value in the exercise. He warned against those who had 'tanks on the brain' and pointed up their limitations, not only as they existed then, but as they might develop in the future. Perhaps it was a mercy that he could not know those same tanks had some 12 years of front line service ahead of them.

The 1926 season, although not on the scale of the previous year, featured a mixture of archaic and progressive actions, from the tank point of view. Among the former, two which took place on Salisbury Plain are worth recording. The first was a combined tank and cavalry attack upon a moving infantry column. The plan was to disrupt the column first with a company of tanks charging through and then send in the cavalry to wipe out the scattering enemy in detail. As it turned out the tanks launched their attack prematurely, and only hit the enemy's advance guard so that his main body, bringing machine-guns swiftly into action, was judged to have wiped out the attacking cavalry instead. The second action involved a company of tanks supporting infantry in an attack. Tied to a walking pace, and channeled into lanes left open in the artillery barrage, most were judged to have been knocked out by enemy guns. Towards the end of August an exercise in the Aldershot area was billed as 'The Largest Tank Attack Since The War'. The idea was that all 24 tanks of 2nd Battalion would make a 33 mile night march around the flank of an enemy force to attack 1st Guards Brigade soon after dawn. The night move was a great success, but when the time came for the attack to go in, tanks got tangled up with hundreds of spectators and their cars which blocked the very roads to which the attackers had been confined. This not only allowed their enemy – knowing exactly which route the tanks must take – to cover their approach with anti-tank guns, it caused the battalion to be split up, so that it delivered its attack in dribs and drabs. Capt. Liddell Hart, writing in the *Daily Telegraph*, also complained about the illogical umpiring procedure laid down by the War Office. This decreed that any tank, travelling at less than 6mph, when within 600 yards of an anti-tank gun, would automatically be declared knocked out when two rounds had been fired at it. If moving at more than 6mph then four rounds were required to achieve the same object. According to this influential military correspondent, trials at Larkhill showed that on average 22 rounds had to be fired at a tank before it could definitely be claimed that it had been destroyed. If this seems to be an inordinately high amount it should be borne in mind that the anti-tank gun in use at the time was nothing more than the regular field artillery 18pr, which was neither designed, nor particularly suited, to the role.

One unfortunate result of these inconclusive operations was that it made RTC officers more frustrated and inward looking than ever. This is nowhere more obvious than in the pages of contemporary issues of the *Royal Tank Corps Journal*. This monthly magazine, published at Bovington, while striking the usual balance between matters professional and personal to the Corps – without detracting from the really serious business of sport – reflected the insularity of a clique which felt itself to be rejected. Contributors were preaching to the converted, and probably preferred it that way. The possibility of a change depended on attitudes at the top, and these seemed most favourable in 1926 when Field Marshal Sir George Milne was appointed CIGS. A self-confessed convert to the creed of armoured warfare, he appeared to be totally committed when J F C Fuller was appointed his Military Assistant. Better yet, the new Secretary of State for War, Sir Lamming Worthington-Evans, gave every impression of being an even more zealous enthusiast than the CIGS, so the latter got instant backing when he announced his intention of forming an Experimental Mechanised Force in 1927. The story of Fuller's nomination as commander of this force, and how he was lost to the cause as Milne suffered increasingly from cold feet, has been told in the Regimental History*. For the present we shall concentrate on the activities of the force itself, and its constitution.

The Mechanised Force has been described as the prototype armoured division. Certainly nothing quite like it had ever been assembled before – the contemporary French experimental light division being little more than a mechanised infantry column backed up by tanks and motorised artillery. The dominant feature of the Mechanised Force was tanks; in this case the mediums of 5th Battalion, along with the armoured cars and tankettes of 3rd Battalion. They were supported by five mechanised artillery batteries, a motorised Field Company, Royal Engineers under the command of Martel and a motorised machine-gun battalion. For certain operations a lorry and half-track borne infantry battalion was added while the RAF contributed four squadrons for Army Co-operation, bombing and fighter cover. The area selected for operations was Salisbury Plain, where the maximum amount of space was available with the least risk of troubling the civilian population. The Mechanised Force came together in the middle of August 1927, and for the next three weeks carried out a series of trials to accustom its commanders in handling techniques. These mainly concerned the movement of such a force by road, or the establishment of a protected camp for nights spent in open countryside – a sort of 'circle–the–wagons' scheme based on the old Boer wagon laager. This last was a great success but the route marches were hampered by the need to adhere to special standing orders. These were drawn up far too rigidly, demanding accurately spaced columns on the road, which failed to take the respective merits of wheeled and tracked vehicles into account. On the roads, for instance, the Rolls-Royce armoured cars that formed the Fast Group would streak ahead at more than double the official 25mph they were

---

*Liddell Hart. *The Tanks.* Vol. 1. Cassell, 1959.

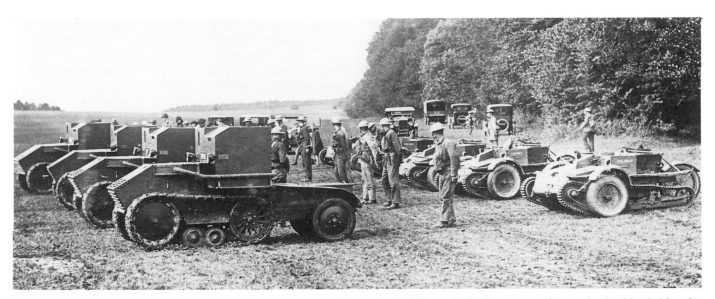

60 Two sections of 3rd Battalion RTC, the reconnaissance element of the Mechanised Force. In the front row are four production Morris-Martel tankettes (note the longer wheelbase) and behind them four Carden-Loyd Mark Vs.

supposedly tied to, while the medium tanks and other tracked vehicles of the Slow Group, limited to 7mph on the roads, left everything else behind across country. Thus these orders stifled initiative and forced the commanders to behave as a 'mechanical menagerie' to quote Liddell Hart, instead of exploiting the mobility that mechanisation conferred.

These training manoeuvres culminated in a wide ranging mock battle in September. In order to derive the maximum potential each of the opposing forces started out some 35 miles apart. The Mechanised Force – Eastland – moved out from Micheldever in Hampshire, while a much larger conventional force, 3rd Infantry Division supported by a brigade of cavalry – Westland – began their march from Heytesbury in Wiltshire. Their objective was the high ground around Andover; the task of the Mechanised Force was to stop them. Since it was essential for the two forces to meet somewhere on the Plain, Eastland was given a head start, and within an hour the armoured cars had covered nearly 40 miles, evaded enemy cavalry patrols and gained possession of a series of bridges that would enable the main body of the force to cross all the major rivers in the area. The tanks first made for the airfield at Old Sarum, just north of Salisbury, but they were spotted from the air while trying to hide in the aircraft hangars and attacked by enemy bombers which accounted for some tanks. Soon, however, reports were coming in of the progress of the main enemy force, and the tanks moved out once more, only to get snarled up when one of them broke down in a narrow, sunken road. Once this was sorted out the tanks made for the ancient Iron Age hillfort of Yarnbury Castle, while the armoured cars followed the main road to Chitterne and met the enemy column head on. This brought Westland to a halt while, unseen in the hills to the south, the tanks and artillery of the Mechanised Force prepared to attack. In the gathering dusk the long infantry column was first assailed by low-flying aircraft, which concentrated on the defending artillery before the tanks came thundering down from the ridge, in three waves, firing on the move and causing Westland's forces to break and run.

Overnight the umpires allowed Westland to steal a march, while the Mechanised Force went into laager near Shrewton. The enemy move was detected but, being without wireless, the information was sent by a despatch rider whose machine broke down. By the time the tanks were made aware of the situation and caught up, half of Westland's force was across the River Avon, but this advance was contained by the tankettes and armoured cars, which detoured through Amesbury, crossed the river and moved north, driving the enemy infantry to take shelter in the woods. Those remaining on the west side of the river turned to face the tanks, but they too were forced to seek 'tank proof' cover in the woods, where they chose to sit it out, under constant attack from Eastland's air force. In the sense that they had arrived on their objective, albeit in a rather harrassed condition, Westland were deemed to have won through, but at this point the exercise, and the 1927 season of the Mechanised Force came to an end.

When operations were resumed in the following year – 1928 – the most significant change was in the title. It was now to be known as the Experimental Armoured Force, although to be accurate this could only be applied to a certain part of it; Gunners, Sappers and the infantry still travelled in unarmoured vehicles, as did the newly formed Signals Company which, it was hoped, would improve communications and lessen the reliance on despatch riders. This season's exercises were of a more specialised nature and, apart from some demonstrations laid on for Members of Parliament and other dignitaries, was concerned mainly with tactical handling of various combinations of equipment. There was no major operation, as in the previous year, and once the trials were over it was announced that the force would be broken up and experiments continued in other directions. Subsequently the events of these two years were discussed and dissected throughout the Army. The general opinion was that, as constituted, the force was unbalanced: it needed to be more flexible. Effective reconnaissance demanded vehicles with a much better cross-country performance, while the tanks were too noisy for a surprise attack to be mounted. It was agreed that the armoured element was the core, but that the ancillary arms, the infantry and artillery in particular, should be adjusted to suit the demands of the situation. Of particular interest, however, were the considered reactions from both sides. Brig. R J Collins, who had commanded both the Mechanised and Armoured Forces, speaking in 1929, emphasised the problems of selecting good ground, and of vehicle reliability. In reply, Col. A P Wavell, who had served on the staff of 3rd Infantry Division, explained how the very presence of such a force posed problems for the infantry. Not knowing where it was, or when it might attack, introduced an air of caution, along with frustration at the virtual impossibility of hitting back. There was no means whereby foot soldiers could seek out a tank force and destroy it because mobility and armour protection allowed the tanks to choose when they might attack or break off an action.

The effectiveness of armour in this situation was further borne out by other exercises carried out by RTC units not involved with the Mechanised Force during these two years. The 2nd Battalion in Sussex and the residue of 3rd in East Anglia, had repeatedly demonstrated that they could contain much greater forces of infantry and cavalry if well handled. In view of this it might seem rather surprising that the War Office announced a complete change of emphasis in 1929; in fact, bearing in mind the prevailing attitudes, the need for economy and a sentimental attachment to horsed cavalry, it is probably not surprising at all. What it amounted to was the formation of two experimental infantry brigades, each of which was given a light tank battalion, equipped with Carden-Loyd carriers. The ultimate object being to train the infantry to handle such machines for themselves. Until this could be organised the RTC was required to operate them. The result, as that season's manoeuvres proved, was that the carriers, masquerading as light tanks, literally dominated the assault role, further diminishing the value of infantry who could only mop up in the wake of the tanks and revert to their traditional role of holding whatever ground the tanks captured. Not that the cavalry got off the hook entirely, an experimental divisional cavalry regiment was formed for a War Office exercise in 1929 from elements of the Queen's Bays, 3rd Carabiniers and 16th/5th Lancers. They operated in an odd assortment of vehicles ranging from Carden-Loyd carriers and six-wheeled trucks for the machine-gun troop, to Jowett light cars representing anti-tank vehicles and Austin Seven two-seaters playing the part of Scout Cars.

Before proceeding to examine events in the 1930s it is perhaps best, at this point, to look for a moment at some of the men whose commitment to the concept of mechanised warfare proved to be so vital and stimulating in these years. Presiding over all, like some shadowy mentor, was J F C Fuller, the academic whose stubborn single mindedness during the planning stages of the Mechanised Force let the chance to command it slip from him. With it went the only chance Fuller would ever have of commanding a tank force from ground level and putting his theories into practice. Yet it is an activity, one suspects, that might not have suited his intellectual approach. Among the practical men of action George Lindsay might be singled out, not only as an advanced thinker on armoured matters, but particularly for his skill at picking men who could

convert his ideas into actions and then advance them further. Men like Charles Broad who commanded 1st Tank Brigade in 1931, Justice Tilly who commanded 5th Battalion in 1932 and 'Tim' Pile, whose inspired handling of the reconnaissance group in 1927 gave the Mechanised Force its eyes. There were others, too numerous to name; yet above them all, at a practical level, stands P C S Hobart. No mean intellectual in his own right, Hobart, a Royal Engineer during the war, was at his best when it came to training, inspiring and handling men and tanks. From 1931, when he took command of 2nd Battalion, he demonstrated almost uncanny skills which led him, allowing for setbacks, to the peak of his profession; and professionalism, as we shall see, was his hallmark. Enough has been written elsewhere of these men, and others like Martel working outside the Corps, to show that they formed a powerful nucleus of profound thought and opinion, yet it appears to have been largely isolated from the wider fields of military thinking. Through correspondence and personal contact they certainly inspired one another, but this rarely seems to have affected those outside their circles and hardly, if ever, penetrated the upper strata of military life where political considerations clashed with service ideals.

1929 also saw the publication of a small booklet, *Mechanized and Armoured Formations*, otherwise known as the Purple Primer, although Martel insisted on referring to it as the Mauve Manual. Compiled by Broad, it was issued by the War Office for both service and public consumption; a curious move since it was in no sense a policy document but a sort of stock-taking review of the effects of mechanisation on traditional thinking since 1919. Among its more interesting contents were possible establishment tables for a medium and light armoured brigade, along with a progress report on the development of wireless in armoured vehicles. Each brigade would include a signals section, three tank battalions, a close support artillery battery and anti-aircraft battery. They would be homogeneous formations, compact enough to be handled as an entity and reasonably uniform in cross-country or road performance. As the next ten years would show, this sort of formation with some modifications would form a most effective constituent for an armoured division, yet sufficient in itself to form an independent striking force if required.

The early tank wireless sets that started to appear in 1926 were bulky things and heavy on power consumption, although sufficient progress had been made to enable morse key signalling – W/T – to be transmitted effectively over quite long distances, with voice communication – R/T – available at shorter ranges. The three sets available were the MC, which could be fitted fairly comfortably into the turret extension of a medium tank, but limited to a range of two miles on R/T only; the very similar MB which offered five miles R/T and 12 miles for W/T, but was only suitable for hull mounting in command tanks since it weighed 2cwts and took up a lot of room; and the MA which, with its independent power unit weighed about ·75 ton. It could transmit speech at 30 miles but could only be carried in a 3-ton lorry or half-track. By 1932 the first two were about to be replaced by the No2 set, which had a range on R/T, albeit only from a stationary tank, of 12 miles. However, it was too big for the old mediums and only fitted the Mark III and A7 tanks, or the bigger armoured cars. At the same time the No7 set was designed for use in light tanks, but its range was

61 Medium Mark II tanks and Carden-Loyd Mark VI carriers of 1st Brigade RTC manoeuvering en masse on Salisbury Plain in 1931. The tanks are still finished in the old Mechanised Force colour scheme of light grey over brown, divided by a broad black line.

only about three miles on R/T. Until this was ready the early light tanks had to make do with modified No1 sets. Marconi provided the sets used in the two prototype Light Mark IV tanks, but trials revealed that they did not even come up to the standard of the No1 set, so they were rejected. Increasing use of wireless led to further investigation towards reducing engine interference. Metallic screens proved unsatisfactory and suppressors were adopted instead. However, it was discovered that no hard and fast guidelines could be drawn for their installation, and each type of AFV had to be prepared on a trial and error basis. Power supply was another problem. Extra batteries could be fitted, but they soon drained down if they had to rely on the tank's standard dynamo to keep them charged up, so the next stage was the fitting of a second dynamo, capable of maintaining an adequate power supply even while the tank's engine was ticking over. By the late thirties the No9 set had appeared, replacing both the Nos2 and 7 sets, and it was joined by the No11, which went into the new infantry tanks. The Signals Experimental Establishment was also working on the No10 set, but this work stopped in 1938, and was not resumed for nearly two years, by which time the designation had changed to the No19 set, which proved so successful during the war. Although it is outside our period it might be mentioned that one of the most progressive features of this set was a facility to combine both external communication with other tanks, and two-way internal links for the crew. This was the first satisfactory solution to another problem of the period. The Laryngaphone has already been mentioned, but it soon faded from the scene, as did a system of speaking tubes, tested in the medium tanks, which were normally drowned out by engine noise. Most tank commanders relied on what has been called the 'voice and boot' method. The Tannoy company later produced a reasonably effective system which did not require all the crew to be wired up, but it had the disadvantage of working in one direction only.

Based on the Purple Primer much was anticipated for 1930, but in the event it was an anti-climax. An Experimental Medium Armoured Brigade was formed from 3rd and 5th Battalions, each comprising one light tank company (represented by Carden-Loyds) and two medium companies. They were pitted against 2nd Battalion with various infantry and cavalry combinations, with predictable results. However, the year was marked by a noticeable upswing in reliability. By restricting the march speed to 10mph, and taking frequent rests on the road, a distance of 50 miles could be covered. Even after four two-day exercises, the average number of tanks hauled off to workshops during each exercise was only three. Bearing in mind the age of the medium tanks, and renowned fragility of the Carden-Loyds, this was no mean achievement; a tribute not only to the RAOC personnel who did the repairs, but also to the crews, whose increasing familiarity with their vehicles, and expertise, anticipated trouble before a serious breakdown occurred. The key year, therefore, was 1931, when the 1st Brigade RTC was formed under Charles Broad, who operated from the Medium Command Tank 'Boxcar'. The brigade was formed with 2nd, 3rd and 5th Battalions, with the same establishment as before: a close support battery and an experimental Light Battalion raised as a temporary measure. Most of the 'light tanks' were still Carden-Loyds, but a few examples of the real thing were now available, and these were

62 *The command group of 1st Brigade, the famous wireless tank* Boxcar *and its attendant Light Tanks Mark II.*

issued to company commanders. For all that, they served a useful purpose, for the theme was movement and manoeuvre. Gathering round the command tank, the lights would take their instructions and then speed off to locate their own units and then guide them in accordance with the commander's wishes. By 1932 there were enough light tanks to equip the Light Battalion, but training that year was overshadowed by the Disarmament Conference in Geneva which, if it had succeeded in agreeing its original proposals, would have outlawed all tanks except light ones, on the grounds that they were machines of offence, in more than one sense of the word. Possibly because of this the Brigade was not called together for 1933. Instead each battalion was allotted to an infantry division, to practice close co-operation. However, it was announced that in 1934 the Brigade would be re-established on a permanent basis, and that the light battalion would likewise become a fixture as the 1st (Light) Battalion, RTC. The brigade commander for the training season would be the Inspector of the RTC, P C S Hobart.

The history of 1st Tank Brigade in 1934 has been amply dealt with in the Regimental History. Here it is only necessary to explain that Hobart, operating from his command tank – one of the new Medium Mark III 'Sixteen Tonners' – created a new milestone in armoured warfare by the extensive use of wireless control. In passing it is worth noting that the RTC worked almost exclusively on R/T, since the idea of having a trained W/T operator from the Royal Signals in each tank had been rejected, in favour of a crew member who might also act as loader. By organising a special transport element within the brigade, escorted by armoured cars from two Territorial RTC companies, Hobart provided his tank force with enough freedom to break away from traditional supply techniques, and use its mobility to the full. Movement and manoeuvre was now much more than a catchphrase, it came to stand for a battle winning combination, allowing the brigade to range far and wide as it circled the opposition out of sight, before striking its blow from the least expected direction at a time of its own choosing. Then the light battalion, formed by extracting the light tank company from each mixed battalion, distracted the enemy while the medium battalions manoeuvred for position. Such was the success of a whole series of these attacks that towards the end of the season the senior director, Gen. Sir John

63 The Medium Mark III tank T907 in the command role with 1st Tank Brigade in 1934.

Burnett-Stuart, felt obliged to change the conditions and apply every stratagem of gamesmanship he could think of to try and create an artificial defeat. His object, in which he only partly succeeded, being to restore some degree of confidence to the shattered 'enemy'.

From the peak of 1934 events can be seen to deteriorate. The 1935 Tank Brigade season was marked by a partial return to training in the infantry support role for the three medium battalions, following the conversion of 4th Battalion to what was called an (Army) Tank Battalion in 1934. However the light battalion did some remarkable night operations under Lt. Col. J A L 'Blood' Caunter. By 1936 and 1937, although enthusiasm for the cause was undiminished, tank stocks were running low. Most of the mediums were around ten years old, and besides using up spare parts at an alarming rate, were just

not capable of performing at the pace demanded by Hobart and his battalion commanders. Only the light tanks were improving, as the new three-man models came into service, but as fast as they appeared they were being issued to newly mechanised cavalry regiments, which had already siphoned off most of the RTC's serviceable Mark IIs, leaving only obsolete machines and lorries to fill their place. Threatening moves by the Italians in Libya created an increased demand for tanks in Egypt, and it was only after the Munich crisis of 1938 had sharpened up awareness in the most entrenched minds that the trend was noticeably reversed, and by then it was almost too late.

7　The Royal Tank Corps in India

India, in the days of Empire, besides being a source of great wealth and prestige to Britain, was also a cauldron of troubles. Various political movements adopted anti-imperialist attitudes when it suited their purpose, while religious factions kept the pot continually on the boil. Tribal groups, especially in the North West, turned out to try their mettle against the British Army at regular intervals when they weren't fighting one another. Nurtured on warfare and a grim landscape they proved formidable opponents, even against armoured vehicles and aircraft, while across the border their Afghan cousins were occasionally goaded into war, often with a little help from Russia. Yet for all this a posting to India was considered well worth any hardship in the years between the wars, and it proved a superb training ground for officers, men and equipment.

Armoured cars had been introduced to the sub-continent in 1915, and their impact has been recorded in a previous title.* Yet when the Great War ended the desire to return to 'proper soldiering' was every bit as strong in the East, and moves were made to disband the armoured car force. It survived by the skin of its teeth, and almost immediately justified its existence when the Third Afghan War broke out in 1919. There were internal security problems too, and if it had not been prevented by a low arch from entering the square in Amritsar, an armoured car would have been involved in Brig-Gen. Dyer's unnecessary massacre of rioters in April 1919. By this time, naturally, most of the improvised war-time cars were getting a bit weary, but all that was available to supplement them were some old Austins and Rolls-Royces, surplus to requirements in the Middle East. Of the original home-made cars, only the three Rolls-Royces of 1st Armoured Motor Brigade were still fit for service and, in 1919, one of them was rebuilt to the Brigade's design, by the Gun Carriage Factory at Jubbulpore. The open-topped body was replaced by a turreted pattern covering the entire chassis. Since no suitable curved plates were available the hull and turret were formed from flat panels. The latter was an odd lozenge shape, with quite an enormous aperture for the Vickers machine-gun, while the crew compartment was equally large. In 1920 the car was used as the bridal coach at the nuptials of the Brigade adjutant, and from that day on was always known as 'Wedding Bells'. It was later modified to improve the driver's view ahead, but remained in service until 1940 before being scrapped.

In February 1920 it was decided to place the armoured establishment in India on a proper footing so it was absorbed into the Tank Corps. Five armoured car companies were raised at Bovington, another was transferred from Iraq, while two more were added in 1925. At first they had precious little equipment and some, upon arrival, had to manage with Ford T pick-up trucks. The 7th ACC took the old Rolls-Royces, some of which were supposed to be able to trace their careers back to the Duke of Westminster's days. The 8th took over the Austins, while the 9th managed on Fords, backed up by three armoured Fiats, and the 10th took on the venerable Jeffery Quads from three redundant armoured motor batteries. The humid conditions in India had played havoc with pneumatic tyres during the war, new casings rotted even while they were in store, so an alternative was sought. It was found in a curious patent system known as the MacIntosh Normal Air Pressure (NAP) tyre; a euphemism if ever there was one. The tyre was in reality a solid, and a very narrow one at that, but in order to provide some extra cushioning the outer surface was perforated by a series of triangular holes. These cavities were supposed to trap pockets of air when squashed against the ground giving, it was claimed, the softness of a pneumatic without the risk of punctures. In practice the system only worked moderately well on a firm surface. On anything less each cavity soon filled with soil and stones, turning the tyre into a genuine solid with a completely smooth tread. However well it may have suited a heavy, slow moving vehicle it was an unmitigated disaster on a heavy, fast one, as many surviving pictures testify. They show Indian armoured cars of all makes, that have skidded on a wet surface and rolled over, usually shedding the turret in the process. Tyres of this type were first fitted to the imported Austins and Rolls-Royces.

New cars were urgently required and the Government of India naturally looked to Britain. In particular they looked to Rolls-Royce; experience throughout the world over the past six years having shown that no other make of chassis could take the weight and punishment and yet remain unshakeably reliable no matter where they were used. They also appreciated that combat conditions in India, especially in the frontier regions, were peculiar to say the least and felt that the standard War Office design of body and turret would not do. In such a rugged landscape, and in the face of so wily an enemy, there was literally no telling from which direction the next attack might come. The only certainty was that it would be from an unexpected quarter, invariably from above and most probably from behind. The outline for a new design was therefore worked out in India and, with this in his pocket Maj. A J Clifton – who had commanded the Indian armoured cars during the war – was despatched to Britain to place orders and oversee construction. The first stage was to build a mock-up of the proposed design on a 40/50 hp Silver Ghost chassis, much of the detail design work being undertaken by a naval draughtsman from Vickers, for the cars would be built in their plant at Erith in Kent. The most significant feature was the

---

*Fletcher, *War Cars*.

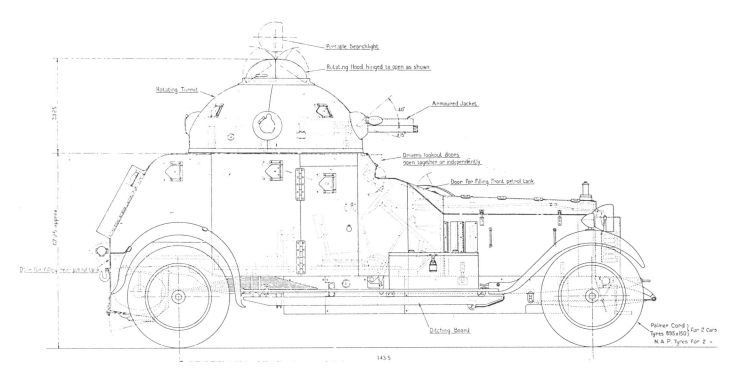

D14 *The Rolls-Royce Indian Pattern armoured car, as supplied by Vickers. It is shown with pneumatic tyres as sold to Iran.*

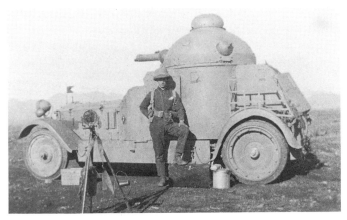

64 An Indian Pattern Rolls-Royce armoured car waits while a heliograph is set up.

turret, which was dome-shaped. It will be recalled that Erith was building the first Vickers tank for the British Army at the same time and that it too had a dome-shaped turret, so some mutual influence may be suggested. Atop the turret was a small, dome-shaped cupola, capable of independent rotation and fitted with a clamshell type of hatch for the commander. The shape was ideal for the frontier since it could deflect bullets fired from any angle and, although more expensive to manufacture, also saved weight. Further, with all-round protection in mind, the turret was provided with four, self-sealing ball mounts capable of taking Vickers machine-guns. Each car would carry two guns and, depending on the situation, these could be fitted side by side, or with one pointing forwards and one aft in diagonally opposite mountings. Since the tactical situation might change at a moment's notice, crews were trained to switch guns from one mounting to another in 15 seconds. The mountings were designed to give the gunner a choice of geared elevation, holding the weapon steady for accurate long range shooting, or free movement during close encounters.

Unlike the wartime cars these Indian Pattern models, as they came to be called, had armoured hulls covering the entire chassis. Double doors were provided at the back, but side doors were fitted as well and these were so arranged that the nearside one opened forwards while the offside door had its hinges at the back. Thus it was always possible for a crewmember to dismount under fire from the side which gave him best protection. Inside, each hull was lined with an asbestos and woven wire material called Raybestos, which not only reduced heat but prevented flakes of metal from flying about when bullets struck the armour. Hull and weapons weighed a little over two tons.

Good as the armoured bodies were, the chassis, surprisingly, gave cause for concern. To begin with Rolls-Royce were most unhappy with the idea of using semi-solid tyres on such a vehicle, as well they might be, but were over ruled by the Indian Government. However, the real shock came when a sample chassis was submitted for cross-country trials. Put at a steep bank it failed to get up, despite repeated attempts. Clifton considered that the gear ratios were too high, but the makers refused to consider an alteration and in due course Sir Henry Royce himself was dragged into the argument. He proposed a two-speed epicyclic reduction and agreed to include this at an extra cost per chassis of £600. Since the price already stood at £2,100 per unit, this was rejected by Clifton; the chassis had to be accepted as they were. Cost had already proved a critical factor. Clifton had been sent home with instructions to order 32 cars, sufficient to equip two companies, but in the end he considered himself lucky to be able to afford 19. These were ready for delivery by the summer of 1922, and upon arrival in India they went to equip 9th ACC. As events turned out these cars proved to be as effective as any supplied to the Indian Government between the wars. An NCO of the RTC, posted temporarily to the Southern Provinces Mounted Rifles at Fort Madras in 1939, who had been with 9th ACC at some stage, found three of them stored there in good running order. Under his direction the armoured hulls were removed and sent to Ahmednagar, where they were remounted on more modern Chevrolet truck chassis.

During a visit to Bovington Maj. Clifton was informed that the Tank Corps already had just the armoured car for him, and a demonstration was laid on. What he was shown was a twin-turreted Peerless which, by way of demonstration, described a few stately circles on a patch of concrete in front of him while various officers pointed out its many marvellous features. Clifton appeared unimpressed and requested that the car be driven off the hard standing and over the adjacent sandy ground, into which it duly sank. There would be no Peerless armoured cars in India. Yet more were urgently required, and Clifton still had an extra string to his bow. The cross-country trial that the Rolls-Royce chassis had failed, was also attended by another make, under consideration as a medium transport vehicle for India, which must have earned a few condescending glances from the Rolls-Royce engineers. This was a 40/50hp Crossley, a four-cylinder unit built originally for a Russian contract that was cancelled by the Revolution. Rough and ready as it was, by comparison with the Rolls, it had sailed through the trials without a hitch. Where the Rolls-Royce people had carefully nursed their entry, the representatives from Crossley Motors told Clifton to do his worst with theirs – he wouldn't break it! Impressed by this – and the quoted price of £900 per chassis – Clifton purchased one on the spot and, loading it up with four tons of ballast, set off on a 4,000 mile drive all around Britain. It survived the test and, following further negotiations, an order was placed for 32 chassis, to be armoured in the same style by Vickers.

65 'Tiny' Clifton at the wheel of the Crossley test vehicle before setting off on his round Britain trip. Notice the special alloy spoked wheels which were fitted to a number of light trucks at this time.

Deliveries began in 1923, followed by a further order in 1925, but the exact number built is not known. In time Crossley armoured cars were serving with at least six companies in India, so production must have been close to 100 units, if not more. There were differences, mostly of a detail nature, not

66 An impressive view of Repulse, an Indian Pattern Crossley armoured car seen here in an unusual camouflage scheme and with an unofficial mascot on the bonnet.

only between the Rolls-Royce and Crossleys, but also between the two groups of Crossleys; in the latter case mostly in respect of engine ventilation and how the wooden ditch crossing planks were carried. Most of these Vickers built armoured cars were finished in a silver-grey colour which was intended to reflect the heat, but at least one company tried pure white for a while and disruptive, two-tone camouflage schemes were popular from time to time. A noticeable feature of all the Indian armoured cars was the attention given to names, usually in groups such as wild fowl, hunting dogs or famous generals, battles and even warships. The style of lettering was always the same and was more prominent than that used in Britain, as well as being more common. Modifications were few, but quite interesting. Some cars carried wireless sets, and these can easily be identified by the aerial wires, strung from uprights at each end. One company commander devised a sort of cow-catcher attachment for pushing road blocks aside at a potential ambush site, while other cars were seen with light, steel discs mounted above the cupola to keep the sun off.

Most of the armoured car companies saw action at one time or another, especially when they did a 12 month tour of duty on the North West Frontier. Their regular work here was as convoy escort to the lorries that took supplies and reinforcements to the outlying forts, cantonments and lonely picquets. Two cars would take the lead, with others scattered at intervals through the column and a final pair bringing up the rear. They would also take part in major punitive expeditions, escort political officers on their rounds and patrol the network of military roads. A major operation was undertaken in Waziristan in 1930, when the Afridi rose and threatened Peshawar. A massive attack on a supply depot was only beaten off by the timely arrival of Crossleys from 1st ACC, but the attackers simply melted away into the surrounding countryside, with hardly any casualties. Earlier that year the same company was involved in a serious disturbance in the city of Peshawar itself. A section commanded by Maj. S J King MC was called to deal with a large crowd which had gathered near the Edward Gate, but in the ensuing chaos two of the cars collided, fracturing the fuel line of one which was immediately

67 *2nd Lt. Synge's Crossley burning after the trouble in Peshawar, 23 April 1931.*

68 *The Crossley body fitted to a Guy six-wheeler chassis in India. A double radiator has been fitted, with extra air scoops at the sides. The commander demonstrates the effectivness of the clamshell cupola in the half-open position.*

set on fire. The crew managed to escape to the cover of a nearby police post but a despatch rider who should have kept out of the way was knocked from his machine, run down and killed. What makes this little action so interesting is the restraint shown by the crews. In escaping from their burning car some

were obliged to use their revolvers against individuals, but the other cars only resorted to machine-guns on two occasions in a tense period of some two hours.

The appearance of six-wheeled lorries soon attracted the attention of the armoured car men in India, as they had in Britain. Although the Crossleys were reasonably satisfactory on the roads, despite their narrow, solid NAP tyres, it was another matter when it came to pursuing the enemy across country, as already noted. And the opposition clearly understood this, as they demonstrated on inumerable occasions. A six-wheeler, it was hoped, might help to redress the balance. The first experiment on record dates from 1927, when the body of a Rolls-Royce armoured car was fitted to a Morris-Commercial 30cwt lorry chassis. Since no photograph of this experiment has yet been discovered it is impossible to say whether the body used was one of the earlier wartime models or a Vickers-built car, although the former seems more likely. Nothing came of this, probably because the chassis was overloaded, but later that same year a heavier six-wheeled Guy chassis was fitted with the body from an Indian Pattern Crossley, and a double radiator at the front to improve cooling. It performed well enough on trial to encourage the Indian Government to adopt it as a standard type, but exactly what happened next is not now clear. The traditional story has it that chassis were ordered from Guy Motors, to which more of the Crossley hulls would be transferred, but there was a mix-up over the order and 16 brand-new Guy armoured cars were delivered instead. Clearly this is improbable; a contract with Guy for 16 chassis is hardly likely to be mistaken for a contract with Vickers for 16 complete armoured cars, the difference in price alone would rule that out. Rather it may be an excuse, invented at some later date to explain how it was that the RTC in India finished up with 16 armoured cars that were so big they could hardly negotiate the frontier roads.

The Vickers-Guys were certainly big cars. When they were delivered in 1928 it was seen that they measured over 20 feet from stem to stern, and weighed about nine tons. The basic layout and armament was the same as the four-wheeled Crossleys, although the bonnet was longer: to enclose the six-cylinder engine and enlarged radiator with its distinctive round fan casing at the front. One Guy was tested in Britain before delivery, alongside a prototype Lanchester, but it did not result in any more orders. Even so the cars had a good top speed of 45mph, and with their articulating rear bogies and broad section pneumatic tyres had a much better cross-country performance. Unfortunately it was on the winding roads of the frontier, where opportunities for cross-country driving were few, that they were most restricted, and this was really where they were most needed. They were too long to negotiate the sharp corners, and too heavy for many of the bridges. They spent their service lives with 10th ACC, but none lasted beyond the mid-thirties, and legend has it that they were then converted into lorries.

In 1930 the Army in India took the unusual step of building a six-wheeled armoured car to their own design on the Morris-Commercial chassis. Possibly this was an attempt to provide a six-wheeler suited to frontier operations, but it was hardly an inspired design. The body was large and box-like, but the turret was a tiny, bevel-topped thing mounting a single Vickers machine-gun. The intention may have been to design a car with some sort of personnel carrying ability. It was named *Chaklala*, and its most curious feature was the way in which the ditch crossing boards were pitched at an angle, to double as mudguards for the front wheels. Presumably it was not a success since no more were built.

Privately owned armoured cars have never been common, except perhaps in fairly recent times, but one example from India warrants a passing mention. It began life as a conventional Rolls-Royce Silver Ghost, purchased by the Nawab of Bahawalpur in 1924. In 1933 the owner returned it to Britain where the coachbuilders, Barker and Co, fitted it with an armoured shell. The martial impression was somewhat compromised by the large windows, although they had armoured shutters, and the shining Flying Lady mascot on the radiator, but in every other respect it was a genuine armoured car, complete with turret and ditch crossing boards. Like many Indian Princes the Nawab had his own regiment; it may be that

69 *A production Guy armoured car on test at the Vickers factory in Britain. Unditching boards and temporary tracks are stowed above the rear mudguards.*

71 *A Crossley body that has been remounted on a Chevrolet chassis.*

70 *The Morris based armoured car* Chaklala *which was built in India. The unditching boards are arranged to serve as front mudguards.*

he felt the armoured car would create a suitably modern image, or he may have had reasons to fear for his own safety, but beyond this speculation little is known about this handsome vehicle.

From about 1932 the armoured car companies in India gradually converted to light tank companies, and the armoured cars were relegated to the axuliary forces or handed on to newly mechanised elements in the Indian Army. The years were beginning to tell on them and under normal circumstances they would probably have been scrapped before long. However, the outbreak of war in 1939 suddenly gave them a new lease of life, which was enhanced by transferring the bodies – of most of the Crossleys and some Rolls-Royces – onto 30cwt Chevrolet truck chassis. They remained as four-wheelers, but now ran on large section pneumatic tyres, which probably gave them a better performance than they had ever had. In this form some even went to war again when Indian armoured regiments took them to the Middle East.

The RTC Centre in India was established at Ahmednagar in 1923 under Lt-Col. W D Croft, but the armoured car and later light tank companies were based on eight major centres, which they exchanged on a fairly regular basis. Such exchanges could be made by road or rail as appropriate, and they included seasonal changes as, for instance the armoured car company stationed at Peshawar would move to Parachinar, in the hills, for the worst of the summer months. Least popular of all such posts was Razmak in Waziristan, on the Indian/Afghan border. Situated over 8,000 feet up in the sterile hills, it was a totally artificial military settlement built as part of a larger scheme to retain a presence in what might otherwise become a secure fastness for some of the King–Emperor's most troublesome subjects. The military road that linked Razmak with the frontier cities was a circular route, of intrepid engineering, along which supply convoys and relief columns would move, escorted by the armoured cars in an unending cycle.

The idea that tanks might prove useful in India was first considered in 1920, when Lt-Col Philip Johnson was sent out to Bombay by the War Office to investigate the possibility. He toured the frontier and seems to have given a positive report since, as recorded in Chapter 1, he then began work on the so-called tropical tanks. Meanwhile, on his visit to Britain, Maj. Clifton had attended a demonstration of prototype Medium D tanks at Charlton Park, where he was told that improved models would soon be despatched to India for trials. When two did arrive in 1922 he was disappointed to find what he described as his 'old friends' from Charlton Park, and his hopes fell. The tanks soon justified his pessimism. At first, under Johnson's supervision, they were tested under hot weather conditions to see how this might affect the crew. Various expedients were tried, from panels of asbestos cladding, to spraying them with water, a singularly impractical solution in such dry climes. Finally they were despatched by rail to Ahmednagar, where the C-in-C was to inspect them. But both tanks broke down between the railway station and the camp, having to be ignominiously towed in by Jeffery-Quad armoured cars and steamrollers. Clifton says that they never moved again.

Then, in 1923, another tracked vehicle arrived. Although described as a tank it was, in fact, an artillery tractor, the prototype AT1 built by the ROF. Being of a more conventional layout than the Johnson tanks it seems to have performed adequately, but after the debacle of the Medium Ds it had a lot of prejudice to overcome. In any case it was not a fighting machine, and although it proved that tracked vehicles could be operated in the wilder parts of India, it made very little impression on the military establishment at the time. Two years later it seemed as if attitudes had changed. The success of the medium tanks in Britain led to renewed interest from India, and when the last Mark IA was completed Vickers built two more machines, T59 and T60, for India. They are interesting tanks for a number of reasons, but mostly because in terms of design they represent a transition between the Mark I and Mark II models already described. Although mechanically the same as the Mark I they had all the outward manifestations of a Mark II, i.e., the raised driver's cab and skirting plates over the suspension. Cooling was improved with the provision of extra ventilating fans and louvres in the hull sides, but strangest of all was the choice of armament. The 3pr gun was not fitted, and the Vickers machine-gun mountings in the hull sides were eliminated. All that remained were two machine-gun positions in the turret. Granted there would be no need for a gun capable of defeating other tanks in India, but one would have thought that a close support weapon which could fire smoke or high explosive shells would have had its uses. One officer involved with the trials remarked on this, saying that it seemed wasteful to provide such a large tank, weighing around 12 tons, with nothing more than two-machine guns.

Commanded by Lt. J T Crocker RTC, and with hand picked crews of capable men, the tanks arrived in January 1925, just too late to take part in the Delhi Manœuvres. They were then put through an intensive four months of trials in all parts of the country, often making day-long marches between stations of up

72 *The Medium D tank that Philip Johnson took to India. Seen here being lifted by a steam crane of the Great Indian Peninsula Railway.*

73 A group of officers view, with apparent scepticism, one of Crocker's medium tanks during the Indian trials.

to 70 miles. Each trip was followed by a demonstration of cross-country manœuvrability and familiarisation exercises with the infantry regiments located in the area. The trials were often extremely tough, but the tanks generally managed to complete them, although one occasion when a tank, defeated by a steep shale bank, was passed by a horse-drawn gun team, was greeted with delight by the old guard. India was still not ready for tanks, at least not this type, and in due course both were shipped home and scrapped.

There matters rested for another three years. But in 1928 two Carden-Loyd Mark VI Carriers were taken out. Basically similar to the British models, these had been built with Indian conditions in mind: they were better cooled, and fitted with overhead canopies to keep the sun off. These, however, were later removed, no doubt because they made it difficult for the crews to disembark. Of course they were not tanks, only machine-gun carriers, but they were tested in other roles, such as towing small artillery pieces, which must have proved quite a strain. In 1930 they were serving alongside 8th ACC when trouble broke out in Waziristan. The officer commanding the armoured cars asked if the Carden-Loyds might join his column and this was approved, provided they were not allowed to go too far forward. Maj. Kenchington's force was moving against a large Afridi *lashkar*, or raiding party, that was operating in the area, and he used the carriers to take their machine-guns on to hilltops commanding the road, or to act as flank protection for artillery batteries. Whether they did actually fire their guns in anger is not clear, but it does seem certain that this was the only occasion upon which Carden-Loyd Carriers accompanied British troops on active service.

74 One of the two Indian Pattern Carden-Loyds at MWEE for its initial trials. The hood is little more than a sunshade and this example has the ammunition panniers on each side.

Although he admitted their limitations, which he saw as being due to their small engines, Kenchington saw that they held some promise, and in an article published in the *Royal Tank Corps Journal* he made a strong case for the employment of light tanks in the sub-continent.

The result was that in 1931 four Light Mark IA tanks arrived in India for extended trials, starting at Chaklala. When these were completed they left by road, in an ordinary military convoy, for Razmak. This trip of 270 miles was accomplished with no serious difficulty, the tanks managing to keep pace

75 A Light Tank Mark IA in India. Extra cooling louvres are fitted over the engine panels and this tank has the clamshell type cupola.

with the wheeled vehicles, and only stopping to replace the occasional broken track pin. At Razmak they were said to have dismayed the local population by their abilities in climbing shale inclines and operating in snow. The four light tanks were virtually identical to those of the same mark built for the British Army, except they were fitted with the Horstmann type suspension from the outset. This proved perfectly satisfactory for conditions in India, although the track had a tendency to break on rough, stony ground, but being light was easily repaired by the crew of two. One feature that the authorities in India saw as vital for light tanks was a cupola, and a variety of patterns were tested on the light tanks. They also required more attention to be paid to cooling and, working on the assumption that the opposition would never be armed with anything more lethal than a rifle – although that could be lethal

76 Taking a tight corner on the climb over the Nahakki Pass. The Light Mark IIB is guided by its commander and watched by a detachment of Sappers and Miners.

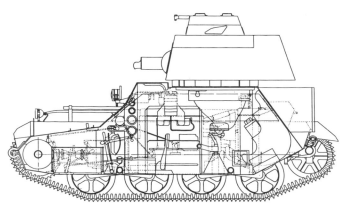

D15 The Light Tank Mark IIB, Indian Pattern.

enough in such skilled hands – the armour need not be as thick as that fitted to British light tanks. With these matters agreed an order was placed with Vickers-Armstrong for a substantial number of Light Tanks Mark IIB, Indian Pattern.

Basically similar to its British counterpart, the Indian Pattern Light Mark IIB can be most easily distinguished by the low, rectangular turret cupola. Other features peculiar to this model were the cooling louvres on the engine cover plate and a large stowage bin at the rear. Otherwise they employed the same Meadows engine and Horstmann suspension, and mounted a single Vickers machine-gun. They soon proved themselves capable of operating successfully off the road in the worst frontier conditions, and this was nowhere more evident than in an operation which took place in September 1935.

The 2nd Light Tank Company (LTC) comprised three sections which, no doubt for whimsical reasons, were distinguished by the letters, T, I and N. It was I – or Impi – Section which took the most interesting part in this operation. The problem was to operate on both sides of a ridge which, at its lowest point – the Nahakki Pass – was some 1,200 feet high. Access to a temporary camp established on the north side was by an old native track, worn into the granite by generations of tribal feet and, latterly, Army mules. Any suggestion that motor vehicles might negotiate such a route was looked upon as impossible by local tribesmen and many British soldiers, however, the tank men were determined to try. With assistance from a sapper party the track was widened as much as possible and cleared of the worst boulders before the first tank started over. It was a nail-biting trip; some of the hairpin bends were so tight that the tank had to reverse in order to get round, and the tracks were constantly slipping on the loose shale. At the crest the ridge was no more than three feet wide, so the tank had to be balanced while the crew surveyed the route down. This was even more difficult than the climb, since wear on the brakes was excessive and there were many halts while the working party made sure that the path was at least as wide as the tank. On the following day the rest of the section went over; having one hair-raising moment when a track broke and the tank ran away on the downward slope before the driver managed to skid it round and bring it to a halt with its nose projecting over a precipice. On the third day tanks went into action on both sides of the ridge, to the confusion of the opposition who regarded this kind of thing as cheating!

Earlier that same year 7th LTC was involved in action of a different kind when a severe earthquake struck its home station of Quetta. Tanks were used first to clear debris of fallen buildings to aid rescue work, and subsequently to patrol vulnerable locations such as the aerodrome. Apart from one tank, which was fitted with the improved Vickers suspension system, none of the Indian tanks were modified in respect of engines or bogies as those in Britain had been. However, a ruse later adopted in the desert was first used in India when two machines from 2nd LTC were fitted with canvas covered frames that made them look like ordinary lorries. The object, presumably, was to insert them into convoys that appeared innocent of any escort, thus tempting the opposition to attack, when the disguise would be thrown off. There is no evidence to suggest they were ever used in this way. The only permanent conversion recorded was of a tank modified into an armoured recovery vehicle. The turret was removed and a tall, square, superstructure mounted in its place, with a large stowage locker behind. It was no doubt capable of towing a disabled tank or repairing it where it stood. On the subject of recovery by the RTC in India, it is worth mentioning that a four-wheeled transporter trailer was developed to a local design, which could carry a light tank or, by erecting a temporary jib, remove its turret for more serious repairs.

We pause now to look at a tracked vehicle, a design study for a tank which had nothing specifically to do with India but for the fact that it was built there. Of the many factors that affect tank design, two of the most critical are length and steering. Length can be an advantage if it isn't taken to extremes; a long tank can pass over wider trenches and be made to run faster with greater stability than a short tank. However, there are compensating disadvantages. A long tank rising over even a small obstacle pokes a lot of itself into the air, presenting a vulnerable target and coming down with an almighty crash when it passes the point of balance. Since, until recent times at least, tanks made most of their longer journeys by rail they had to stay reasonably narrow to conform with the railway loading gauge. Yet unless a tank is made wider as it gets longer, the ratio of length over width becomes so great that it is impossible to steer. Even when this ratio is correct a tank wastes a lot of its energy steering, and for sharp turns has virtually to come to a halt, while at the same time enormous stresses are set up in the tracks and suspension.

Many attempts had been made to resolve these problems, notably in the Medium D series already discussed, but all foundered on the rocks of technology and resulted, instead, in a search for more effective transmissions which, by definition, were invariably heavier and more complex than the designer might have wished. In the early thirties Col. Martel – as he now was – had been posted to India with the Royal Engineers. His efforts to produce a light tank have already been recorded, he now turned his attention to these technical problems. His thoughts were directed towards the concept of an articulated tank which would run on four sets of tracks, and thus solve both problems at the same time. Such a tank could be long, in relation to its width, yet track to ground contact would be short; it would pass over an obstacle in stages without rearing high in the air and it could be steered either by hull articulation or by mounting one set of tracks on a turntable. There might be problems in making very tight turns, because skid steering would be difficult to arrange, but conversely if skid steering was not employed the transmission could be kept as simple as on the average lorry.

77 Martel in his experimental four-track tank. The Morris engine is at the back and steering is effected by the bogie unit beneath it.

Costs and material shortages, which were at their worst in India, limited Martel's options, but by late 1931 he had constructed a small prototype which was ready for trials. It could hardly be called a tank as it stood, being nothing more than a scaled down design study, yet good enough for trying out the principle. The body, which was nearly 12 feet long, was a narrow, mild steel box, open at the top. The driver sat in the front part behind a sloping nose plate, while the rear section was occupied by a 16hp Morris engine, which Martel had

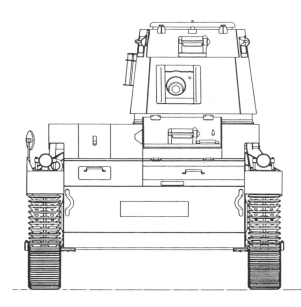

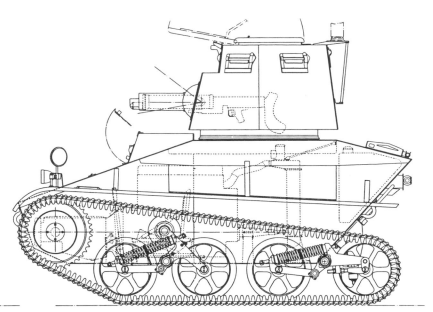

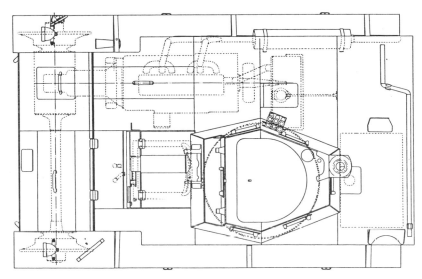

D16 Light Tank Mark IVA built for India.

78 A Light Tank Mark IVA crossing a nullah. *The high turret with its lookouts all round was invaluable on the frontier.*

borrowed from the military authorities, behind which was the radiator. The tracks were light and narrow, with the links connected by rubber blocks instead of pins to try out another

theory. The drive arrangements were rather rudimentary but they linked up to both sets of sprockets, while the suspension system was based on Horstmann. The body was wider at the front than back, since the rear tracks were turntable mounted to provide steering. Martel claims that this was the most difficult problem to solve, but that in its final form the machine steered as easily as a car. Although he published short articles on this and another project tested in India at the time, there is no evidence to suggest that Martel made any serious efforts to market the idea to the British Army. Later, back in Britain, he built a toy-sized scale model of a cruiser tank based on this four-track principle, but by then, as we shall see, he had become involved in another scheme which did bear fruit.

Although the Light Mark IIB was popular with the RTC in India it still fell short of the ideal, due to its power to weight ratio, which was considered insufficient for the rugged conditions it had to contend with. The Indian Government placed the problem with Vickers-Armstrong and, as already recorded, Carden designed an improved version which was taken up by the British Army as the Light Tank Mark IV.

79 The one and only Light Mark V to reach India has its innards inspected. Its cupola seems enormous.

80 A Light Tank Mark VIB tips forward to show the top of its turret. No explanation can be found for the abandoning of turret cupolas at this stage in India.

Another prototype was despatched to India and following acceptance trials was ordered for service as the Light Mark IVA. Production began in 1935 and, inevitably, there are numerous detail differences to note when comparing it with the British variant. The turret was shorter, like the first prototype, but much higher with a prominent cupola surmounted by a large hatch. Hull shape and all mechanical details were the same although the armour was thinner and the weight somewhat less. Ventilation was improved and extra cooling provided for the brakes, which otherwise tended to overheat when the tank was descending the long, winding hills in frontier regions. Tanks were also provided with a combined signalling and spotlight, protected by an armoured shutter.

The actual number of tanks ordered is not known, but it cannot have been less than the 16 required to equip one light tank company. The only known modification looked so outdated in the age of armoured warfare that it seems positively silly. It amounted to a means, in the form of huge wire hooks, whereby a pair of wooden stretchers – of the type normally slung, pannier fashion, from Army mules or camels – could be mounted on each side of the turret to carry wounded. If, as Kipling or Masters tell us, the Afridi or Pathan was no respecter of wounded in those days, then the unfortunate occupant of the stretcher was vulnerable to more than mere dust or sunstroke, and while he was there the tank could not retaliate anyway, since the ropes that secured the stretcher also prevented the turret from turning.

A single example of the Light Tank Mark V was also built for India by Vickers-Armstrong in 1935. The only things that seem to have distinguished it from the British version were an enormous drum-shaped cupola, spotlamp and tubes on the turret side, presumably to stow signalling flags. By the time it had been tested at Ahmednagar, the Light Tank Mark VI was entering service in Britain, so although India was sold on the idea of a three-man light tank, further orders were delayed until 1937. By that time the decision had been made to abandon armoured cars altogether and equip the forces in India entirely with light tanks, and indeed, since 1936, all eight RTC companies in India had be redesignated light tank companies, whether they were equipped with such machines or not. The Light Tank Mark VIB (Indian Pattern) was therefore ordered in considerable numbers and, again, it closely resembled its British counterpart but for one extremely curious detail. It will be recalled how, in Britain, the Light Mark VI was the first such tank actually to enter service with a turret cupola for the commander. Yet for some strange, and unexplained, reason the model delivered to India had no cupola at all, a complete reversal of doctrine. Why this was agreed is a mystery; possibly the authorities felt that the whole cupola concept was getting out of hand, or experience had shown that it was more trouble than it was worth, but the new tanks all arrived with two flush fitting hatches on the turret top instead.

By 1935 it had been decided that the RTC should leave India, and all armoured fighting vehicles would be handed over to the newly mechanised cavalry regiments of the Indian Army, or British cavalry regiments stationed in India. The policy was implemented in 1938, but an acute shortage of equipment led to some odd combinations within the various regiments.

8 Export Drives

The prestige that accrued to Britain as the nation which invented the tank, was turned to credit soon after the war when a lucrative export trade in armoured fighting vehicles was established, largely by Vickers. It is a subject that has never been well documented but it proves, upon examination, to be of considerable importance; not just in terms of trade but for the influence on tank design world-wide which it generated. Even countries that did not buy British tanks took note of design trends and often copied them.

However, at the outset, in 1919, it could just as easily have been France that dominated this trade, for France already had something to sell. Their little Renault FT light tank was built in such large numbers that there were plenty to spare, and the design was copied by at least three other countries. What is more, these tanks, being small, were relatively cheap as well as being simple to operate and maintain. Thus any country, without the industrial capacity or technical expertise to build tanks of its own, if it wished to modernise its armed forces, invested in a few Renaults. The wartime British tanks, by contrast, were great lumbering things of very limited application, for which there was no obvious market. Only the Japanese, who were ready to absorb all and any ideas on military modernisation, took one or two heavy Mark IV tanks, some Medium A Whippets, Austin armoured cars and the inevitable Renaults. France lost out in the end simply because she had too many Renaults and made no serious effort to

replace them, while the British, as we have seen, were obliged to come up with something new.

Not surprisingly, perhaps, one of the first firms to offer armoured vehicles on the post-war market was William Foster & Co of Lincoln, who exploited their reputation as originators of the tank to good effect. However, what they designed was based so obviously on wartime designs that it was clearly a non-starter. Drawings show a long, narrow vehicle running on unsprung track frames like a stretched Whippet. The body design was of the utmost simplicity, with a crew compartment in the front and cargo or personnel section at the back, with the engine – the old wartime Daimler six – and transmission between them. There is no reason be believe it was ever built.

When the Irish Free State was formed in 1921, and the British Army began a gradual withdrawal, they left behind a selection of armoured cars for the new government. These included 13 Rolls-Royces, some Jeffery-Quads and Peerlesses, along with Lancia armoured tenders, all of which came in very useful when civil war broke out in 1922. Yet the name that dominated British military exports between the wars was Vickers, or Vickers-Armstrong as they later became. Indeed, as their contemporary advertising makes clear, they were in a position to supply everything a militant country might need to fight on land, sea or in the air, and they did not hesitate to claim an important place in the origination of the tank; a claim which relies more on their post-war acquisition of the Metropolitan Carriage, Wagon and Finance Co than on anything built at Newcastle or Sheffield. However, as suppliers of tanks and armoured cars to the British Army after the war, their credentials were beyond question. As we shall see, this dual responsibility had to be handled with care when interests conflicted, but in general it seems to have progressed smoothly

81 A party of smart civilians try out the accommodation in a Vickers armoured Peerless lorry. A few were supplied to the Greek Government for internal security work, hence the high wire-mesh roof.

82 One of the commercial Crossley armoured cars as supplied to Argentina and Japan. Compare the front end with that of Repulse *in India; plate 66.*

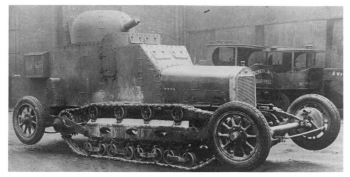

83 The unsold, and probably unsaleable wheel-cum-track armoured car built by Vickers, photographed at the Sheffield factory standing on its tracks.

enough. Among the first types to be built for a foreign customer were some Peerless lorries, fitted with armoured bodies to what might be called the 'Irish' pattern, for the Greek Government who soon found a use for them during civil disturbances. At about the same time the Persian Army took delivery of two Rolls-Royce armoured cars, identical to those supplied for use in India except that they ran on pneumatic tyres. A slightly modified version of the very similar Crossley was supplied, in quite large numbers, to the Japanese, and a smaller batch went to Argentina. The Estonian army also had some Crossley-based armoured cars but the hull design was quite different and may even have been manufactured locally.

In 1927 Vickers' Sheffield Works turned out an ambitious armoured car, presumably as a speculative exercise. Based on a modified Wolseley touring car chassis it had the wheelbase extended dramatically at each end to leave room in the centre for a pair of tracks, on elevating sub-frames, which could be raised and lowered as required. The narrow, upright hull was topped off by a small, domed turret and the entire effect was one of instability. When settled upon its wheels the vehicle did not look too bad, although the wheelbase was something to be reckoned with on sharp corners, but perched on its tracks the car looked ready to fall over at any minute. It must have pitched alarmingly on anything but level ground since, compared with the overall length of the vehicle, ground contact to the tracks was minimal. It seems that no buyer was ever found for it, although there were customers for the most unlikely vehicles. One certainly was the Hungarian official who negotiated with Vickers for the purchase of an armoured car in 1928. As recorded earlier, Vickers had built two big wheel-cum-track armoured vehicles for the British Army which proved more trouble than they were worth, what the Hungarians got was basically one of these without the track attachments. Described by Vickers simply as an armoured car, it had a broad, low hull with the engine and driver's positions alongside one another at the front, the driver sitting to the right of the engine. Beyond was an extremely large, domed turret, mounting but one Vickers machine-gun; larger though similar in shape to those fitted on Indian Pattern armoured cars, including the cupola. At the back the hull sloped down almost

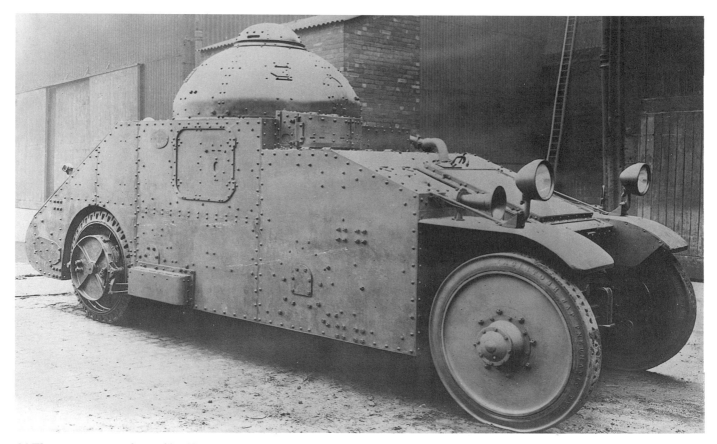

84 The strange armoured car sold to Hungary which appears to have derived from a wheel-cum-track design. Macintosh NAP tyres are fitted and, it should be noted, the brakes only operate on the rear wheels, and external drums at that.

85 *Six Morris-Commercial armoured cars with Vickers bodies paraded at the factory before shipping to Siam.*

to ground level and contained the main access doors. Like the wheel-cum-track vehicles it ran on disc wheels fitted with NAP semi-solid tyres, the rear set being recessed into the hull with the front axle exposed. A more unlikely military vehicle one might have to go a long way to find. It must have been heavy for an armoured car yet cross-country capability would have been pathetic, since the drive, and no doubt the brakes, only operated on the rear wheels, and through a conventional four-speed gearbox at that. The Hungarian police appear to have ended up with the thing but it is not clear how long it lasted.

With the advent of the six-wheeled army lorry Vickers began to investigate the possibilities of making commercial armoured cars based upon it, and came up with a pleasing design based on the Morris-Commercial D type 30cwt. The clean lines made good use of the available chassis space, providing a roomy body surmounted by a small, round turret holding one machine-gun. Temporary tracks could be fitted around the rear bogie wheels, while the radiator was protected by large, hinged flaps and access was gained via a pair of doors at the back. Some eight of these cars were sold to Siam, although at around 4·5 tons they must have been quite a challenge for the Morris chassis with its 16hp engine; it is not known how long they survived in service.

Perhaps for this reason the next Vickers' offering employed the more powerful Crossley chassis. This may also have been influenced by the fact that Vickers had entered into an agreement with Crossley Motors to supply their 30cwt lorry as part of an all embracing mechanisation package, using a 3-ton Thornycroft as the larger model. As an armoured car the design was very similar to the Morris, although the front of the hull was sharply undercut beneath the radiator, no doubt to improve cross-country mobility. The same turret was also used, but an extra machine-gun was fitted in the hull alongside the driver. None are believed to have been sold in this form, although a version with a taller turret – not unlike that fitted to the Indian light tank Mark IVA – was sold to Iraq, one of which was discovered in derelict state by British troops when the country was occupied in 1940. The Vickers' catalogue also

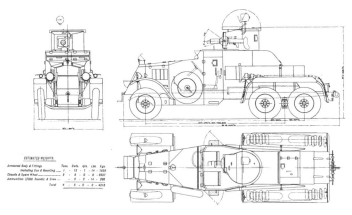

D17 *The Vickers-Morris armoured car.*

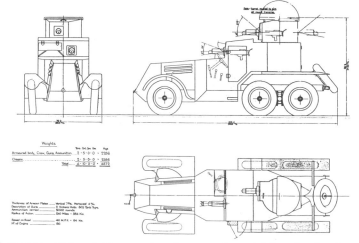

D18 *The Vickers hull mounted on the more substantial Crossley chassis.*

included a domed, turreted, six-wheel Crossley of the type used by the RAF and a drawing showing the same chassis, with an open-top armoured body mounting a heavy pom-pom anti-aircraft weapon.

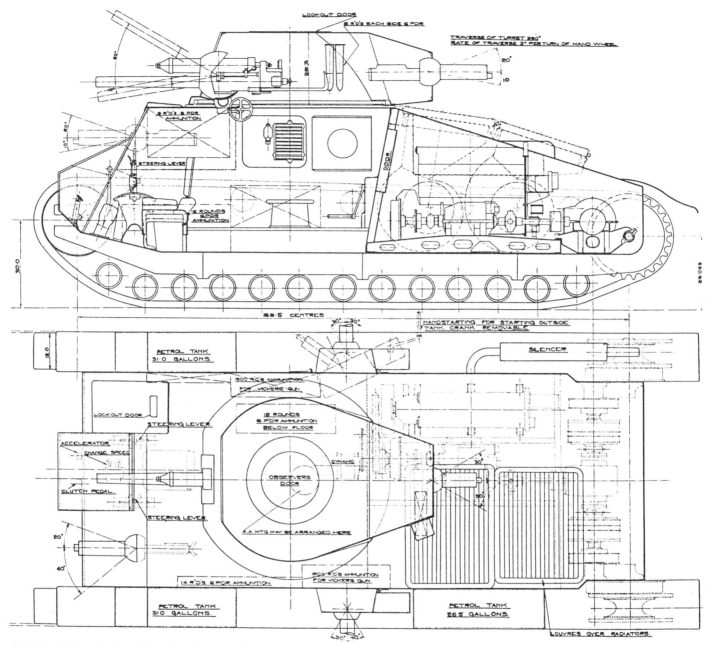

D19 The Vickers Medium Mark C tank as supplied to Japan.

Vickers' entry into commercial tank production took longer to establish and was complicated by national security considerations. Armoured cars were one thing, but where tanks were concerned it was essential to be sure that the nation buying them was a confirmed ally, or that the tanks they got should be inferior to those used by the British Army, just in case they might have to be dealt with at some future time. Eventually an agreement was worked out between Vickers and the British Government, which in essence required that any tank offered for sale by Vickers, should not include any features that had been designed by government employees. This would appear to have given them more than enough leeway, and in any case it was not extended to the point of covering obsolete designs, assuming anybody wanted them. The first Vickers tanks offered for sale abroad were drawn, but never built, in the mid-twenties. Classified as Marks A and B

they were bulky designs, even when compared with the British service mediums, and unlikely to appeal to any potential customer.

The Mark C was a different matter. Indeed it looked so promising that shortly after it was completed, in January 1927, a War Office party visited Sheffield to have a look at it. Apart from the basic method of plate on frame construction, it had nothing whatever in common with the contemporary Medium Mark II. In a sense it had more similarities with those first two Vickers tanks of 1921, at least in terms of the rear-mounted engine; but in view of the official limitations a comparison is interesting. First the suspension: this consisted of the inevitable small rollers, grouped in bogie, but then connected by a system of levers and coil springs to provide a compensating effect between each cluster of bogies, as distinct from the independent action of the service type. The track links were cast in steel with a depressed centre, but open-ended, possibly to improve mud clearing. The engine was a water-cooled six-cylinder Sunbeam Amazon rated at 185hp, located at the rear right-hand side of the hull. The War Office party remarked that the radiator and fans seemed to take up a lot of room, but to save space the clutch and gearbox were located alongside the engine, driving back to the steering epicyclics and rear sprockets. The fighting compartment, at the front, was covered by a large diameter turret, slightly conical in shape but with a flat top and extended rearwards into an ugly bustle that contained a Vickers machine-gun, there being no co-axial weapon. The main armament was a short 57mm (6pr), less suitable for anti-tank work than the British 3pr, but a better dual-purpose weapon. Extra machine-guns were mounted in the sides of the hull and to the left of the driver's position; all of which would have kept a crew of five busy. The driver himself was located in a very strange place. His visor formed part of the sloping front plate of the tank, but the lower half of his body, and the controls, were housed in a curious box-shaped compartment that protruded from the front of the hull and looked as if it had been added as an afterthought. To his right was the main hull access door which, like the Medium tank A7 seems to have been designed to dismount the crew in the least sensible place if they left their damaged tank in the heat of an action. The same might be said of the main fuel tanks, which were located in armoured containers on the trackguards. Despite its size the tank weighed no more than 11·5 tons, accounted for by the use of very thin plate – a mere 6·5mm maximum – which hardly warrants the name of armour when used on such a large tank. Tests revealed that it was a noisy machine and, to the embarrassment of the Vickers engineers, it could not be persuaded to do more than 11mph, although it was designed for 18mph which, it was hoped, would be achieved once it was run-in. It also proved difficult to steer, due to the long stretch of track in contact with the ground.

86 The Medium Mark D tank is introduced to Irish Army soldiers; the turret is reversed, showing the rear machine-gun position, while both the cupola and front hull door are open.

The Medium Mark C was purchased by the Japanese Government, who had it shipped out to the Fuji testing ground, accompanied by two Vickers engineers. Trials began in March 1927, but were marred by an accident when the tank backfired on a steep slope and caught fire, severely injuring one

of the British engineers in the process. This seems to have had a profound effect on the Japanese, who soon began to design a series of compact military diesel engines, which in time they developed to a very high standard. However, it is quite clear that the general design of the Vickers tank influenced Japanese thinking on the subject, because their Type 89 Medium, which first appeared in 1929, was similar in general layout and many details, albeit with a much better design of track.

If Japan is seen as an unlikely customer for Vickers' first commercial tank then the second was even more improbable; it was the Irish Free State. This is not to suggest that Eire had ambitions to become a great user of tanks, but the Government obviously regarded them as important machines and felt it would be wise to train a cadre of troops in the use of tanks and to familiarise the rest of the Irish Army with them. The tank they chose was known to Vickers as their Mark D, but the only obvious difference between it and the Mark C was the fitting of the turret cupola for the commander. It was a big tank for such a purpose, but at least it was up to date and in any case was probably all that was available at the time. Lt. Collins-Powell of the Irish Army was sent across to Sheffield to oversee final construction and to study the tank in detail. He then came back with it to Dublin and took charge of training others to operate it at the Curragh. In fact it remained in service until 1940, when it was damaged beyond economic repair in anti-tank defence trials; its turret dismounted to form part of a pillbox; the hull being scrapped. Now only the gun survives as a treasured relic of Ireland's first tank.

For every successful sale Vickers produced a large number of designs which never got beyond the drawing-board stage. Plans survive for tanks of the Mark C type with various alterations, wheel-cum-track machines of different types and, of course, armoured cars, none of which were ever built. However, this work was combining to increase experience, which culminated, in the pre-Carden era at least, in a medium tank of exceptional design which appeared in 1928. There is often a tendency for certain design trends in all fields to become stereotypes, often for no better reason than unqualified tradition. Thus, for instance, the definition of a medium tank might be taken, at this time, to be a machine of substantial size, weighing about 12 tons; this held true for most tank producing countries. Matters such as crew and armament also took on an essence of the inviolable. Vickers' management appreciated that the medium tanks they had been offering were probably too large for many of their potential customers, and made serious efforts to come up with something more compact. The result was one of the most effective and influential machines to appear in the 20 years between the two world wars; although it was rejected outright by experts in the British Army, possibly for the very reason that it did not match up to their concepts of what a medium tank ought to be.

Known as the Mark E, or Six Ton tank, the prototype was described in a publicity booklet as 'the best possible combination of firepower, mobility and protection'. It was offered in two basic forms although, as the booklet went on to make clear, the makers were willing to adapt it in any way to suit customer requirements. Indeed, another quote from the booklet makes the following strange claim: 'The superstructure of the Tank is removable, and the available space can be utilised to meet varying requirements as regards armament.'

87 The original Vickers Mark E tank with its turrets facing to the flanks. The high rear end of the hull is thought to have covered a Dorman water-cooled engine.

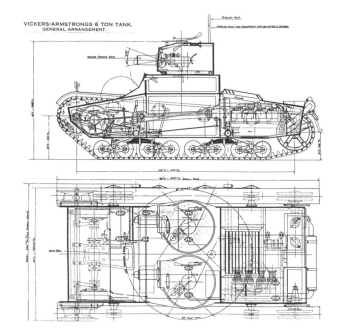

D20 The Mark E in its twin-turreted form.

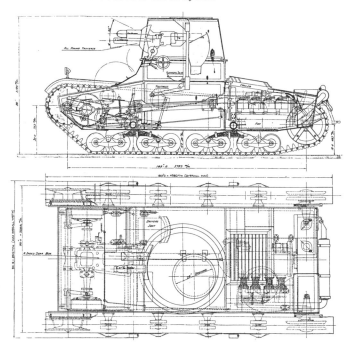

D21 The single turret version of the Mark E.

The new tank was 15 feet long, just over seven feet wide and a little under eight feet high. The rear hull on the prototype was quite high, and some sources suggest that it contained an 80hp Dorman water-cooled engine. Production models were much lower in this region because these tanks were fitted with a horizontal air-cooled, four-cylinder version of the Armstrong Siddeley engine. The drive shaft then passed through the fighting comparment to a five-speed gearbox in the nose of the tank, with simple clutch and brake steering acting on the front sprockets. Lightweight manganese tracks ran around a tough, if rather basic suspension based on two bogie clusters at each side. These supported the hull on cross tubes, using a quarter-elliptical leaf spring linking the bogies of each unit. The central fighting compartment included a position on the right for the driver and sufficient space for two or three more crew members depending on the type. Apart from the inconvenience of a drive shaft running through the middle, this gave the crew plenty of room to work, with everyone in close touch. Armour was advertised as being 13mm maximum on the fighting compartment and turrets, although this was again left up to the customer's choice and as much as 17mm was available if requested. Speed was a respectable 22mph, although the weight was usually a ton or two above the nominal six tons of its title.

Two basic versions were offered. The first, like the prototype, carried a pair of one-man machine-gun turrets mounted side by side, each capable of covering a 100° arc of fire, while the other mounted one, much larger turret that contained a short 47mm gun with a Vickers machine-gun alongside it. Wireless was an optional extra. On the twin-turret version it was usually located inside the hull, but the single-turret model could be supplied with an armoured bustle to house a Marconi tank set if required. Sample tanks were tested by, and sometimes sold to, many countries, while others bought substantial numbers. It would be tedious to cover them all, but some of the more interesting can be dealt with. The single example tested by the US Army was something of a milestone, since it is a rare event at the best of times, and it says much for the potential that the design represented. It resulted in the appearance of Medium Tank T1E4 which, as things turned out, was never developed. A Polish order for twin-turreted tanks was later regretted, but rather than replace them

Vickers were asked to supply new upper hull plates and single turrets to convert them. Poland later built its own version of the tank, the 7TP, but they are also thought to have been the potential customers for two more heavily armed versions that were produced as drawings only in about 1930. Both had twin machine-gun turrets, while one had a larger gun in the hull structure pointing to the front and the other had two such weapons, facing in either direction and presumably offset to some extent, which would have been a nightmare to fight. The Chinese order included single-turret tanks with wireless bustles, while the Finns took their main delivery unarmed, since they wished to fit a 37mm French weapon instead. The

88 *A 47mm armed six tonner in Chinese service although the original caption claims that it was built in 'one of General Chiang Kai-shek's 2,000 war factories'!*

largest customer was Russia, which took both versions and then developed them into a range of tanks under the series designation T26. Odd sample tanks were supplied to Greece and Portugal among others, and modest orders were delivered to various countries, including Bolivia, Bulgaria and Siam. Their influence can also be detected in tanks built by Czechoslovakia, Hungary and Italy in particular.

Two six-ton tanks, one of each pattern, saw action during the Gran Chaco War between Paraguay and Bolivia; in service with the latter. The small tank force, commanded by a German officer, included some Carden-Loyd carriers as well, but the country was semi-forest which inhibited tank operations and Paraguay, which had no tanks, won the war, destroying the single turret Mark E and capturing the other. Both Chinese and Siamese six-tonners saw action against the Japanese and a few captured examples no doubt served with the Imperial Army. But it was in Europe that these tanks did most of their fighting. Poland and Bulgaria committed theirs, while the Winter War between Finland and Russia saw British-built six-tonners of the Finnish Army taking on Russian T26 derivatives. Finland captured so many of the Russian tanks that they took them into service and even instituted a rework programme, which resulted in a sort of Mark E/T26 hybrid mounting the Soviet gun and with a hull machine-gun installed to the left of the driver.

British criticism of the tank, following preliminary trials, centred mostly on the suspension which was considered noisy, and not robust enough. However, a few of the tanks, still on the stocks at Newcastle when war broke out in 1939, were

89 *A Mark E, fitted with Straussler's trench crossing leg attachments. Just the sort of added complication a tank crew can do without.*

taken into British service for training purposes, and, the criticism notwithstanding, the same suspension was used for an artillery tractor and the first infantry tank, A11. Vickers used one of the twin-turret models as a demonstrator and at one stage it was equipped with an ingenious, if rather complicated, trench crossing device invented by Nicholas Straussler. It consisted of hinged legs attached to each end of the tank, which swung outwards as the tank crossed a trench, and held the relevant end up while it was over the gap. Clever as it was it seems that no one was persuaded to buy it. The statement, quoted earlier, about the tank having a removable superstructure may explain an unusual variant of the Mark E

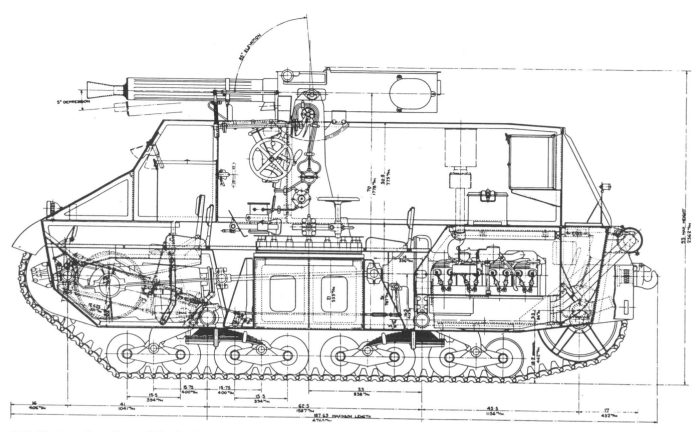

D22 The 6-ton Pom-Pom vehicle showing details of the gun mounting.

90 Looking down into the fighting compartment of a 40 mm Pom-Pom vehicle, built on the six tonner chassis for the Siamese Army.

supplied to Siam in small numbers. It retained the basic chassis and automotive layout, but the original superstructure was replaced by a large, open-topped box, containing a water-cooled 40mm Pom-Pom on a high-angle mount, with the crew located around it. Clearly the main role was anti-aircraft, although it was capable of being used against ground targets as well, if one was prepared to accept a high silhouette.

The idea of an amphibious tank has always intruiged both designers and soldiers since the earliest days of armoured warfare. It appears to confer the maximum potential for mobility, for such a tank is not even stopped by inland waterways; but this ideàl is flawed in many respects. Such a tank must be carefully built to seal the hull, while the mechanical parts have to be designed with the same thing in mind. There is the additional complication of driving a propellor off the gearbox and fitting a rudder, which also increases the maintenance burden. Without careful inspection and lubrication after a swim, bearings will soon dry out and seize; rust is another consideration. From an operational point of view there are more problems. Generally, for instance, one might say that a tank built to float without external assistance – in the form of pontoons or screens – will be very light on armour and thus vulnerable, while a tank capable of resisting armour-piercing shot will be so heavy that it would not float unless built unacceptably large. In practice even mobility is compromised since a suitable crossing point in a river must be selected first; steep banks, mud-flats or thick reed beds can stop a tank as effectively as a trench. Yet the demand was there and Vickers-Armstrong, as they had now become, set out to meet it.

The result was a two-man tank of striking appearance, based on Light Tank Mark I components but with an enlarged hull to ensure buoyancy. This included kapok filled trackguards and

91 *The original Vickers-Armstrong Light Amphibious Tank in the Stour at Christchurch. The plate covering the suspension was a counterbalance for the Meadows engine.*

extra compartments beneath the floor, which unfortunately also reduced the effective ground clearance. The hull was formed from armour to a maximum thickness of 9mm, which was hardly very effective, although it resulted in an all-up weight of less than three tons. Tar was used to seal the hull joints, rather than using close pitch rivets. Power was supplied by a six-cylinder Meadows engine driving through a four-speed gearbox, with a take off to the propellor at the back. This gave the tank a top speed of 6mph in the water and an amazing 40mph on land due to the high power to weight ratio. Yet this proved to be a mixed blessing because the suspension units could not take such punishment for long and the unstiffened hull was prone to distortion after a good cross-country hammering. The usual circular machine-gun turret was fitted, offset to the left, while the engine was located on the right. This still meant that the tank was out of balance in the water, so on the prototype a steel ballast weight was fitted over the nearside suspension unit, although production tanks were balanced in a less obvious way. Photographs reveal two basic versions, those – like the two British Army trial tanks already mentioned – that had cowls around the propellor to effect steering, and those that had rudders. The prototype, built at Chertsey, was first tested in the River Thames near Teddington Lock. It floated well down by the stern and with precious little freeboard forward, but it soon attracted customers. Apart from the British Army a few were sold to Holland, Finland and Siam, while both Russia and China ordered quite large numbers. Only the Russians developed the type to any extent, through the T37 and T38 series, but many similar machines developed in Japan certainly drew inspiration from the Vickers design.

When it came to conventional light tanks Vickers-Armstrong found that there was a very large potential market to exploit. This was not due entirely to the matter of cost, although this was important, but to another factor that suited many smaller nations – simplicity. By their very nature such tanks could hardly be described as complex; they were driven by ordinary commercial water-cooled engines, linked to familiar crash gearboxes, while the basic clutch and brake steering was not only simple in itself, it eliminated the need for a differential and reduced complications even further. Such a machine would be easy enough to drive with the minimum of training, reliable, since the components were tried and tested items not subject to any undue stress and, in the final analysis, reasonably easy to maintain. Vickers' publicity might be going a bit over the top when it described them as 'no way less reliable than a modern touring car', but it was not far off.

By the time the first commercial example was offered for sale, in 1933, similar tanks were in service with the British Army both at home and in India. This was an additional bonus for Vickers since, as the originator of the tank, Britain was still seen by many as a leader in the field and therefore if the British Army used Vickers light tanks it enhanced their credibility. Nevertheless, the constraints on the use of officially designed components meant that those tanks advertised for sale were not quite the same as their counterparts in the RTC. This was most obvious in respect of suspension, which still featured leaf springs, and the tiny round turret. The Meadows engine was naturally chosen, located on the right so that the driver's compartment and turret were offset to the left. In their sales brochure Vickers offered the choice of a standard, rifle-calibre machine-gun or the heavier ·5in version, but surviving records suggest that customers did not take up this particular option. It is also interesting to note that the long, sloping front hull plate, formed of 9mm armour, was pointed out as a feature intended specifically to deflect bullets. Obvious as this appears, it is rarely mentioned in official British documents on tank design, even during the Second World War, and the impression is often given that some doubt existed in the minds of British soldiers that it was a worthwhile practice.

92 A builder's publicity photograph of the 1933 model Light Tank, the first of which was sold to Finland.

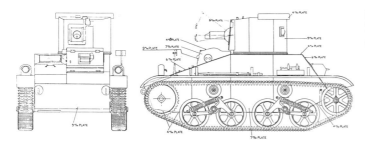

D23 The commercial light tank in its second guise.

The first tank sold went to Finland, but they didn't order any more and the next batch, of 16, went to Lithuania, followed by two for Switzerland. These were interesting. To begin with they were supplied with teeth on the idlers as well as the sprockets. This practice is not popular since the track will soon stretch to a point where it cannot be matched up to the teeth at both ends, but it may have been intended as a means of dislodging packed snow from the tracks. It probably caused trouble, because plain idlers were later supplied for both machines. However the strangest thing about this order is that each tank had a different suspension, although they were both delivered on the same day in July 1934. One had the leaf spring suspension while the other had the latest Vickers' double spring system, which soon became standard on later export models. In passing it is interesting to note that none of the tanks sold abroad had the Horstmann pattern of horizontal springs used on the British Light Mark II. Switzerland ordered five more tanks in 1935, all with the later type of suspension,

and all seven were delivered without armament. This trend also proved popular. In their publicity material the company made it clear that it was prepared to be as flexible as possible in meeting customer requirements; as some armies were already committed to types of weapon that Vickers could not supply this was an obvious solution. A more extreme example of this flexibility was the first Belgian order for 18 tanks placed early in 1934. They were required to take a 13·5mm Hotchkiss machine-gun, for which a larger turret was required so Vickers

93 Argentinian soldiers, in German style helmets, and British Light Tanks taking part in a parade. This is the second model with double coil-spring suspension.

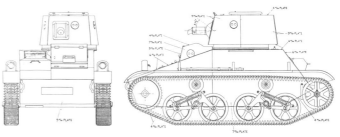

D24 The commercial light tank with an angular turret as supplied to the Dutch East Indies amongst others.

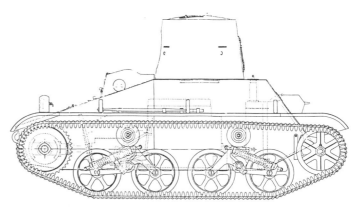

D25 Known to the Belgians as the T15 this light tank mounted a conical shaped turret.

produced a special pattern, taller than usual and conical in shape. These were delivered early in 1935, to be followed by another order for 24 that arrived in Brussels towards the end of that year.

The next development also dates from 1935, when the round type of turret was superseded by a six-sided flat one, not unlike the type developed for the Indian Pattern Mark IVA, but without the special cupola. Orders of some size were received from China, Latvia and Lithuania, in addition to a small one from Holland. Among these the Dutch order is interesting on account of the armament, which consisted of twin Colt-Browning 7·7mm air-cooled weapons, and the Lithuanian because four out of the sixteen they had were modified to take Gambrella wireless sets. However, it was the Latvian order which brought about the next development. Of the 18 tanks they took between 1936 and 1938, six carried 40mm guns in lengthened versions of the angular turret. This was quite a substantial weapon for such a small tank, and apart from some experimental types built for the British Army, made it the best armed of any light tanks supplied by Vickers up to that point. Described as a quick-firing, semi-automatic weapon, it was Vickers' own design and was claimed to have a performance only slightly inferior to the 2pr anti-tank gun of the same calibre developed by the Royal Arsenal. Shortly before the war another order was received from Holland, for tanks to be supplied to their army in the Dutch East Indies. These were to be machine-gun armed. As it was the war broke out before all of them had been delivered, and the balance were delivered to the Royal Armoured Corps for use as training tanks under the designation Light Tank Mark IIIB, although they were popularly known as Dutchmen.

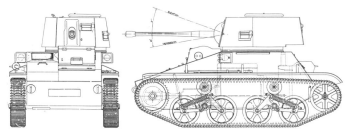

D26 The 40mm gun light tank as supplied to Latvia.

94 The commercial light tank with an enlarged turret to carry the Vickers 40mm gun. Tanks of this type were supplied to Latvia.

The original Vickers-Armstrong files for this period, concerned as they are with future business, make interesting reading. Rival companies such as Marmon-Herrington in the United States, and Praga in Czechoslovakia, were making inroads into what had once been a Vickers monopoly, and it was difficult to keep ahead without incurring great costs in research. A letter from Sir Noel Birch, one time MGO but now a Vickers director, written in 1938 poses the question whether the firm should concentrate on work for the British Government or foreign sales. Either way, as Sir Noel sees it, they would be in for a lean time. The design under discussion – a new medium tank – might take two years to design and another 12 months would pass before the War Office was ready to accept it, so production might not commence until 1942. He writes, 'It would be a brave man who would prophesy in 1941 or 1942 the War Office will have any money to spend on anything . . .'. Knowing, as we do, that war would break out within a year, it seems extraordinarily naive, for the Munich Agreement was still in the future. Birch, of course, was purposely taking a pessimistic view (if the prospect of continuing peace could be a cause for pessimism) in order to make a point, for his job was to sell tanks and keep his firm in business, but still it seems to be an amazing thing to say at a time when air-raid shelters were being dug all over London. In an earlier document on the same theme Birch outlined some of his ideas for the future to Sir Charles Craven at Barrow-in-Furness. One of the ideas he put forward was for a crewless tank, controlled by radio from the air, which he believed would come in time. He also discussed the protection of tanks from aerial attack and pointed out that the Fraser Nash company had already interested the War Office in a power driven anti-aircraft turret for a light tank, and warned Sir Charles that they must keep a careful eye on the Morris company. Prospects were not improved by a letter which he received from Sir John Carden's erstwhile partner, Vivian Loyd. Writing from Switzerland, where he had gone for his health, he claims to have heard rumours that the Germans were developing a sort of wireless death-ray that stopped the magnetos of petrol engines on land and in the air, which came within its range. Loyd was trying to persuade Vickers to adopt diesel engines, which would not be vulnerable to the ray, but once again development costs made the project unworkable, and in any case Sir Noel had little time for Loyd, whom he regarded as a burden to the company.

Returning to the subject of tanks, by 1936 Vickers were anxious to take some commercial advantage from the current British trend towards three-man machines. Forbidden to sell the Mark VI, they worked up a design of their own which they called the Command Tank. In a paper explaining this development they pointed out the advantages of having a third man in the tank who was free to undertake command duties. The object, clearly, was to persuade existing customers with two-man light tanks to provide their section, company and battalion commanders with these bigger tanks to ensure more efficient operations. A design was prepared and a prototype built, probably towards the end of 1937. It was both longer and wider than the Light Tank Mark VI and, by moving the engine and transmission to the front there was room for a larger turret, which mounted a 40mm gun, although twin machine-guns were offered as an option. Armour was to 11mm standard and

95 *The Vickers-Armstrong Command Tank was a good deal larger than it looks. A sort of combination of the six tonner hull and turret with light tank suspension components. It was offered to Belgium but never sold.*

the turret was similar in shape to that fitted on the Mark E, while an access and escape hatch was provided at the back. The suspension was based on the Vickers double spring type, but with extra shock absorbers to ease the burden of greater weight. The tank was on test in Belgium in February 1938 when, to their dismay, Vickers learnt that the War Office had added it to the Secret List because it possessed 'so many features of the Mark VIB', which they regarded as secret. Following protests it was released again in July and discussions went ahead on the possibility of Belgium building the tank, under licence, for their own use. Just a couple of months before the war broke out there was even talk of having the tank built in Belgium for sale to other foreign customers but, of course, all this came to nought. The tank was last seen, in somewhat battered condition, among a collection of relics outside the MEE buildings just after the war, after which, presumably, it was scrapped. The Belgians had also expressed an interest, in 1934, in the Six Ton tank, on condition that it was fitted with a Rolls-Royce engine. A prototype was duly built, and fitted with the six-cylinder 20/25hp engine, which was naturally too big to fit into the low, rear compartment originally designed to house

96 *The prototype Medium Mark F, showing how the turret was offset to the right to clear the engine, and the air inlet cowl on the front deck.*

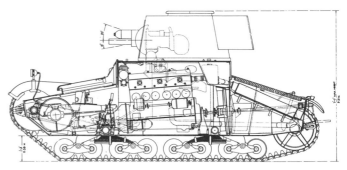

D27 *Internal layout of the Mark F medium tank, showing how the Rolls-Royce engine dominated the central compartment.*

the flat four-cylinder Armstrong Siddeley unit, so it was moved forwards into the fighting compartment instead. This required a redesign of the hull, which was inevitable anyway because the new engine was water-cooled, and space had to be found for a radiator. The alterations involved enlarging the centre section, mainly at the expense of the rear, and then placing the engine upright in the left side, tilted forwards slightly to line up with the transmission. The engine was then partitioned off from the crew compartment and the turret moved so far across to the right that a portion of the turret ring was actually visible protruding through the side of the hull. An air-intake cowl was fitted on the front of the hull and the radiator mounted at the back; armour was to 13mm standard. In this form the tank was classified as Mark F, but following trials in Belgium no further orders were placed, despite some interest from Portugal. The Mark E Six Tonners that ended up in British service have already been mentioned. They are believed to have been part of an order placed with Vickers-Armstrong by the Siamese Government in 1938, but they are of greater interest because examination of the survivor reveals an outward similarity to the Mark F. Presumably the order specified the old Armstrong Siddeley engine because that was already well known in Siam, but Vickers may by now have been gearing up to produce the Mark F and chose to use that hull form instead, with the turret moved in towards the centre.

In 1931 the War Office made some concessions to Vickers in the matter of what they could export and two designs, hitherto restricted to British and Commonwealth armies came on to the open market. One was the Medium Tank Mark II, a design which was by then some six years old. They were not exactly trampled in a rush of customers and, indeed, it seems a bit surprising that any were sold at all. However, the Russians, who were rapidly building up a tank force, appear to have been ready to try anything, and added an order for 15 to one for Mark E Six Tonners. The two types were assembled side by side at Sheffield, and writing of this in July 1931 Sir Noel Birch refers to the 'old service bus Mark II', adding that 'the Russian order . . . has already saved the situation as far as Vickers-Armstrong is concerned'. In a spirit of egalitarian solidarity the Russians called these tanks *English Workman*, and kept them in service at least long enough to commit some to action during the Russo-Finnish War. Basically similar to the British version they featured less pronounced turret bevels because water-cooled Vickers machine-guns were fitted to the turret sides, and cowled ventilation fans on the hull sides.

The other type released for sale in 1931 was, of course, the Carden-Loyd Mark VI Carrier, and this, it seems, the world had been waiting for. A Vickers-Armstrong sales brochure issued at about this time described it as 'SMALL, ARMOURED, SPEEDY, HANDY AND POWERFUL', they might, with some justification, have added 'CHEAP' too, for at around £400 per unit it did represent a bargain of sorts. A version was advertised with small, hinged head covers for the crew: pyramid-shaped lids that closed over the central compartment. Single examples were tested by many countries and purchased by some, but quite large numbers were sold to the Russians, who developed their T27 Carrier from them, and to the Siamese Government, which took at least 30. Among those countries that used them as the basis of their own designs were Czechoslovakia, France, Italy and Poland, while the

97 Awaiting export to the Soviet Union, an 'English Workman' Medium Tank. The altered style of turret, with machine-guns mounted, is well shown.

98 Two Carden-Loyds in Sweden. In the foreground is the unique narrow type in which the gunner sits behind the driver. Beyond it, on the snow, is a standard Mark VI with hinged head-covers.

Swedes ordered a special narrow version in which the crew sat in tandem. The idea was presumably to produce a vehicle capable of moving along narrow channels cut in the snow, but it remained the only one of its kind. The Belgians used the open-topped version, fitted with a single return roller instead of the skid rail, and at least two of theirs carried 47mm guns mounted on the front hull plate. Vickers offered a similar idea, mounting their short 47mm gun, but they do not appear to have sold any.

Later versions, of the Mark VI★ type, also reached the commercial market. Finland had one, and the Japanese bought quite a few, while those purchased by Bolivia saw active service in the Gran Chaco War against Paraguay. Since reports of these little machines in action are rare, it is worth recording the opinion of Wilhelm Brandt, the German officer who commanded the Bolivian armour. He found the Carden-Loyds too small and low to the ground for operations in rough country, especially where they encountered fallen trees upon which they invariably got stranded and broke their tracks. Since the idea of overhead protection seemed to appeal to foreign buyers Vickers went a stage further in 1932, producing what they called their Light Patrol Tank, which was basically a turreted version of the three-man carrier tested by the British Army. The suspension was improved by the addition of tiny

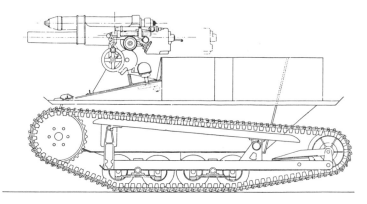

99 Trials of the Vickers-Carden-Loyd Light Patrol Tank. This is the later version with coil-spring suspension.

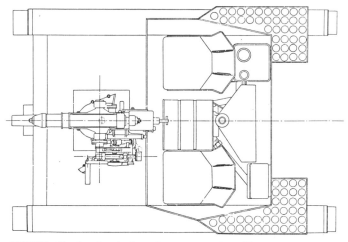

D28 The Carden-Loyd adapted to mount a short 47mm gun.

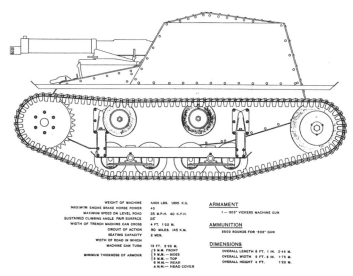

		ARMAMENT
WEIGHT OF MACHINE	4400 LBS. 1995 K.G.	1 — '303" VICKERS MACHINE GUN
MAXIMUM ENGINE BRAKE HORSE POWER	40	
MAXIMUM SPEED ON LEVEL ROAD	25 M.P.H. 40 K.P.H.	AMMUNITION
SUSTAINED CLIMBING ANGLE FAIR SURFACE	25°	3500 ROUNDS FOR '303" GUN
WIDTH OF TRENCH MACHINE CAN CROSS	4 FT. 1·22 M.	
CIRCUIT OF ACTION	90 MILES. 145 K.M.	
SEATING CAPACITY	2 MEN.	DIMENSIONS
WIDTH OF ROAD IN WHICH MACHINE CAN TURN	13 FT. 3·95 M.	OVERALL LENGTH 8 FT. 1 IN. 2·46 M.
MINIMUM THICKNESS OF ARMOUR	9 M.M.— FRONT / 9 M.M.— SIDES / 6 M.M. — TOP / 6 M.M. — REAR / 4 M.M.— HEAD COVER	OVERALL WIDTH 5 FT. 9 IN. 1·75 M. / OVERALL HEIGHT 4 FT. 1·22 M.

D29 The Mark V★ version of the Carden-Loyd as sold to Japan, Bolivia and Finland.

coil springs by Horstmann and the Ford A engine was used. It looked decidedly unstable with the tall, offset turret, and hardly suitable for use over rough ground, but at least one was purchased by Denmark, and fitted with a Madsen machine-gun. But since it cost over £1,000, and hardly warranted the title of tank, it was a commercial failure. In 1933 it was decided

to offer a cheaper version, with thinner armour and leaf spring suspension as a Police Tank. This sold for £700, with a bullet-proof glass cupola as an extra for £50, if the customer wished. An advertisement, published at the time, showed one of these machines in a city street, chasing a gang of theatrical looking ruffians and followed by a group of policemen straight out of the Keystone Cops. But there is no reason to suppose that even this persuaded anyone to buy one.

As already mentioned, in addition to armoured vehicles, Vickers-Armstrong offered a full supporting range of military vehicles ranging from lorries to tracked tractors of various types. In Belgium an armoured version of the standard light tractor was developed, mounting a 47mm gun in a partly enclosed turret, and this saw service with their army as the T13. They even went so far as to armour versions of the one-man utility tractor, for front line resupply work, and exported a few. It is worth noting also that Vickers sold tracked tractors to at least two commercial organisations in Germany, ostensibly for civilian use. However, it now seems clear that they were used during development work for the Panzer I light tank, which showed Vickers' influence in its suspension and tracks.

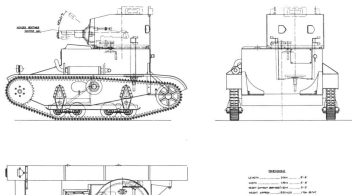

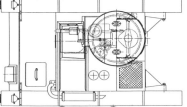

D30 The Vickers-Carden Loyd Light Patrol Tank showing the earlier suspension and optional cupola.

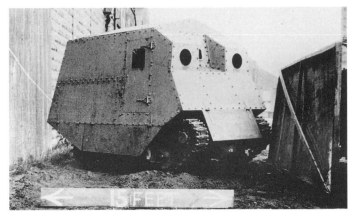

100 An Alvis-Straussler chassis fitted with wooden mock-up turret and hull of the design sold to the Dutch East Indies.

101 The strange little Garrett tractor-based fighting vehicle demonstrates its ability to turn in confined spaces. The round holes in the front could presumably be fitted with machine-guns.

Vickers-Armstrong so dominated the commercial military scene in Britain between the wars that the few other contenders in the armoured vehicle field are easily overlooked. Fosters' abortive effort has already been mentioned but one that was reasonably successful was the Alvis Company of Coventry. In 1937 they joined forces with the Hungarian engineer Nicholas Straussler, to form Alvis-Straussler Ltd, and marketed a range of vehicles to his designs. Prototypes of both armoured cars and light tanks had already been developed by the Manfred Weiss company in Hungary, so by the time he came to Britain Straussler was virtually ready to go into production. The armoured cars were of strikingly modern appearance, with almost streamlined hulls formed from well angled plates. They were four-wheelers with rear mounted Alvis 4·5 litre engine and tubular backbone chassis with independent suspension all round. Primary and auxiliary gearboxes gave eight speeds in either direction, driving all four wheels; the central turret mounted a machine-gun. Twelve were built in Britain for the Dutch East Indies, under the designation AC3D, which featured an extra machine-gun alongside the driver, but the situation is confused by the fact that similar cars continued to be built in Hungary. As the next chapter will show, a few more were built in Britain for the RAF, and we have already noted a light tank that was tested at MEE; this was also offered on the export market, although apparently never sold.

It is probably unnecessary to stress that the production of armoured vehicles is an expensive business involving research of a technical nature to very high standards, and a familiarity with military requirements. It is probably fair to say that even Vickers-Armstrong never made a great deal of money out of it, while Alvis-Straussler Ltd probably did little better than to break even, so it would be a bit much to expect a firm already on its financial uppers to get anywhere at all. However, the trade no doubt looks lucrative from the outside, and desperation can force a company to try anything. Such was the case with the old established traction engine builders Garretts, of Leiston in Suffolk. By 1932 this company was ready to go under when it was rescued by the famous locomotive manufacturers Beyer Peacock and Co of Manchester. Among the new products marketed by the rejuvenated company was a type of commercial crawler known as the Multi-Speed Tractor, one of which was tested at MEE as a possible artillery tractor

for the 60pr gun. It was rejected as unsuitable, but in the report it stated that, 'it can also be converted into a somewhat crude AFV', which was close to the truth. It was powered by a rear-mounted Gardner diesel, driving through a three-speed gearbox and two-speed auxiliary drive, and in top gear it could manage a respectable 12mph. The armoured version, which was demonstrated in prototype form in 1933, was a most peculiar vehicle, the precise purpose of which is almost impossible to determine, especially since the firm itself was rather vague on the subject. The hull was nothing more than an armoured box, almost as tall as it was long, with a gabled roof and flat sides. The driver sat centrally at the front, with the engine behind him, and flanked by panels containing circular holes which are presumed to be forward facing machine-gun mountings. Doors were provided in both sides, and hinged skirting plates covered the suspension, while another hinged panel at the back gave access to the engine. It is tempting to see the thing as some sort of armoured personnel carrier, except that there would hardly be room inside for more than three, or four at the most; say a driver, two machine-gunners, and possibly a commander. Publicity photos show it posed in the work's yard, either on a slight slope or in a very narrow passage way, and marks on the ground show it could spin around in its own length. The implication is that it was being offered as a simple type of internal security vehicle which could manœuvre in narrow alleyways, but the advertising campaign had no effect at all, and this curious little vehicle quietly faded from the scene.

In addition to those tanks sold commercially by Vickers-Armstrong it appears that some were supplied direct to foreign armies from War Office stocks. The Egyptian Army received a few Light Mark III tanks which became surplus to requirements in the Middle East, and then shortly before the war obtained ten Light Mark VIBs. A single example of the same type was supplied to Iraq, and nine more went to the Turkish Army. There were hopes, at one time, that the Government would allow Vickers to offer the A9 Cruiser for sale, and Poland was thought to be interested, but this never happened. Yet there is photographic evidence to suggest that at least one A11 Infantry Tank reached Poland by some means or another. The Polish Government sometimes proved a rather difficult customer as far as Vickers-Armstrong were concerned.

102 *A puzzling photograph from Poland, said to have been taken in September 1939. A damaged A11 Infantry Tank Mark I, a type not known to have been exported yet clearly at that date not a captured British Army type from France.*

Lengthy negotiations for some military equipment often went awry for financial reasons and there was always a suspicion that some British designs were being pirated. However, there remains this photograph of a knocked out A11 with cheerful German soldiers climbing all over it, and the logical explanation seems to be that one was supplied to Poland shortly before the war and committed to action in the desperate days of invasion, although no documentary evidence can be found to support this. An alternative explanation might be that the tank was one of those captured in France, in 1940, from the British Expeditionary Force, and then placed in German service for security duties in occupied Poland. The only reason for questioning this is that one rarely sees troops posing for a photograph in such a jovial manner if the knocked out tank they are sitting on is one of their own.

The situation in India has already been covered, but this might be a suitable point at which to examine the equipment supplied to, or built by, other Commonwealth and Empire countries. Australia obtained four Medium Mark II tanks in 1929. Although built as part of a larger contract placed with Vickers in 1926, and numbered in sequence with the tanks supplied to the British Army, they had turrets like those sold later to Russia, with smaller bevelled areas to accomodate Vickers machine-guns. Eleven Mark VIA Light Tanks followed in 1937. Meanwhile the Australian Government was making efforts to produce armoured vehicles of its own. In 1935 a prototype armoured car was built, on a modified Ford

Chassis. The first to be produced in that country since 1915. Clearly based on the design of the British Rolls-Royce it was a big vehicle which soon acquired the nickname *Ned Kelly*, for obvious reasons. Some accounts suggest that it was such an unwieldy vehicle very few commanders would allow it out on the streets, preferring to keep it locked in a shed where it could not come to any harm. Yet it remained on the strength as a training vehicle until 1942. The possibility of buying armoured

103 *Ned Kelly,* a large Ford armoured car based on the Rolls-Royce design, which as its name implies was built in Australia. Here it demonstrates the use of ditch-crossing boards.

105 *Two of the big Shanghai Volunteer Defence Force armoured cars follow the armoured staff, or command car on a patrol.*

cars from Britain was discussed and laid aside before another model appeared in 1937. In that year two Ford-based cars appeared to a design which may have been influenced by the British Morris Light Armoured Car. They had high, box bodies, surmounted by what passed for a turret, although in reality it was little more than a shield, mounting a single machine-gun. They were issued to 1st ACC, the erstwhile 19th Light Horse. Six more were built to an approved design in 1938, again on Ford chassis, in the South Australian Railways workshops, and these were soon followed by nine more which featured Marmon-Herrington four-wheel drive.

Canada bought a few Carden-Loyd Mark VIB carriers in the early thirties, which they used as tractors for ski-troops in the winter, but an approach by Vickers in 1931, through Mr Pacuad of the Canadian High Commission in London failed to interest his government in the idea of allowing Canadian Vickers to build AFVs for home use and export. Shortly before the War some Light Tanks Mark VIB were snapped up from an order that was intended for Australia, when the government in Canberra failed to make up its mind quickly enough. Both Ford and General Motors of Canada built prototype armoured cars based on the design of the six-wheeled British Crossley, which has hardly the most inspiring of prototypes. They were left-hand drive chassis, but the panel alongside the driver, which housed a machine-gun in the British cars, remained blank on the Canadian version. Whether such a mounting was contemplated is not clear, but without it these large cars could only deploy one machine-gun each. However, they were not developed and no further attempts were made to produce armoured vehicles until war broke out.

104 Canada also used a Ford chassis for one of their early armoured cars, based loosely on the British Crossley design. A similar vehicle appeared on a GMC chassis.

South Africa received a Medium Mark A Whippet tank shortly after the First World War, apparently in answer to an internal threat. Named HMLS *Union* it put in a few brief appearances before vanishing. In 1931 two Crossley armoured cars, similar to those supplied to India, were obtained, both later being remounted on Ford chassis with large section pneumatic tyres. At some stage South Africa also acquired two Vickers Mediums. The exact date is not known, but it must

have been fairly late since one of them, T14, had been used in Britain as a test-bed for a Ricardo diesel engine, before presumably being converted back to an Armstrong Siddeley unit. The fact that both tanks came from the very first batch of Mark I Mediums supplied by the ROF in 1922 implies that they must have been given away, and the only benefit the South African forces might have derived from them can only have been in the form of a challenge to keep them running at all. Surprisingly, one still survives, as a gate guardian outside the barracks in Bloemfontein.

Following the 1927 emergency in Shanghai, and the withdrawal of British regular forces, the European settlers had to rely on their own resources to some extent. Residents had formed the Shanghai Volunteer Defence Force and this had its own armoured car section, using locally constructed vehicles. More imposing than effective, they were based on heavy American truck chassis with solid tyres, possibly Packards, and the armour layout was based on the Rolls-Royce design, only on a grander scale. There were eight of these vehicles and one armoured command car, probably on a Ford chassis.

106 In Singapore they took a D Type Morris-Commercial six-wheeler and fitted it with the biggest body and turret they could think of. Mercifully it was only in wood, this bulk in armour plate would have flattened it.

The disturbances in China sent ripples of discontent spreading throughout the Far East, and soon reached Singapore. As early as 1927 a very strange sight appeared on the streets of that city, in the form of a 30cwt Morris-Commercial truck, fitted with an outsize body, complete with turret, but made of wood. Whether it was the prototype for an armoured vehicle is not certain, but if so it suggests a misplaced confidence in the load-bearing capacity of the chassis, since the body was large enough to do justice to a single decker bus, while the turret was of such size that one Vickers machine-gun appeared quite lost in it.

In due course what might be described as a standard type of armoured car, designed to suit local conditions, appeared. The first of these, a Thornycroft nicknamed *Leaping Lena*, was

107 Albion and Thornycroft (left) six-wheelers of the Hong Kong Volunteer Defence Force. The figure circled is P J (Pip) Gardner later to gain one of the two Victoria Crosses for the RTR in the Second World War.

constructed by the Whampoa and Hong Kong Dockyard for use by the Hong Kong Volunteer Defence Force. It was a six-wheeler with a long, enclosed body and two machine-gun turrets arranged either side of the centre line and staggered fore and aft. This gave the maximum possible field of fire for either weapon but also permitted both to concentrate on a single target if necessary. The Thornycroft was soon joined by another six-wheeler, thought to be an Albion, and the Dockyard supplied similar cars on the same chassis to Singapore and the Chinese Government in the early thirties.

9 Middle East Mandates

If the transition from war to peacetime soldiering was traumatic for the Tank Corps in Britain, it passed almost without notice in those regions of the Middle East for which Britain held the League of Nations mandate. Bolshevik activities on the Iraqi–Persian borders, added to internal Arab struggles for the control of specific regions – aided and abetted by British and French politicians – kept the pot continually on the boil. As manpower was reduced closer to peacetime levels in the Army and the advantages of mobility became even more apparent, so the surviving Light Armoured Motor Batteries (LAMBS) took on a greater share of the duties: with a motley collection of wartime armoured cars.

From early 1920 onwards this task fell increasingly to the Tank Corps. As already explained new armoured car companies were raised, and as these arrived at their allotted stations in the Middle East they took over the cars, and to some extent absorbed the personnel, of the wartime units. Thus, for instance in Iraq, Nos 1 and 2 ACC inherited the Rolls-Royces of 6th, 14th and 18th LAMBS in March 1920, while early the following year 6th ACC arrived to be given the venerable Austins of 7th LAMB. Meanwhile, in Egypt, 3rd ACC arrived and within a short time had a detached section operating out of Sollum, in the Western Desert; following almost literally in the tyre marks of the Duke of Westminster. They were joined, at Alexandria, by 4th ACC, which took over the Rolls-Royces and surviving Ford T tenders of 11th and 12th LAMBS before, later in the year, being moved up to Palestine.

New Rolls-Royces were at a premium. Many of those originally destined for warmer climes were shipped instead to Dublin where, for the time being, the need was more urgent. In order to remedy the situation in Iraq a number of new Rolls-Royce chassis were shipped out, to have the bodies of 1914 Pattern cars transferred to them by local workshops' personnel. Soon there were enough of these to enable 6th ACC to relinquish their Austins, which were then sent to India. In June 1921 the War Office appointed Lt-Col. George Lindsay to command the armoured cars in Iraq. His early reports suggest that the situation he found out there was none too rosy, but he had the enthusiasm and skill to change things. His first step was to combine the three armoured car companies into No 1 Group, Tank Corps, and then to show them how they might train themselves. This was achieved by staging long-range reconnaissance trips. Groups of armoured cars and tenders would leave Baghdad on sweeping tours through the desert, often lasting a week or more, covering hundreds of miles in virtually barren terrain. In many instances Lindsay sought, and received, the whole-hearted cooperation of the RAF, who flew contact patrols and resupply flights: making the motorised units free of a supply train or previously laid stores dumps. Armoured cars were equipped with wireless to maintain

108 *A Rolls-Royce armoured car and Commer tender in RAF service in the Middle East. Both have Scarf type machine-gun mountings on top since RAF personnel preferred to shoot in the open.*

contact with HQ and to guide in aircraft but, in a sense, Lindsay's success backfired, at least if one supposes that Tank Corps' ambitions lay in these regions.

Based on his own experiences in Arabia, the one-time Col. T E Lawrence, now a political advisor to Churchill at the Colonial Office, promoted the concept of a combined air and armoured car scheme to control the region, in just the way that Lindsay was demonstrating. This he regarded as the most economical solution to the problem, which immediately appealed to the Government. The War Office response was lukewarm, to say the least, so Churchill dangled the idea before Sir Hugh Trenchard at the Air Ministry, who quickly took it up. However, to ensure a totally harmonious administration in the region it would be necessary for the RAF to operate its own armoured cars. It appears that until this was suggested the War Office was starting to look upon armoured cars generally as rather old-fashioned things of limited value. Now they suddenly changed their minds, although it was too late for Iraq. The changeover was completed by the end of 1922, by which time the personnel from 1st and 2nd ACC had returned to Britain while those of 6th ACC had gone to India, passing their cars to the two companies in Egypt. Of these the 4th, since moved up to Palestine, were embroiled in a Jewish–Arab conflict. Riots broke out in Jaffa in April 1921, and the armoured cars were employed in keeping the angry factions apart. Some two months later they had a much more interesting and congenial task. They were required to cross the desert from Cairo to Baghdad, to assist in the establishment of the All Red Air Route, which would ultimately create an airline link between Britain and Australia. The stage in question was part of the route to India, and the original idea was that the armoured cars should act as escort for a Fordson tractor and plough, which had the lonely task of cutting a furrow clear across this desert stretch. This, ultimately proved an impossible task, so the tyre marks of the armoured cars were used instead, circling continuously at likely landing grounds and then setting up cairns and huge arrows of whitewashed boulders before moving on.

The 3rd ACC in Egypt was soon caught up in more civil unrest, notably in Alexandria and Cairo, while the section at Sollum was gaining valuable experience in desert operations. Then trouble was reported from the Sudan and a section of Rolls-Royces was shipped from Suez to Port Sudan aboard the cruiser HMS *Caradoc*. From here they moved to Khartoum and then to Omdurman, crossing the White Nile in barges. When things had settled down, late in 1925, they moved back to Cairo via Suez. Although wireless was used to a limited extent it was still very much the exception, and it is probably worth emphasising that in many cases detached sections – amounting to no more than three or four armoured cars with some transport – might find themselves face to face with rioting city mobs, or miles away in the middle of an inhospitable desert without hope of help or advice in any form. Such a section could easily be commanded by some young and inexperienced lieutenant, who was expected to deal with whatever came along, without reference to higher authority.

Just such an incident can be told. It concerned the section from 4th ACC which had travelled from Jerusalem to Baghdad, mapping out the Empire Air Route. The commander in this case was Lt. H M E Bradshaw, whose Military Cross suggests that he was neither as young nor inexperienced as his rank might imply. Late in June 1921 they left Baghdad on the return journey, having been seen off by King Feisal and Air Vice Marshall Sir Geoffrey Salmond. Some days into the trip one of the Crossley tenders broke its back axle and the party was forced to wait while repairs were organised. They had already received reports from the RAF of a large Bedouin group – some 600 strong – in the area, who were already suspected of hostile actions. Inevitably it was here, in a narrow wadi, that this mass of horsemen suddenly appeared and surrounded the cars in a threatening manner. Its leader was no less a personage than Sheik Auda of the Abu Tayi, who had been one of Lawrence's principal lieutenants under Feisal during the war. Any previous allegiances had long since ceased to interest the Sheik, and the atmosphere was distinctly fraught, so while Bradshaw attempted to explain the situation in faltering Arabic his crews slipped into their Rolls-Royces, released the locking pins of the Vickers guns and quietly loaded them. This incident passed off without any trouble, but it could just as easily have finished in an altogether less satisfactory way.

When the RAF accepted the idea of controlling Iraq, and later Palestine, entirely with aircraft and armoured cars, the first step was to acquire suitable vehicles, but this was more easily said than done. All previous experience pointed to the Rolls-Royce as the ideal vehicle but they were in short supply. Some ex-War Office cars of Great War vintage were taken over

109 The unique turreted Lancia armoured car of the RAF. The rest of these cars had open-top box bodies.

in Iraq while new models were ordered; the chassis from Derby while the bodies would be fitted at Woolwich. It seems that at most only 24 Rolls-Royces flew RAF colours, and of these only 13 were brand new and seven of them were not delivered until 1927. So in order to provide more fighting vehicles a number of Lancia armoured tenders were also obtained. These were mostly of the open-bodied type originally built for service in Ireland, which became available when the British Army withdrew from the South on the formation of the Free State. In many cases they were still crewed by ex-Black and Tans who transferred to the new service. Among these cars was an odd turreted one, apparently built for service in Ireland, or modified there, which finally founds its way out to the Middle East. Although armoured cars would appear to be ideal for desert work, being fast and light enough to cover considerable distances over such terrain, there were still places that they could not go, and to overcome this it was suggested that some tanks should be obtained. It might seem to be a rather drastic step for the air arm to take, and an expensive one, but in due course a curious compromise was worked out. Early in 1923 two tracked vehicles were ordered from the ROF. They were of a type known to the Army as Dragon, Field Artillery Mark I, a full-tracked gun tractor, powered by a Leyland engine but otherwise, in terms of basic layout and suspension, not dissimilar to medium tanks. The Royal Artillery version came complete with cross benches on top of the body for the gun crew, with an open driver's position at the front*. In the two built for the RAF this cab was surrounded by raised panels of armour, while the rear section was left open, forming a well between the tracks. The idea was that when a tank was required the entire body and turret – less bonnet – of a Rolls-Royce armoured car would be placed inside the Dragon and anchored down to create a tracked, armoured vehicle with a fully rotating machine-gun turret, in effect a tank, which could carry the armoured car's gun and crew to places they might otherwise not reach. Whether it was a wise choice is another matter, these early Dragons were notorious for overheating, even in Britain, so it was not surprising to find that the armoured radiator shields were removed at a very early

---

*See *Moving the Guns* p 28.

110 *Sporting what was, no doubt, a very unofficial nickname, the RAF armoured dragon with a Rolls-Royce body and turret installed.*

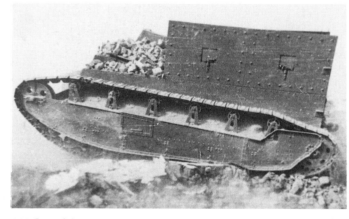

111 *One of the two RAF armoured dragons was later seen with this fixed superstructure.*

stage, while the riveted tracks were equally vulnerable to harsh conditions. Yet the pair seem to have lasted for a remarkably long time. One was photographed with a much smaller turret in about 1932 and either it, or the other one, was seen with a permanent armoured body fitted, like some crude type of armoured personnel carrier. The Air Ministry even bought a Carden-Loyd Carrier in 1931. It was a Mark VI export model with armoured head covers, which must have been distinctly unpleasant to operate in the Middle East. The contract sheet shows that it was made from CTA plate, which is also unusual.

In 1928 the Aden Protectorate was added to the list of RAF responsibilities. Some Rolls-Royces went down there but it soon became clear that the armoured car fleet would have to be expanded. By this time the War Office was purchasing six-wheeled armoured cars, so not to be outdone, the RAF ordered three from Vickers in 1930. Two were built on the Crossley 30/70hp 6×4 chassis, in the style of the big Indian Guys, with dome turrets and twin Vickers gun armament. However, the RAF cars came complete with long, ditch crossing troughs on both sides and – a popular continental feature – spare wheels mounted low down on each side, and free to rotate, so that the long chassis was less likely to get caught, or 'belly' on some uneven ground. The cars were numbered AC1 and AC2, but AC3, for some odd reason, was a lorry. The next armoured car, AC4 – otherwise His Majesty's Armoured Car *Enterprise* – used the bigger Crossley 38/110hp chassis. The layout in this case was in many respects closer to the six-wheeled Crossleys built for the British Army, except that the turret was of the typical Vickers round pattern as used on some light tanks. All three cars were permanently equipped with wireless.

In 1935 the Air Ministry took delivery of one of the prototype Straussler armoured cars which had been built in Hungary and then driven from Budapest to Coventry as a prototype for Alvis to work on. It was subjected to strenuous tests in the desert, including at least one long-distance run from Port Said to Baghdad. This must have been satisfactory since 12 more were ordered from Alvis, although deliveries did not commence until shortly before the war began. They were based on the commercial AC3D pattern, but the RAF required more

112 *Two of the three Crossley six-wheelers supplied to the RAF by Vickers-Armstrong. AC4, the leading car, was unique but there were two of the dome-turreted AC1 type.*

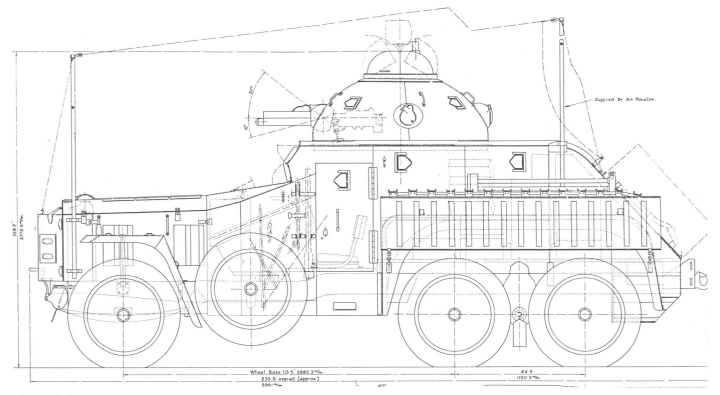

D31 The dome-turreted Vickers Crossley six-wheeler as supplied to the RAF.

113 RAF personnel checking over their Alvis-Straussler armoured car. This view shows the wider style of body designed for these vehicles.

internal space, so the bodies were flat-sided instead of being undercut, and they lacked the hull mounted machine-gun. Very little is known of their performance; most, if not all of them were stationed in Aden, but it is worth noting that for all their efforts to find something better, and presumably more reliable, the RAF discovered that it was the Rolls-Royces that lasted longest. Granted most exchanged their chassis for Fordsons early in the Second World War, but this does not detract from the fact that most of them had 20 years' service under their belts by then, and some might claim even more.

To return now to Egypt: in 1926 a detachment from 3rd Battalion arrived from Lydd with some mediums, the first British tanks to operate in the Middle East since the Gaza

Detachment of 1917. It is worth recalling that while these tanks were undergoing their initial trials in the desert the rest of the Battalion was taking part in the Mechanised Force exercises on Salisbury Plain. Early in 1929 the 5th ACC, returning home from its sojourn in Shanghai, was diverted to Egypt. The War Office had decided to convert the 12th Lancers into a mechanised cavalry regiment and the plan was to hand over the 5th's Rolls-Royces to them while the personnel returned to Britain for disbandment. A stay of execution was achieved when the 5th was given the task of training the Lancers for the new role and, when this was done, the RTC company was kept in being by a variety of stratagems, which included keeping quiet about them and prevaricating whenever London tried to find out what was going on. By 1930 more tanks, and some Carden-Loyd carriers had arrived, and these were divided up between the two armoured car companies so that 3rd ACC – which had absorbed the section from 3rd Battalion – had ten medium tanks while 5th ACC had six mediums and the Carden-Loyds. As previously noted these tanks were specially prepared for operations in a hot climate by fitting spaced panels of asbestos over the hull, and various camouflage schemes were tried, both to disguise the vehicles in a desert landscape and to reflect the worst of the heat.

Suggestions had already been made that a branch of MWEE should be established in Egypt to test equipment under local conditions, but this was rejected on the grounds of expense by the Secretary of State for War. In order to circumvent this an Experimental Section – listed as Z Section of 3rd Battalion – was formed in 1927 on a scale so small that it would not attract attention. The general lack of roads in areas away from the Nile

114 A Medium Mark II tank of 6th Battalion RTC in Egypt. The insulating skin of asbestos panels shows up well, having not yet been painted.

and the rough nature of the ground, proved very hard on all kinds of suspensions; the fine sand, whipped up by enormous storms, was ground to an even finer dust by the tracks, and this dust got in everywhere. Early types of air-cleaner were completely overwhelmed, and even the latest types could only cope if a special dustproof carburettor was used. Dust even worked its way in through the crankcase breathers and led to complaints of excessive cylinder wear; all of this had to be investigated, and hopefully cured, if prodigious quantities of spares were not to be used up. Examples of the Light Tank Mark IA and Carden-Loyd Mark VI★ were tested and a few of the big Lanchester armoured cars were supplied for troop evaluation. The five six-wheeled Crossleys arrived too, in 1933. They had been fitted with the new Dunlop bulletproof tyres to avoid the need to carry spares, but they were not popular. A report described them as being, 'definitely inferior . . . to the Rolls-Royce four-wheeled armoured car', and it was recommended that no more be built. In 1934 and 1935 they were reported as being 'with a Service Unit' in Egypt but, by 1936, it was admitted that the transmission, front axle and suspension all suffered on cross-country jaunts, so they were confined to roads; which was a lot of use in the desert. In fact one service unit that had them, the 11th Hussars, seems to have shut them up in a hangar and left them there, preferring to operate only Rolls-Royces. It was not all plain sailing for the Rolls-Royces either. Numbers of the 1924 Pattern had been delivered in order to meet the demand but both types suffered from the harsh terrain, especially on trips like the long-range

reconnaissance to Siwa Oasis which George Lindsay organised for 12th Lancers in 1931. Front axles, half-shafts and springs continually gave trouble until they were replaced by stronger types; in the case of springs, for instance, a cadmium-plated type was developed for the front-end of Rolls-Royces. Other improvements included extra header tanks for the radiators and wider Dunlop sand tyres fitted to heavy-duty split rims. Indeed these wheels were so wide that it was no longer necessary to fit twin tyres on the rear axles. The original Rolls-Royce type of

115 A Crossley Mark I armoured car of 12th Lancers in the desert. In addition to mechanical problems these cars were just too heavy for the conditions and the crews spent most of their time digging them out.

carburettor would not accept an air-filter so the engines were modified to take a Solex type that would.

Since tanks were now clearly going to form a permanent part of the Egyptian scene, the two RTC armoured car companies were merged, in 1933, as a two company tank battalion: the 6th, commanded by Lt-Col. C B Costin-Nian MC. It was a wise move for, in 1935, the Italians invaded Abyssinia without warning and tension in the area increased dramatically. British forces in Egypt were in the worst possible position, with a regular, if rather one-sided, war going on in the east, and another huge Italian army to the west, in Libya, whose intentions were uncertain. As part of a larger countermeasure the 1st (Light) Battalion and a medium tank company from 4th (Army) Battalion RTC, arrived in October and remained for 12 months until the trouble died down. Even so, while they were there, problems arose again in Palestine on a scale that was beyond the scope of the RAF to control. Diverse Arab factions, angered by a marked increase in Jewish immigration, came together in open revolt.

The first step was to despatch 6th Battalion, equipped with 18 Light Tanks Mark III, by rail from Egypt. On arrival they were split up into sections and despatched to various parts of the country. By July 1936 they had been joined by the 11th Hussars in their Rolls-Royces, and other units including a mechanised Royal Horse Artillery battery. Contact with armoured cars of the RAF led the Hussars to adopt extra armament, in the form of a Lewis gun mounted on a stalk at the back of the turret, which was worked by a member of the crew

standing in the open. Naturally the Royal Navy was present off the coast, and with little to do the sailors exhibited their usual tendency to get ashore and look for something more dangerous to get involved in. They began by hiring three civilian lorries and starting an army of their own. Crew members from the cruiser HMS *Sussex* mounted a 40mm Pom-Pom behind a shield on one lorry, a 3pr saluting gun on another and a searchlight on the third. This team, known as Pip, Squeak and Wilfred after a contemporary comic strip, was soon in action alongside the Army, using the searchlight at night to tempt snipers, and then hitting back at their positions with the

116 Ford based armoured railcars used on the Palestine Railways during and after the 1936 emergency. Two units operate back to back which allowed the leading vehicle only to be powered, whichever way they were going.

117 Fords, especially American ones, have always been popular in the desert. These V8 armed pick-up trucks were operated by the 8th Hussars in Egypt and Palestine, and although regarded as poor substitute armoured cars, were in fact direct and worthy descendants of the Ford T Light Patrol Cars of the First World War.

self-propelled guns. The 2nd Battalion, Cheshire Regiment, charged with the protection of the railway system, built armoured bodies onto Ford V8 truck chassis and converted them to run on rails, in pairs coupled back to back, as patrol vehicles to check for sabotage and precede any trains that the rebels might attack. It is worth recording at this point that similar armoured rail units, based on Model T Ford cars, were operated over a vulnerable stretch of line in Egypt by the RASC at around the same time.

The worst of the trouble was over by the end of the year and most units withdrew, leaving only the 11th Hussars to back up the RAF. The 6th Battalion returned to Egypt where, among other things, it was engaged in testing samples of the new

118 *The Sudan Defence Force also had a strong affinity for Fords. These lightweight vehicles must have been very stirring to drive over firm going, especially with a Vickers gun firing over your head!*

three-man light tanks, Marks V and VI, which would soon replace the two-man models. The Palestine Emergency had interrupted training of what was known as the Mobile Force, based at Mersah Matruh. As a mixed cavalry and RTC formation it was held up as an example to those in Britain who were resisting the inevitable creation of a Royal Armoured Corps. In mid-1938 this was followed by the creation of a Mobile Division consisting of 1st and 6th Battalions RTC (the former having returned to the Middle East) and a brigade of three cavalry regiments equipped with light tanks, armoured cars and, for the time being, some Ford pick-up trucks. It was commanded by Gen. Hobart, whose expertise and energy laid the foundations of what was to become the 7th Armoured Division; described by General O'Connor as 'the best trained division I have ever seen'.

Before leaving this region it is worth mentioning three locally manned units that operated fighting vehicles under some form of British control. Officers and NCOs served on detachment with many native units in Africa and the Middle East, but the use of armoured vehicles was uncommon. The Sudan Defence Force had a motor machine-gun section as early as 1926. It began with Ford T light patrol cars and graduated to Model A Fords mounting Vickers machine-guns, but in the late 1930s it could also boast a few weary Rolls-Royces of First World War vintage. The Arab Legion formed a mechanised unit which originally used Ford-based armoured cars of a type also operated by the Palestine Police. Later, turreted armoured cars were built to their own designs, which saw service during the war. Security on the Jordan / Palestine border was the duty of the Transjordan Frontier Force, which was, by its very nature, highly mechanised. The vehicles used were mostly of British origin, mounting machine-guns but the use of armour was limited.

119 *The Trans-Jordan Frontier Force preferred more substantial vehicles and used these rugged looking Commer Raiders with oversize tyres and various weapon combinations.*

10 The Reckoning

In 1933 Hitler became Chancellor, and a year later Führer, of a virile Fascist Germany. In 1935 Mussolini adopted an aggressive foreign policy and in 1936 General Franco took a prominent part in the civil war that, three years later would place him at the head of a Fascist Spain. By 1937 the Japanese were embroiled in a similar harsh conflict in China, and the prospect of continuing world peace looked shaky. For Britain it was a matter of deciding where the greatest danger lay; one year it would be Italian ambitions in North Africa, the next a threat to European peace from Germany. The 12th Lancers, and their Lanchester armoured cars, formed part of an international force, under the auspices of the League of Nations, to keep peace in the Saarland while a plebiscite was organised to decide its future allegiance. The profusion of swastika flags and banners that greeted them left little room for doubt as to the outcome and, following this vote of confidence, Hitler occupied the Rhineland in 1936.

Although Britain appeared largely unmoved by these events, a degree of urgency could be detected in weapon development. Warship construction was expanded, while the RAF would soon receive a new generation of fighter aircraft that would, in effect, save the nation in the not too distant future. Unfortunately the same sort of progress could not be detected where tanks were concerned. Production of light tanks increased, and of their kind they were as good as any, but the larger types present a sorry picture, pointing to a state approaching utter confusion. The faithful old mediums, notwithstanding their dubious origins, had been in service for ten years or more, and every attempt to find something to replace them had got no further than a few prototypes. In the meantime the entire concept of armoured warfare had undergone a profound change as a result of the major exercises held on Salisbury Plain. There was no shortage of ideas on future requirements, what was lacking was money and a formed body of opinion upon which the War Office could draw before placing any orders. For example one can look at the Middle East. Although the need for tanks to operate in temperate climes was clearly the priority, the risk of trouble on Egypt's borders could not be discounted and the various armoured regiments had built up a great deal of experience operating tanks in that region. One would be entitled to expect that any new tanks developed around this time might at least include some features that reflected this, but it seems they did not. It was, apparently, quite difficult enough to design tanks at all, never mind considering such awkward details, or looking too far into the future.

Before we examine the development of tanks up to the outbreak of war there are some other fighting vehicles worthy of attention; many of which were among the best examples of British ingenuity and engineering of this period. The scout car

120 *Two of Martel's Sappers demonstrate how to lift their Austin scout car over obstacles. Not something they would want to have to do very often. Just to the left of the nearest man's head can be seen the platform on which the observer could stand to peer over hedges and walls.*

is a case in point. One could see its origins in the Ford T Light Patrol Cars of the First World War, but this is not strictly a fair parallel. A much better case can be made for two little vehicles that appeared in 1928. It was the year of the Experimental Armoured Force and, as in the previous year, Giffard Martel was commanding 17 Field Company RE, yet his mind, as ever, was considering wider matters. He managed to borrow two Austin Sevens from their manufacturers; or at least running chassis complete with bonnet, radiator and front mudguards, but precious little else in the way of bodywork. Both were fitted with crude wooden seats and a sort of pedestal on which a man could stand to get a better view. A stout plank beneath the chassis protected the sump and gearbox and rope slings hung down on each side. The cars carried a crew of two: driver and observer, armed only with their rifles. In these lightweight cars they could set out on scouting missions at considerable speed while remaining inconspicuous and quiet. Their task was to gather information, not fight for it. To observe from behind cover and then report what they had seen as swiftly as possible. Many would argue that the horse was still the best means of accomplishing this, since it could cross any kind of country and jump ditches, but Martel claimed that a mounted horseman was too high up to make the best use of cover, and ultimately too slow. He had the rope slings fitted so that the crew could manhandle their car bodily over those obstacles which the horse might jump. In the event nothing resulted from this experiment, at least along the lines that Martel suggested, although the baby Austin was adopted as a liaison vehicle and, later, as a wireless car for many years.

121 Believe it or not this was the prototype of a serious military vehicle, the FWD/Douglas four-wheel steer and four-wheel drive battery scout car. Where the crew were supposed to sit is not at all clear.

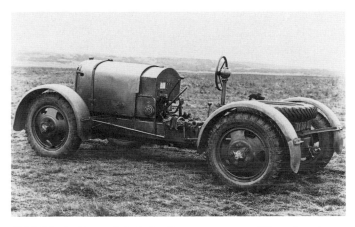

122 Nicholas Straussler's design for a scout car would have been large, had it ever been completed, and no doubt very difficult to steer with a pillar-mounted steering wheel.

Two years later, in 1930, the Royal Artillery took a hand. They were looking for a cross-country car suitable for battery commanders to use, but had it been adopted no doubt a scout car version would have resulted as well. The original scheme, promoted in 1929, was to adapt the six-wheeled Trojan light truck for the purpose, but for some reason the project was passed on to the FWD Motors Company of Slough. It was an odd choice; although they had experience of all-wheel drive technology this firm specialised in large trucks, so what they built was more along the lines of a design exercise than a true prototype military vehicle. It had a short chassis with a wheel at each corner, on the end of a long, cantilever spring. Separate drive shafts ran from a central three-speed gearbox to each wheel and the engine, a second-hand Douglas 1200cc unit, was mounted crosswise in the middle, with the radiator on the right. This formed the highest part of the vehicle, but with springs and drive shafts sprouting in all directions it is not at all easy to see where the driver was supposed to sit, let alone the battery commander, and MWEE was not impressed, beyond commenting on the general advantage of light, four-wheel drive vehicles.

Next on the scene was Nicholas Straussler with what he meant to be a true scout car. This had a four-wheel drive, four-wheel steer chassis, powered by a Ford A engine mounted beneath a conventional bonnet at one end. There was no front as such, the steering wheel, controls and driver's seat being mounted on an upright column in the centre which could be turned to face either way. Tests at MWEE indicated an excellent cross-country performance, but steering, with a vertical handwheel, was very difficult and the cooling not up to standard. It was rebuilt to remedy these faults, but the War Office decided to wait and see how the Straussler armoured cars for the RAF behaved before making a decision and, in the event, nothing more was heard of it.

While the engineers designed and MWEE tested, some regiments could not wait, and at least one took steps of its own to achieve a result. The Inns of Court, a Yeomanry regiment, for their camp in 1932, produced two old Morris Cowley cars with imitation armoured bodies, which they operated as machine-gun, or scout cars. Both were probably acquired at the

123 Examples of the do-it-yourself school of scout car design. Two improvised Bullnose Morris Cowleys owned by the Inns of Court Yeomanry.

124 If it was style you were looking for then this partly armoured Hillman Minx was the scout car for you. The weight must have affected the performance which, across country, would not have been good anyway. It was tested by the 3rd Hussars.

expense of the officers involved, and there is no particular reason to associate it with the next official development, although there were striking similarities. In 1934 MEE took delivery of a smart little Hillman Minx two-seater, fitted with armoured doors over the radiator, tiny armoured flaps to cover the aero-type windscreens and a lightly armoured body with hinged rear-viewing flap. It looked sporty, and quite unmilitary, with its wire spoked wheels and coachbuilt mudguards, but it was taken seriously enough to be handed over to the 3rd, King's Own Hussars, for trials.

While on the subject of the 3rd Hussars it is worth digressing for a moment to examine another type of armoured vehicle they were evaluating at this time. The two cavalry armoured car regiments already mechanised, the 11th Hussars and 12th Lancers, were continuing the tradition of cavalry operating in the mounted role. Yet cavalry fight dismounted as well, and an attempt was made to mechanise this function. The first vehicle to be developed for this purpose was called the Cavalry Portée; basically a lightly armoured version of the newly developed Morris 15cwt Platoon Truck, with seats for a section of cavalrymen and stowage for their weapons. The armour was quite high, where it was fitted, but the roof was just canvas and there were great gaps in the sides to enable the men to dismount. Vehicles of this type entered service in small numbers, and photographs exist of a subsequent version, on the same chassis, which appeared in mock-up form and may have been at attempt to develop a true armoured personnel carrier.

125 The 3rd Hussars was selected to field test these Morris-Commercial Dragoon Portée vehicles for the dismounted cavalry role.

Returning now to scout cars, and before examining the ultimate developments in this field, another unusual contender deserves consideration. This was the Guy Demon Scout Car that appeared in 1936. It was intended for use by cavalry motor regiments and the scout companies of machine-gun battalions, although it is not clear from pictures of the prototype where a weapon was supposed to be mounted. It was a rear-engined vehicle, powered by a big 3·7 litre, four-cylinder engine, driving the rear wheels only, through a four-speed gearbox. The driver sat low down at the front, in a sharply pointed nose; the number of crewmen carried in the rest of the body is not known. MEE reported that handling was good in all respects,

126 The big Guy Demon scout car looks a good design from the front and a clumsy mess from the back. However, the lack of a driven front axle must have been very limiting.

with a high power to weight ratio and top speeds of around 45mph. But since this was achieved with a wooden mock-up body it might not have been a fair appraisal of its ultimate performance. In the event, however, the requirement for such a vehicle changed, even while tests were under way, so the project was dropped.

In 1938 four new designs were submitted; two of which formed the basis of the final development, the other two soon falling by the wayside. One of these was by Victor Riley, but since his firm went into liquidation before the prototype was built and was absorbed by the Nuffield organisation, nothing more was heard of it. Nuffields themselves were involved at this time with the Austrian Steyr, and Czechoslovakian Tatra companies, so they offered a design based upon the latter. MEE tested it in August but found it so riddled with faults that it was returned to the makers and never seen again. The two more successful contenders were Alvis and BSA. Both produced very similar vehicles in 1938: lightweight four-wheel drive two-seaters, with low silhouette and high mobility. The Alvis, nicknamed the 'Dingo', was apparently produced without any advice from Nicholas Straussler. It was powered by a rear-mounted four-cylinder engine, offset to the right, which drove through a four-speed synchromesh gearbox into a transfer case, and from there through a propellor shaft contained within a tubular backbone. All four wheels were independently sprung and driven, but only the front set steered. Armour protection for the crew consisted of panels to 14mm standard covering the front and sides only, the driver and gunner being provided with adjustable seats so that they could travel head out, or down behind the armour as the situation demanded. In the lower position the armament, a Bren gun, could be aimed through a slot in the front, but when elevated the gunner had a full 360° sweep, as long as he did not shoot the driver.

The BSA entry was powered by a six-cylinder Daimler engine, again at the back, but on the centre line. A Daimler fluid flywheel carried drive to a Wilson four-speed pre-selector gearbox, which had a separate reversing level so that all speeds could be used in either direction. This transmission system, without the separate reverse, had been adopted some years earlier by many bus manufacturers, but when it was first

127 The prototype BSA scout car in its original form, with armour at the front and sides only. This is the true predecessor of the famous Daimler Dingo.

examined by MEE in 1930/31 it was dismissed with the comment that it was 'a welcome luxury on a pleasure car'. Steering worked on all four wheels, but it was a complicated system. The rear wheels did not come into play until the front set had reached maximum lock, but when driving in reverse the front steering was held rigid and only the rear wheels turned. Again all wheels were individually sprung. The crew arrangements were similar, and the Bren gun could be used in the same way, but the layout of the engine afforded better protection for the crew from behind. Both cars were thoroughly tested by MEE and, in October, took part with a number of other vehicles in the annual North Wales trials.

128 The Alvis contender for the Army's scout car contract, seen here in its second form with the raised body sides and a folding roof at the back.

There were good features on both sides. The Alvis was quicker and more agile, with a superb cross-country performance, although it was found to be a bit less stable when cornering fast. The BSA was more stable, and comfortable, with a much tighter turning circle, but from reading the reports one gets the impression that the most popular feature was the fluid flywheel and Wilson gearbox. They made starting easier, especially on steep hills or in soft sand, and allowed the car to creep gently

up to the crest of a hill with the engine on very low revs, without the risk of stalling; a great advantage on a stealthy reconnaissance mission. In 1939 both scout cars were modified to conform with the latest Mechanisation Board requirements. For the BSA this meant no more than the addition of a sliding roof to the fighting compartment, but the Alvis was virtually rebuilt. The track of both axles was widened, to improve stability, and the hull enlarged all round to provide better protection. It also had a roof, but when the two were compared the BSA design was still prefered by MEE. In the end the Alvis was regarded as acceptable, with modifications, as a despatch rider's vehicle, but it never entered service in any form. Modifications required for the BSA were of a minor nature and it was noted as suitable for War Department use as a scout car. Production began almost immediately under the Daimler marque, but by one of those quirks of fate often perpetrated by soldiers it was unofficially christened with the name of its erstwhile rival; in time this became semi-official and, as the Daimler Dingo, it turned out to be one of the most effective fighting vehicles to serve the Allies during the Second World War and beyond.

By the early thirties British armoured car design had rather fallen by the wayside. The Rolls-Royces continued to give good service, but the bigger six-wheelers, the Lanchesters and Crossleys, had been a disappointment and in any case their role as combat vehicles was considered to have been superseded by light tanks. In 1934 Morris-Commercial came up with a design for a lightweight six-wheeler based on their type CDS 30cwt chassis. It was demonstrated with a wooden mock-up body, but rejected when attention focused on the new Morris 15cwt four-wheeler, the type CS8T. Thoughts on the role of armoured cars also changed; reconnaissance was seen as their proper role so that light weight and mobility counted for more than armour protection or firepower. A design was therefore prepared for 1935, to be known as the Morris-Commercial experimental armoured reconnaissance car, Series I. It would be tested in conjunction with a Leyland, which will be mentioned later. The Morris featured a fully enclosed body, with armoured louvres covering the radiator, but its most curious aspect was the turret, which not only rotated, but went up and down. The idea was to reduce the silhouette, so with the drum-shaped turret retracted the lid was virtually flush with the top of the hull. Driver and wireless operator were located within the hull while the gunner and commander occupied seats in the turret, which was raised and lowered by hydraulic gear modified from a tipping lorry. The problem was what to do with the weapon – a machine-gun – when the turret retracted, and this was solved by fitting a channel into the roof of the body, at the back, in which the gun barrel rested. Field trials with a cavalry regiment soon proved it to be an unworkable arrangement and the elevating gear would not function at all unless the car was standing on level ground. They also revealed cooling problems which would have to be resolved before any further designs could be built.

The War Department's tame cooling expert was Capt. M. Payne, and he designed a complex cowl arrangement that fitted over the Morris radiator and directed a good flow of cooling air without the need for hinged doors or louvres. Once this was accepted the Superintendent of Design at Woolwich was asked to come up with a new design of hull. The truth about this

129 *The first Morris armoured car with its disappearing turret. Here it is in the raised position and from this angle one can see the groove in the back into which the machine-gun fitted when the turret was down.*

vehicle is clouded by comments made by Brig. G. Macleod Ross in his book, *The Business of Tanks*★, in which he makes a valiant effort to establish the reputation of his superior at the Department of Tank Design, the Director, Maj-Gen. Sir Campbell Clarke. Briefly, according to this source, the vague order for an armoured car was telephoned to the Department; no specifications were offered and Campbell Clarke chose the Morris chassis entirely on his own initiative. Further, since there was no directive on whether the car had to simply gather information, or fight for it, the Director opted for the latter. The result was a large armoured car of conventional layout, surmounted by a turret which, not surprisingly perhaps, looked remarkably like the type fitted to the Woolwich designed light tank L4E1, even down to the enormous octagonal cupola. A quick-acting driver's shutter was one of the better features, while MacLeod Ross claims to have contributed a rather jazzy comouflage scheme which was applied to both prototypes. It was this, the writer goes on to say, that contributed to its downfall because it offended the eye of the Assistant Director of Mechanisation, while the Director of Cavalry, whose troops would be expected to use it, was opposed to the big turret and wanted something which was open at the top.

While there is an element of truth in all this a great deal is left unsaid. For a start there is good evidence to show that the Morris chassis had already been selected as the basis before these cars were built, having been used for a prototype that the author does not mention. Again we know that the War Office

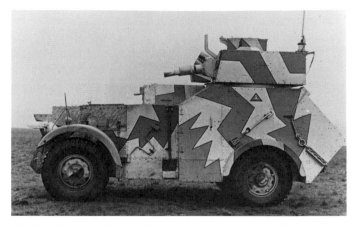

130 *The Ordnance Factory Morris armoured car finished in the exotic MacLeod Ross camouflage scheme, which is supposed to have enraged the Director of Cavalry. Compare the turret with the Light Tank L4E1.*

was looking for something to suit the reconnaissance role, so the armament of one ·5in Vickers gun and a 9mm Solothurn automatic rifle was unnecessarily heavy. In any case the high turret and even higher cupola resulted in a vehicle that was nearly eight feet tall! The cars were repainted in service green and issued for trials to the 12th Lancers, then based at

---

★Op cit.

131 The first Morris armoured car rebuilt with the reconnaissance car open turret.

132 A production model of the Morris CS9 Light Armoured Car, seen here with a canvas cover on the turret.

available. So, while development work on four-wheel drive cars went on, the Morris would just have to do; supplemented in the desert by Rolls-Royces that would be modified to take the same type of open turret. As a measure of how pressing was the need to provide new equipment it is worth noting that the 8th, King's Royal Hussars, carried out their reconnaissance duties in Ford V8 pick-up trucks of American origin when they were stationed in Egypt shortly before the war.

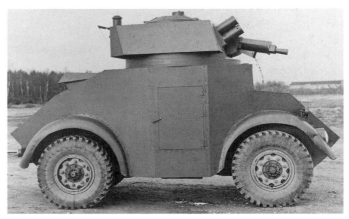

133 The large and ugly Morris/Steyr armoured car which at least had the virtue of four-wheel drive.

Tidworth, before being rejected for a variety of reasons.

Meanwhile the Series I chassis had been fitted with a mock-up for the next design of body which was to become the Series III. In accordance with the Director of Cavalry's wishes this featured an open turret ring protected by a low shield at the front only. However, there had been some criticism of the internal space available so the longer wheelbase Morris CS9 chassis was adopted, mounting a similar mock-up body. This proved more successful and resulted, in 1937, in a contract being placed for 99 such vehicles under the designation, Armoured Reconnaissance Car, Morris-Commercial type CS9 LAC. The same basic hull form was adopted, but the turret was altered. It was still open at the top but with high sides all round to improve crew protection, and an armament consisting of dismountable Bren and Boys weapons which were normally mounted alongside a fixed smoke discharger. The crew remained at four and the wireless set was fitted in the front nearside corner of the body.

Satisfactory as they were for reconnaissance it was quite clear that the Morris armoured cars were not ideal. Four-wheel drive, for instance, would be very desirable but such types would take longer to develop and, as the Summary of Mechanisation frankly admitted in 1937, time was not really

The quest for four-wheel drive was taken up first by Morris who, as already noted, had links with Steyr in Austria. A number of that firm's vehicles were on trial with the British Army on account of that connection, and one was even fitted with a mock-up armoured car body, resulting in what was probably one of the most hideous designs ever offered to the War Office. It would appear that all these imported samples were rejected by MEE on mechanical grounds – always allowing for a bit of patriotic bias – but when Austria was annexed by Germany in 1938 the future of such trade agreements was bound to be questionable. Morris-Commercial therefore adapted Steyr and Tatra technology to produce a four-wheel drive artillery tractor, and a rear-engined version, using the same tubular backboned chassis was offered as the basis for an armoured car. A well-shaped hull was designed by Woolwich, but it is at once instructive to note that no attempt was made to fit the apparently ideal body from the Morris Armoured Reconnaissance Car. Instead the new design featured a central driver's cab and fully enclosed turret, although the six built for evaluation were not at first armed. One went out to Egypt where, bearing the name *Ursula* it served for a while with the Egyptian Police while at least one other was used by the Derbyshire Yeomanry in the early part of the war. However, the type was not accepted for production, following a poor showing in the 1938 North Wales Trials.

Interest now switched to a model designed by Guy Motors. This company was also in the running to produce a field artillery tractor – the Quad Ant – for the War Office and, like Morris altered it to rear-engine configuration for an armoured car, producing six prototypes. The original specification called for 14mm armour, a three-man crew and armament comprising a Boys rifle and Bren gun along with a top speed of 40mph.

134 Morris-Commercial's own attempt to build a four-wheel drive armoured car was based on a rear-engined version of their new field artillery tractor. This is the sample vehicle tested in Egypt.

Now, however, the War Office went through another of its periodic changes of mind, which drove producers and designers mad and sowed confusion everywhere. Presumably prompted by the usual idea of saving money they suddenly realised that a good four-wheel drive vehicle might perform nearly as well as a light tank, with a considerable saving in costs, so it was decided to increase the armament, bringing it into line with the Light Tank Mark VI. To emphasise the point the term Wheeled Tank was coined; it was the sort of title that always seems to appeal to the press – who thought anything armoured was a tank anyway – but in practice it soon proved to be a silly misnomer. In terms of performance, however, the Guy proved very effective and the prototype, which took part in the 1938 North Wales Trials trumped the Morris in no uncertain manner.

Powered by a four-cylinder Meadows engine, driving through a four-speed gearbox, the Guy weighed about five tons. Two were troop tested with the Queen's Bays in Britain, following which the suspension was modified, tyre sizes increased and wheel to mudguard clearances enlarged. Meanwhile, one car sent out to Egypt developed serious cooling troubles and blotted its copybook to such an extent that the type was cordially hated out there for the rest of time. The armament, of course, consisted of co-axial ·5 and ·303in Vickers guns with a fixed mounting alongside for two smoke dischargers. These prototypes were all of riveted construction but, as related elsewhere* welding was adopted for production machines.

The North Wales Trials also included an Alvis Straussler armoured car of the RAF pattern, along with a new model by the Hungarian inventor classed as a light armoured car. This is recorded as having twin Ford V8 engines which delivered a power to weigh ratio of 36·1bhp per ton, a staggering figure nearly double that of its nearest rival. Mention of the RAF raises the subject of another mysterious vehicle, which they acquired in 1936 from Armstrong Siddeley Motors Ltd in

Coventry. Very little information on it is known to survive, but photographs show a large six-wheeler with a well-shaped hull, mounting a large round turret. The front axle is undriven and the rear-mounted engine appears to be an air-cooled V type which, if based on their 1922 90hp V8 medium tank engine, must have seemed rather old-fashioned. The armament of one Vickers machine-gun was a bit pathetic for such a large car and there is no evidence to show that it ever left this country, let alone that any more were built, so it must have proved a failure.

Before leaving the subject of armoured cars mention must be made of the 1934 Leyland design alluded to earlier. Based on the SKG1 chassis, powered by a six-cylinder, 4·4 litre engine, it drove through a four-speed and auxiliary gearbox and appears to have been considered originally as a rival to the Morris, which ultimately became the armoured reconnaissance car. However, for want of further written evidence we can only fall back on photographs and these show what appears to be a front-engined armoured van, so it may have been a modification of the original design. In this form it was tested as

135 A rear view of the Armstrong-Siddeley six-wheeler built for the RAF. Overall tracks for the driven bogie are stored in boxes on each side. The turret only held a single Vickers machine-gun.

136 The original Leyland-based armoured command vehicle does not appear to have been a very inspired design.

---

*Fletcher. *The Great Tank Scandal*.

137 *The original Morris ACV, compared to the Leyland, was a well thought out design. The open door reveals how well it was insulated from extraneous sounds and one can also see the various roof hatches, ventilators and aerial mounts. It is shown serving with HQ, 1st Tank Brigade along with a Medium Mark II** and, just visible on the right, a Medium Mark III.*

the prototype of what would become known as an armoured command vehicle, a somewhat simpler version of the modified medium tank *Boxcar* described earlier. It was, undeniably, an ugly looking vehicle but it was soon joined by a much smarter type based on the Morris CS11/30 chassis, with radiator protection to Capt. Payne's well known design. The body was low, compared with the Leyland, and well provided with doors, roof hatches and aerial mountings, while photographs suggest that the body was also well insulated, no doubt to reduce the volume of sound from outside. As the Experimental Armoured Office it served for a season with 1st Tank Brigade, who reported:

This vehicle was tried by Headquarters, Mobile Division, during the collective training season of 1938 and found to be adequate in every respect save that of performance . . . In order to give some measure of cross-country performance a four-wheel drive chassis is essential.

But that had no immediate effect; the War Office simply altered the contract for armoured reconnaissance car bodies on Morris CS9 chassis so that 15 of them were completed as armoured office types. Some of these saw service in the Western Desert although, presumably, they were not so roomy inside as the 30cwt prototype.

Students of military vehicle design in Britain between the wars cannot fail to be struck by the paucity of really effective prototypes emanating from the official bodies responsible for

such work. Despite what MacLeod Ross and others might have us believe, the lack of originality evident since the disestablishment of the Department of Tank Design and Experiment in 1923 is striking. Bureaucracy lay at the root of it, there can be little doubt of that, for the men who undertook the actual design work were proficient engineers backed-up by the proper resources; perhaps the most striking thing is that their names are hardly known. This is inevitable to some extent in a Government sponsored organisation, and it is often seen as the hallmark of good team work, but it also suggests that none of them had that extra ingredient one might call flair, that elevates an individual from the mundane. This, it seems, was one factor that set them apart from their great rivals, Vickers-Armstrong. They too had their quota of competent engineers, and the spur of commercial accountability, but above all they had Sir John Carden, whose flair raised him to the level of genius. Yet his involvement in what was to become one of his company's most successful designs is difficult to ascertain, although the prototype appeared in 1934, and at that time Sir John was the chief designer of fighting vehicles.

The design in question was a lightweight, tracked tractor which was designed purely as a speculative venture – although clearly with War Office custom in mind – under the company designation VAD50. Basically it was a two-man vehicle which was demonstrated as a gun tractor or machine-gun carrier with seats at the rear for six members of the weapon detachment. Like the Carden-Loyd carriers from which, in a sense, it was

138 VAD 50, Vickers-Armstrong's original fighting tractor, ancestor of all Bren and Universal carriers.

derived, extensive use was made of Ford commercial components. The engine, located in the centre, was a V8, while the four-speed gearbox and differential axle mounted at the back were standard items from their truck range. The suspension was based on the double spring system developed for light tanks and Dragons, but comprised what amounted to one and a half units per side. What set it apart from all previous Vickers' products, and suggests that someone with more than the average degree of skill and imagination was involved in its design, was the steering system. The larger suspension units on each side were located on the ends of a cross shaft that passed through the hull. This tube was free to move sideways by the action of the steering wheel, and in doing so it moved the bogies and forced the track out of alignment. This caused the vehicle to steer on a large radius path and meant that at the high speeds for which the vehicle was designed it was possible to corner without resorting to track brakes, which would naturally slow the vehicle down. Of course brakes had to come into play for sharper turns, and this was achieved by further movement of the wheel, causing the vehicle to skid steer in the normal way. Another advantage, from the user's point of view, was that this system totally eliminated the risk of reverse steering which plagued light tracked vehicles equipped with clutch and brake steering.

Following Carden-Loyd practice VAD50 was left-hand drive, but it was soon followed by a similar machine laid out for right-hand drive, and this latter chassis also formed the basis of a self-propelled 40mm gun, which was displayed in a gaudy camouflage scheme. At this stage the War Office took an interest and ordered a prototype of their own, known as the Experimental Machine Gun Carrier, which appeared in 1935. The layout was more or less the same, with the driver sharing a narrow front compartment with a machine-gunner, while six more crewmen sat facing one another across the engine, at the back. Tests at MEE revealed cooling problems in both water and oil. The former was easily improved by air-flow, but the latter was more serious since it affected engine life, and was found to be due to a design fault. In using commercial components without modification, the designers allowed a branch pipe from the exhaust manifold to pass directly beneath the engine sump, and this pipe was invariably red hot after the engine had been running for any length of time. As the engineers at MEE pointed out 'a more efficient form of oil

heater could hardly be devised'. In order to remedy it, the exhaust pipes were led down through the floor plates and then beneath the hull to the rear. An external oil-cooler was also added, but in order to do this the Ford Motor Co had to be prevailed upon to alter the design of their engine. To quote the report again this was, 'a remarkable achievement in consideration of the adamant nature of Ford production methods'. Improved water cooling required a better location for the radiator fan, and this was obtained by lengthening the hull by a mere three and a half inches in all future production models.

139 The General Scout Vehicle showing the enlarged fighting compartment. Observe how on this and all subsequent models the leading bogie is turned around, compared with VAD 50.

Production began in 1936 with an order for 14 Carriers, Machine Gun, No 1 Mark I, which were regarded as pilot models and therefore completed in mild steel. They differed from the prototype in having boxed in headlamps and a shield fitted to the mounting bracket of the Vickers gun. At the rear an extra armoured panel continued down the nearside while the opposite compartment was left open. They were now designed to carry a crew of three: two in the front and one in the compartment at the back. Also, to give a better ride, the front idler was raised by five inches to stop it from bumping on the ground. In the meantime the prototype was altered to a new configuration as an armoured general scout vehicle for cavalry reconnaissance. It had 10mm armour at the front and the gunner's compartment was enlarged so that it stuck out proud of the front plate. This obscured the driver's view to his left but was essential since, in addition to operating a Bren gun in the normal position, and a Boys anti-tank rifle on a rail around the top, the gunner/commander had to work a No 1 wireless set, and consequently had his work cut out.

In addition to serving as training machines some of the pilot models were converted into prototypes of other proposed versions. Some reappeared as scout or cavalry carriers which will be discussed later, but another was modified into a carrier for the 3in mortar, in which form it had ammunition lockers along both sides. Its companion was the Equipment Carrier, which not only had side lockers, but more along the top of the engine cover and another across the front. The latter was never developed and the mortar carrier only appeared in a different

140 Men of the 2nd Battalion, the Cheshire Regiment, manning a Machine-Gun Carrier No 2, Mark I during a parade. Comparison with plate 136 will show the practice of that time whereby A and B vehicles were marked accordingly (in red).

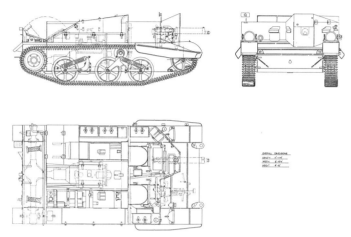

D32 Machine-gun Carrier No 2 Mark I.

141 The prototype Cavalry Carrier with the men seated for long-distance travel. When action was imminent they could turn round and be ready to dismount in a hurry.

form during the war. A further batch of 41 machines appeared under the designation Carrier, Machine Gun No 2 Mark 1. These were fully armoured, and differed from the earlier version in having the enlarged gunner's compartment and a long stowage locker on the right-side track guard. The bigger fighting compartment also eliminated the need for a separate shield for the machine-gun.

The Cavalry Carrier was a strange variant. The front was similar to the new machine-gun carrier but the rear was entirely open, with bench seats for six men, three on either track guard like the first prototypes. They would normally travel facing inwards, although heat from the engine caused a considerable nuisance. Clips to hold their rifles were provided above the engine and a Boys rifle for dismounted use was also carried, while the front gunner had a Bren. The idea appears to have been a development of the Cavalry Portée idea in that men simply used the vehicle to carry them onto the battlefield and dismounted to fight if the need arose. When this was imminent the men would turn round and sit facing outwards with the backrest now serving as a chest restrainer while wire mesh guards prevented their legs from becoming tangled in the tracks. Such little comfort as there was could be enhanced by erecting a canvas canopy which covered the entire vehicle and, in the words of the official report 'provided protection' – but only from the weather. A prototype was field tested by the 9th, Queen's Royal Lancers and 50 production machines were built, although a later report admitted that no decision had yet been reached on their precise role and, in the end, they were never used on active service and, in this form, the idea of dismounted cavalry was dropped.

The fate of the original 40mm gun carrier is not known, but in 1938 another one appeared, described as a 2pr anti-tank gun platform, which mounted the regular service 40mm gun above

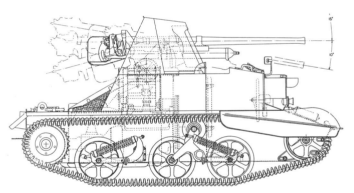

D33 Details of the 2pr mounting on a Vickers Carrier.

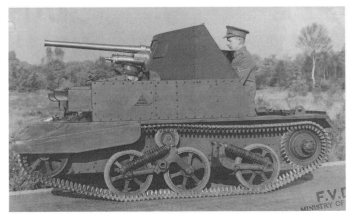

142 The self-propelled 2pr anti-tank gun mounting on a Vickers-Armstrong carrier chassis.

the engine, facing forwards. A large shield was fitted to the weapon, covering the front and, to a limited extent, the sides. The gun itself was capable of being swung 20° either side of the centre line, with elevation of 15° and depression of 10°. Since it would be firing over the heads of the two men at the front they were provided with hinged flaps that enclosed the entire compartment when in action. Interesting as this design was it never reached production. Doubts were expressed about the security of the gunner and loader since the shield only provided limited protection, while it also created minor aerodynamic problem that caused dust, raised in the wake of the vehicle, to be drawn into the rear compartment. Thus, if they were not shot, these two unfortunates were liable to be choked to death.

These experiments aside the basic reliability and utility of the design was quickly proven. With a high power to weight ratio these carriers were fast and manoeuvrable, as well as being inconspicuous and readily adaptable to various roles. Consequently a massive production programme was envisaged, but at this stage Vickers-Armstrong dropped from the scene. Instead contracts were issued to various engineering firms including Aveling-Barford, Morris Motors, Nuffield Mechanisation and Aero, the Sentinel Waggon Company and Thornycrofts. Two basic types were ordered. Most were simply an improved version of the No 2 Mark 1, adapted to mount a Bren gun instead of the Vickers; indeed many hundreds were completed as Bren Gun Carriers, a title which soon, in popular usage, applied to every member of this family of vehicles. They were partnered by a type known as the Scout Carrier, which in effect was a mirror image of the Bren, at least in the layout of the rear compartment. This model was open on the left side and enclosed on the right, except overhead of course, and the compartment thus created housed a third crewman and a No 11 wireless set. Scout Carriers were issued to Divisional Cavalry (Reconnaissance) Regiments in conjunction with light tanks, while the Bren Carriers served, initially, with the infantry. Early in 1939 the sense of building two very similar vehicles for distinct roles was called into question, and a new design prepared which had armoured panels to the same height as the front compartment, enclosing both sides and the back. Bren and Boys guns were still carried, but the vehicle was adaptable to both roles and, in time, many others. Officially they were known as Universal Carriers, although the name Bren Gun Carrier had obtained such currency, both in the service and through the media, that it has stuck ever since.

On the evening of 10 December 1935 an aircraft of Sabena, the Belgian airline, with seven passengers and a crew of four aboard, came down near Tatsfield on the Kent–Surrey border, while approaching Croydon aerodrome, killing everyone on board. One of the passengers was Sir John Carden, returning from an official visit to the Vickers' licensee in Belgium where sabotage was suspected. Nazi involvement has been suggested, both in the sabotage and plane crash, but it may have been an accident; more than one aircraft coming into Croydon was found to have foliage caught in the undercarriage after passing over Tatsfield. Ten days later Vickers announced that Carden's long time partner, Capt. V G Loyd, would take charge of their Chertsey development establishment, with Mr L G Little acting as his technical manager. Leslie Little would prove a worthy successor to Carden, but Loyd was not in the same

class, and certainly did not enjoy the confidence of Sir Noel Birch. By 1937 Birch was doing his best, not only to free the company of Loyd, but also from an agreement made with the two partners which paid a five per cent royalty on all Carden-Loyd designs sold. The main problem concerned the suspension system since, as Birch argued, matters of hull and turret design were more easily avoided. The task of designing a new suspension system fell to Little. Reading between the lines of Sir Noel's correspondence it seems that the original idea was to develop a commercial tractor which, apparently, was not ready in time for the interested customer. It was therefore adapted, in about September 1936, to a light tank of 14mm armour thickness, which was then offered to the War Office. They showed no great interest, deeming the Light Mark VI to be entirely suitable for the immediate future, but it was agreed that development should continue with a commercial option in view, although by this time 14mm was considered to be insufficient protection for anything but small reconnaissance machines. Of course it was the fact that the new running gear freed Vickers-Armstrong from the Carden-Loyd patents that pleased Sir Noel Birch, but its revolutionary nature should be emphasised, to Leslie Little's credit. It consisted of four large-diameter road wheels, the rearmost of which also served as the drive sprocket. In place of conventional springs these wheels were suspended on tubular struts containing a pocket of air and a cushion of oil, giving excellent independent springing on all wheels. This was unusual enough, but Little took the dangerous step of incorporating a second revolutionary feature which involved the steering. The road wheels were all pivoted on brackets and linked to a steering wheel in such a way that movement of this wheel caused all eight of them to lean and turn, adopting a complicated geometry which curved the track and allowed the tank to drive round curves as small as 94 feet radius without having to skid a track. Skid steering was available for tighter turns, but for ordinary road work or across country where there was room, the vehicle steered like a car, although it was much harder work. It was the sort of system Philip Johnson had tried hard to perfect in the early twenties, and a certain Mr Ingoldsby, working for a Vickers' subsidiary in Kent, came close to perfecting shortly afterwards; whether Little knew of this or not is impossible to say. It does, however, raise a question over the matter of who actually designed the steering system for the Bren Carrier; Carden was still there but it has more than a touch of Leslie Little about it. What mattered was that it worked, it still had its faults but they could be cured. Since the tracks had to curve, the pin joints were purposely made loose, and in order to get the best form of contact between roadwheel and track Little chose ball section tyres and designed the inner face of the tracks to match. When skid steering, even at the slowest speeds, the tracks kept jumping off.

War Office representatives who examined the drawings thought they were looking at something similar to the little Straussler light tank, which they did not care for at all, but Sir Noel was now intent upon adapting it to suit both a medium and cavalry tank. Indeed he described it as, 'an unqualified success . . . a landmark in constructive progess'. Vickers-Armstrong simply called it the type PR, and in their yearly reports noted that the wheels, being fitted with armoured hub caps, not only protected themselves but the inner hull as well,

143 *The prototype Light Tank Mark VII here fitted with a dummy turret similar to the type ultimately adopted.*

doing away with the need for skirting plates. It was also claimed that if the tracks broke the tank could run on its wheels, although one wonders if they ever tried this. The engine was another original item. Vickers remained loyal to the Meadows concern who developed a horizontally opposed twelve-cylinder unit, the type MAT, rated at 180hp. It was situated at the rear, driving through a conventional gearbox. As first designed the tank was to mount twin machine-guns in line with other light tanks, but it was capable of taking something bigger so, when the pilot model appeared it had wooden representations of the 40mm Vickers gun and co-axial machine-gun fitted. Vickers also showed it fitted with a mock-up, open barbette style turret mounting machine-guns capable of both ground and anti-aircraft fire. By 1938 Vickers knew the tank as their Mark VII, and in May of that year again offered it to the War Department. The problem now was to find a category for it. A tank with the armour protection of a light, but the firepower of a cruiser was clearly a Light Cruiser, but since no requirement existed for such a thing it was cobbled together rather vaguely as GS specification A17, and the tank delivered to MEE as A17E1; ultimately to enter service as the Tetrarch.

Apart from the usual problems with cooling the tank performed very well indeed; the main concern of the authorities was the location of the fuel tanks, in front of the driver. It seems an odd arrangement, but space was at a premium so Vickers overcame the objections by fitting an internal 14mm bulkhead ahead of the driver and arranging for the fuel to drain down through the floor if the compartment was penetrated. The road wheel tyres and tracks were also altered to a square section to cure the problem of track shedding, and the turret adapted to take the War Office 2pr and co-axial Besa machine-gun. In this form the tank was known as the Mark VIIA, but later reverted to Mark VII. The last change listed before the outbreak of war concerned the carburettors. For obvious reasons the Italian Zenith type were replaced by the home-produced Solex pattern.

Before proceeding to examine the mainstream development of tanks up to the outbreak of war, it is relevant at this stage to say something about War Office policy at this time; although whether this eliminates, or increases confusion is debatable. Vickers-Armstrong obviously had a vested interest in this, and two revealing documents from their files, dated late in 1936,

serve as a good starting point. The first concerns a discussion between Sir Noel Birch and the Master General of the Ordnance. This post had been held, since 1934, by Sir Hugh Elles, the original commander of the Tank Corps in France, and it was an interesting reversal of roles. In the immediate post-war period, as we have seen, Sir Noel was MGO and Elles the somewhat desperate supplicant. To quote the first paragraph of Birch's report:

The MGO said that he has again changed his mind about tanks and now thinks that instead of them being useless owing to anti-tank guns, rifles, mines etc., they will be of some good to the Army but they will occupy a secondary position to what they have done in the past.

Elles also told Birch that he was keen to promote competition and had approached the Nuffield Organisation and Vulcan Foundry with this in mind. Furthermore, he wished all firms involved in tank design, including the ROF, to examine one another's designs. Birch, in spite of his former appointment, was now the very essence of the company man, protective and jealous of his firm's designs, so this idea must have given him a shock. He also reported Elles as saying that he regarded 30mm as the minimum armour thickness for medium tanks and at least 60mm for the new generation of infantry support tanks that he had in mind. What Sir Hugh Elles had in mind was one thing; what the War Office knew of it, or even agreed with, might be an entirely different matter. The day after Sir Noel issued his report another appeared, from Capt. A J Nannini, who had visited Woolwich on Sir Noel's behalf and at Sir Hugh's invitation. Ostensibly the object of the exercise was to allow Vickers to look over the A7E3 Medium tank then nearing completion, but Nannini also used his service connections to sound out the personnel there. He said that the staff of the ROF were:

unable to obtain concrete specifications for armament, armour and performance of future medium and heavy tanks, owing to the fact that the General Staff are unable to arrive at agreement with regard to the tactical employment of tanks.

Nannini was also given to understand that Gen. Ironside and many senior officers disagreed with the concept – usually attributed to Elles – of using tanks to assault fixed defences in company with infantry. The reason given was that it would always be possible to make anti-tank guns powerful enough to destroy tanks at a fraction of the cost. Woolwich estimated that a tank, protected to 40mm standard, could be built which weighed up to 30 tons and had a speed of around 10mph, but they imagined the cost would be prohibitive. They had therefore settled for 30mm at present, although this was only capable of resisting anti-tank rounds up to about 20mm calibre at normal fighting ranges. Indeed, according to Nannini, they had been asked to work out a design for A7E3 on a 30mm basis but found this impossible, expecting at best to settle at 25mm for a drop in speed of about 3mph.

Some details of a meeting held at the War Office just before Christmas 1937 have already been mentioned in another title*. On this occasion the Chief of the Imperial General Staff (CIGS) had indicated that there was no foreseeable risk of conflict in

---

The Great Tank Scandal.

Europe involving Britain, but that Italy presented a serious threat in North Africa. Although all present agreed that tanks should not be launched directly against prepared defences, they were a bit vague about how they should be used, talking about close co-operation with the air force. Since there could be few fixed defences in the desert anyway, the important factor would seem to be mobility, and the only tank available which filled that bill, was the A9 Cruiser, although the meeting agreed that the General Staff 'did not set much store' by this tank. In fact, they claimed the A9 was rated as being of less value than the A11, although the new A12 design should be superior to both. Yet for all its other faults an A9 could run rings around the other two in open country, and they had both been built with direct assault in mind! Before they all departed on Christmas leave a decision was reached: 60 A12 tanks would be ordered at once, authority would be sought for a further 60 either of A11 or A12 type, 'whichever could be produced fastest' – and there is little doubt that A11 would fall into that category – and as a general principle A11 should have priority over A9. This last was a most amazing decision, for if every other factor was discounted the difference in armament was staggering; a fully armed A11 mounted just one ·303 machine-gun, A9 disposed three of these *and* a 2pr.

When it came to designing the new generation of tanks for the late thirties the keynote was still economy, although this was compounded by the lack of a suitably powerful engine, designed for the job. GS specification A9 was issued for a medium tank that would be a cheaper alternative to A7E3 or A8, yet having the same firepower and armour protection as the Medium Mark III. It seemed a tall order, but it was placed with Vickers-Armstrong in June 1934, when it was being referred to as the Medium Mark IV, and naturally Sir John Carden was responsible for the design. Due in part to a change in the specifications, and on account of its performance in the early years of the war, A9 has always had a bad press, but judged for its time there is no denying that, given the restrictions imposed, Sir John did a fair job. The War Office wanted a tank weighing no more than seven tons, with a top speed of 25mph, a good trench crossing ability and an armament layout which gave a 190° arc of fire with front-mounted machine-guns. They also required it to take a single commercial engine, instead of the pair specified for A7E3 and A8. Armour was to be on a 14mm standard and, in order to keep the weight down, Carden designed the hull as far as possible with thinner plates set at oblique angles that would equal 14mm plate set vertically. Carden carried this arrangement down to the underside of the hull, resulting in what amounted to a boat-shaped floor. The engine, a Rolls-Royce Phantom II six-cylinder unit, was located at the rear, driving through a Meadows five-speed gearbox. Steering was by clutch and brake, but an ingenious feature was the way the brake drums were mounted on the outside of each sprocket, where the passing air-flow helped to keep them cool. Of course they were rather vulnerable, so armoured covers were added later. The turret was based on the A7 design, and was intended originally to carry a 3pr and co-axial machine-gun, but in order to achieve the required frontal arc of fire two small machine-gun turrets were fitted, flanking the driver's cab and mounting a single Vickers gun

144 A9E1, which would have been the Medium Tank Mark IV, shown in its original form before the suspension was modified. It had a nasty habit of shedding tracks.

each. They were topped by odd conical lids that looked like Chinamens' hats. Probably the most ingenious feature was Carden's so-called 'bright idea' suspension. Each bogie, of which there were two per side, had one 24in rubber tyred roller and two slightly smaller, sprung on a variation of the light tank system with coil springs. The bogies on each side were reversed so that the larger rollers were at the front and back, and the degree of flexibility was remarkable. The new tank appeared at a time when there was a renewed interest in lubricated tracks, so the type devised for it were of a smooth-faced, double-pin pattern with external guide horns; the pins being sealed with rubber washers to keep the oil in and mud out. In theory these seals were supposed to work so well that when they were connected up at the factory they should never need lubricating again, but it turned out to be rather a pious hope. Among the detail features the most significant was the hydraulic turret power traverse – fitted for the first time to a British tank – but the tank also had a small, air-cooled auxiliary engine mounted on the gearbox. This powered a gas filtration fan in the turret and charged the wireless batteries, and it could be lifted out and run separately as a battery charging unit away from the tank.

Despite every effort the tank was three tons over its specified weight when it left the factory, and performance suffered accordingly. It was first demonstrated at MEE in July 1936, although the front turrets had not then been completed, and were represented by lumps of lead; it was also without wireless or armament of any kind. However, its more modern, streamlined appearance seemed to promise speed so, for the benefit of the CIGS, a race was arranged between it and the Medium Mark II, and Mark III. Unfortunately the latter won and, over a flying quarter mile the A9 did no better than an 11 year old Mark II. It also pitched violently on its suspension and, on subsequent trials, revealed a tendency to throw off its tracks, despite the fact they were supposed to be kept as taught as a bowstring to prevent this.

Vickers-Armstrong then took the tank back and worked on it for 12 months, spacing out the bogies, fitting hydraulic shock absorbers to correct pitching and exchanging the engine for something more powerful. At one stage a big Fowler-Sanders diesel was examined, but in the end they settled for a six-cylinder AEC unit, a petrol version of that firm's 9·64 litre diesel bus engines. By this time the matter of armament had also undergone a change. The old 3pr had finally been replaced by a new, high velocity 2pr with, for its day, an exceptional armour piercing performance, but in keeping with the original requirement, the mounting was also capable of taking a close-support weapon. In this form, and again for its day, the A9 was in most respects a very good tank. The entire automotive set up, from engine through to tracks, was eminently reliable and it was armed with a superb anti-tank gun, which led one over-optimistic commentator to suggest that the Germans would now have to scrap all their existing tanks to avoid having them destroyed! In 1937 an order was placed for 50 of these tanks, which a bulletin from Vickers-Armstrong's Tank Department at Elswick described as the largest single order for tanks that it had ever received – which is not saying very much. Deliveries began early in 1939, by which time a further 75 had been ordered from Harland and Wolff in Belfast, but the tank had now been downgraded to an interim

145 A10E1 as first built, showing the well-sloped hull front that was ruined when the War Office demanded a hull machine-gun.

type, on account of other developments. It was claimed that the tank was generally too complicated for firms without previous tank experience to construct, and its intricate hull shape made it impossible to think of uparmouring to the 30mm standard now required. Vulnerability was further aggravated by a series of dangerous shot traps formed in the angles where the sub-turrets met the driver's cab. A Vickers' bulletin for 1939 makes an intruiging reference to a searchlight turret for A9E1, but nothing more is known of this unless it is connected with the De Thoren system which ultimately developed into the Canal Defence Light.

When first ordered, as a medium tank, A9 was regarded as suitable for equipping battalions of the Tank Brigade, but the General Staff also expressed an interest in something more heavily armoured with which to equip the Army Tank Battalions. A prototype was ordered from Vickers-Armstrong in 1934 and Carden naturally used A9 as a basis. Since it was expected to be slower moving, and therefore an easier target, one inch (25mm) armour was specified. Vickers achieved this by the curious expedient of building the hull from thinner plate, riveted to the structural frame, and then screwing outer panels to this shell to create the required thickness. This practice was known as composite armour since the inner layer was of a malleable material which could easily be cut and welded, while the outer skin was of a good, hard quality armour. The advantages included economy of expensive plate and easier assembly, but generally speaking a single thickness of armour would give better protection. Since the new tank was bound to be heavier than A9, wider tracks were fitted to spread the weight. In all other mechanical respects the two types were identical, except that A10E1, appearing slightly later, never had the Rolls-Royce engine, only the AEC. The main turret and armament also remained the same, but for some unspecified reason no hull machine-guns were demanded for A10. One can appreciate that, for reasons of weight saving, two sub-turrets would be out of the question, but it does seem strange that a slower moving tank intended to work with infantry should not at least have one such weapon at the front. Yet there were compensations: with no such fittings to disrupt it, the front of the hull was well-shaped, presenting a sloping face in every direction, and the overall length was slightly reduced when compared with A9. Thus, despite the extra armour, the new tank, with a crew of four, compared with six in A9, only worked out two tons heavier, and there was little to choose in terms of performance between the two. The prototype went to MEE in July 1937, but following initial trials the War Office changed its mind and decided that a hull machine-gun should be fitted after all. Vickers took the tank back to Chertsey, and it emerged again in September 1938 with its sleek lines spoiled by a vertical front plate. The driver was moved slightly to the left of the centre line and a fifth crew member, the hull gunner, located alongside him to the right. At this time the War Office was on the point of adopting an air-cooled Czech machine-gun – the ZB.53 – instead of the Vickers, and one of these was mounted in the remodelled hull of A1OE1.

The tank went into production in 1939, but by this time yet another change in tactical thinking caused it to be classified as the Cruiser Mark II (A9 having become Cruiser Mark I), being based on the old medium tank function. Orders were placed with Vickers-Armstrong and the Birmingham Railway Carriage and Wagon Co, but there was yet one more twist to the machine-gun saga. Since the turrets were still being produced with a co-axial Vickers mounting, having a different weapon in the hull was bound to create problems with ammunition stowage, so the hull mounting was removed and the aperture plated over. On later models, when the co-axial weapon had been changed to the Czech design – now produced in Britain as the Besa – the hull position was reinstated. This version being classified as the Cruiser Mark IIA, but production of both types only ran to 170 machines.

In 1936 Giffard Martel was Assistant Director of Mechanisation, and in that capacity accompanied Gen. A P Wavell on a visit to Russia to observe their armoured force manœuvres that autumn. Both men were surprised to discover that for a country held, in the West, to be technically backward and still in the grip of post-revolutionary turmoil, here was a tank force to be reckoned with. What impressed them most was the BT type fast tank, of which they saw hundreds travelling across country at high speeds with, apparently, little or no mechanical trouble. Martel was inspired to get such a tank for Britain as soon as possible, but it seemed that a deal with the Soviet Union was out of the question. Then further investigation revealed something that the War Office should have been aware of all along, had they heeded their own resolution to keep an eye on foreign developments. This was that the Russians tanks were based on an American design by a maverick inventor called J Walter Christie. With his lean build, jutting jaw and shock of white hair Christie looked the stuff of which legends are made, in fact he made most of them himself. In terms of his ideas on tank design, if not in age or temperament, he was America's answer to Philip Johnson, for his creed was speed, at the expense of armour protection and almost to the exclusion of anything else. The difference was that Christie was his own man, and not a government employee, so while funds lasted he was free to do as he pleased. An accurate account of his life has yet to be told, but as a result of some 12 years of design work he had, by 1932, built a tank of sorts that was capable of a staggering performance, covering the ground at 65mph on its tracks and then clocking 110mph on wheels alone, which was a unique Christie feature.

One can only take the Johnson/Christie parallel so far; as we have seen the British engineer sought his ideal by the most complicated means, while the American preferred simplicity. What it amounted to was the use of large diameter, independently sprung wheels linked, via trailing arms, to long hellical springs that gave superb deflection. The speeds Christie achieved were almost inevitable, given his preference for huge engines and lightweight hulls, but even this would have been a pointless exercise if the suspension was not capable of handling it. Martel exploited his relationship with Lord Nuffield to get a tank shipped over from the United States, but even that was easier said than done. If an embargo on the sale of war materials were not enough, the only available Christie tank – a prototype built in 1931 – was languishing in a government compound in Washington. However, it still effectively belonged to Christie, even if, as Martel has claimed, one of his creditors had a lien on it; so it was purchased as a Convertible Tractor to get around the official restrictions. Convertible was a term used to emphasise one of the most unusual Christie features, the ability to run as a wheeled vehicle when required, by taking the tracks off. The object was much the same as the old British wheel-cum-track concept: to improve mobility on the approach march and save track wear. In practice, as most armies discovered, it was more trouble than it was worth. One authority has suggested that the Christie tank which arrived in Britain on 17 November 1936 was not M1931 – which had already been tested to destruction – but one of the redundant US Army T3 Mediums supplied as a replacement. It makes little difference technically since M1931 was a T3 pilot model and the latter, with its turret off, would look much the same. Whichever tank it was, it would already have had a hard life.

When it arrived at Farnborough MEE discovered that it weighed 9 tons, so they loaded it up to 10·75 tons in order, as they said, to represent the weight of War Department fighting equipment, but this seems a bit optimistic. They still had a machine with a very high power to weight ratio that put up some astounding performances, both in terms of road speed and hill climbing, all aided by the remarkable suspension. It was not the business of MEE to comment on armour thickness, but had they done so a maximum of just over half an inch (13mm) would have been recorded, which had a considerable bearing on performance. To offset this the nose section at least was sharply angled, giving a good ballistic shape, although this was done to clear the leading road wheels for steering when the tracks were off than for any other advantage. The rest of the hull was anything but streamlined, the sides being particularly high and flat, but they were formed of inner and outer skins with the suspension springs sandwiched between them. The fighting compartment was hardly worthy of the name as far as British requirements were concerned. The turret ring was of such a small diameter that even a light tank turret would not fit, and below that level the crew had to share their space with buffer springs connected to the steering gear. At the rear lay the engine compartment, the second secret of Christie's success. It housed an American Liberty V12, an aero engine of First World War vintage with a capacity of 27 litres, developing 350bhp at 1,800rpm, but capable of being pushed up to 2,500rpm without coming to any harm. The same power unit had been used in the Anglo-American Mark VIII tank of 1918, and since that time a number of tanks had been produced with

146 *The Christie tank purchased by Lord Nuffield, seen here at MEE bearing its British WD number (T2086) and the newly acquired air-cleaners.*

147 *A13E2, the first British built Christie Cruiser at MEE running on trade plates. The large, flat-track plates were a clumsy feature on what was meant to be a high-speed tank.*

aircraft engines fitted (notably some of the Medium D series), but otherwise their potential had been ignored in Britain. In 1937 Martel had located a surplus stock of such engines belonging to the RAF: the 12-cylinder Napier Lion type X1A, which had its cylinders arranged in three banks of four. Tests by MEE indicated an output of 465bhp at 2,500rpm, although it would not run well on service type Grade III petrol without modification; in any case it was turned down by the Army as a possible waste of money. Returning to the Christie tank, now carrying the designation A13E1, the staff at MEE appear to have been most impressed by the gearbox. It was a relatively straightforward four-speed unit, but clearly specially made to suit the engine and hull, with the two top speeds geared up and the lower speeds geared down, yet all as evenly spaced as possible. From here drive passed through a typical clutch and brake transmission to the drive sprockets, where Christie's ingenuity was again evident. The sprockets had no teeth in the usual sense, but were formed as a pair of discs which had a series of small rollers sandwiched between them. The track guide horns were designed to slot between the rollers, giving a positive drive with the minimum of wear and friction. Such a system would only work on the equally unusual tracks that Christie developed, but it was in the design of these that the inventor's genius seems to have left him. Each track plate was little more than a 10in square flat panel, pin jointed to its neighbours, with a huge guide horn, shaped like a mouse's ear, on every alternate plate. Two problems were noted at MEE. The big plates slapping their way around the small diameter front idler gave it a tremendous battering, however, most of the punishment was taken by the track pins which bent out of shape and could not be extracted. Nuffields produced one length of track with a 5in pitch, and a sprocket to match, but this did not work too well either, and it was clear that this feature was in urgent need of attention. However, it was the suspension system that Britain was really after, and to this end the Nuffield Organisation purchased the patent rights from its inventor. The tank ran on eight 27·5in diameter wheels, four each side and of the split type to straddle the guide horns. Each wheel was mounted at the end of a short swinging arm, which in turn bore against a long coil spring that gave each individual wheel the ability to rise through a distance of 14 inches independently of its neighbours, making the tank both

comfortable and, potentially, a good gun platform, even at speed. One thing the British engineers noted, and soon remedied, was the total absence of air cleaners. These were installed above the hull, just in rear of the turret ring, but when the tank was running they found out why Christie had not used them. When the engine backfired it did so with such force that flames shot into the felt-lined cleaners and blew them off again.

By the end of 1936 an order had been placed in the United States for more Liberty engines, while Nuffields got on with the job of designing a British Christie tank. Two pilot models, A13E2 and A13E3 were delivered in October 1937 and February 1938 respectively, and it seems that the contract was agreed in time for them to qualify for the 14mm armour standard, giving an all-up weight of 14 tons. In a way this was a pity, for the Christie suspension was capable of being stiffened up to take much greater weights, and yet, as subsequent developments showed, British engineers consistently built the suspension as close to the immediate design weight as possible, so that it was inevitably overloaded by improvements that increased the weight by too much. Since the convertible facility was not required on the British tanks it was possible to square off the nose, although once again no attempt was made to incorporate a hull machine-gun position. Rather the driver was situated in a central position beneath a box-shaped head cover that stuck out from the glacis plate. The turret was of the normal style, but with a large drum-shaped cupola added, mounting a 2pr and co-axial Vickers gun. The transmission was altered to include a constant mesh gearbox, and Nuffields re-worked the Liberty engine to achieve 411bhp at 2,000rpm, while Amal flame traps were built into the air intakes to spare the air-cleaners. Spacing of the suspension units was rearranged to suit the new hull shape with Newton and Bennett shock absorbers added to soften the rebound effect. A13E2 ran on original Christie size tracks and sprockets, but when A13E3 appeared it had a new type of double link track, of about 4in pitch, which reverted to dry pin joints and marked the abandonment, by Britain, of the lubricated track idea. More or less in this form the tank was adopted as the Cruiser Mark III, of which 65 were built by Nuffield Mechanisation and Aero. Even with governed engines these tanks were quite capable of running at 30mph, and with their fine suspensions clearly suited the cruiser role far more effectively than the Vickers-

Armstrong machines, which were downgraded as a result. When the armour specification changed a new version, the Cruiser Mark IV, appeared with the frontal plates thickened to 30mm and a form of spaced armour added to the turret. Spaced armour was used, later in the war, as an antidote to the hollow charge projectile, but in 1938 it was developed with a different purpose in mind. It had been discovered that if the distance between two plates was slightly greater than the length of a projectile fired at them it would be deflected slightly as it passed through the outer plate, striking the inner one at an odd angle but failing to penetrate. The only drawback was that extra weight did not only mean the new plate itself, but also the brackets that supported it. However, by limiting the increase to frontal areas and the turret, the maximum weight of a Cruiser Mark IV was still less than 15 tons, so performance remained unaffected. The change to air-cooled machine-guns resulted in the appearance of the Mark IVA, which substituted the Besa for the Vickers gun. In all about 240 Mark IV and IVA tanks were built, mostly by Nuffields, although a few were made by the London, Midland and Scottish Railway Co (LMS).

One of Walter Christie's greatest failings, if it can be called that, was an inability to appreciate that there must be a finite stage of development in any programme. It was this trait, more than anything else, which served to alienate him in the eyes of the American Army and administration. No sooner had one of his designs been accepted than he was badgering the authorities with a new model, and then getting very upset if they did not immediately seize upon it. For an inventor committed to progress, this is understandable, but a good businessman knows where to draw the line, at least for a while; for it can be a nuisance where budgets are concerned, and men have to be trained to use each new item of equipment. It was fortunate that British engineers, working on A13E1, did not have the man breathing down their necks all the time, though it did not stop him from trying. Christie was 73 in 1938, yet as pugnacious as ever where authority was concerned, and he decided that it was about time the Britishers were made aware of his latest designs. He had developed a tank in the previous year which he called M1938, and in January 1938 he brought it over to Britain, where it was kept, for demonstration purposes, at MEE. In their report the British examiners referred to it as incomplete, because it did not have a turret, but such things were anathema to Christie; 'high in the sky turrets', he called them. There was space for one, if the crew compartment were enclosed, but, if he must have such irritating details as guns fitted to his tanks, he would prefer that they were mounted in the nose, where they did less to spoil the sleek lines of his machine. In any case if he did not fit weapons Christie might just get by the Federal authorities who did not wish him to export tanks at all. Even without a gun it was a striking looking machine, with the main suspension springs encased in tubes at a rakish angle on the hull sides, a sleek nose and cone-shaped head cover for the driver. The tracks were of shorter, 5in pitch, with each plate slightly curved to conform to the sprocket and idler circumference. The staff at MEE learned that it was powered by a Curtiss type D12 aero engine rated at 670bhp at 2,600rpm, but they were not allowed to look too closely, let alone test the tank as they wished. Whether he was more anxious about having his design pirated or the rough workmanship revealed is debatable, but Christie had gone to the lengths of bringing his own driver, Leo Anderson, over with him. Alas Anderson let his chief down on the very first run, having forgotten to check the gearbox oil after the voyage, and the thing seized within a few miles. The wretched driver had to spend the night with the tank on Farnborough ranges while Christie is said to have scoured the area for an engineering firm capable of supplying replacement gears. Apparently he succeeded, for the next day, during a trial run over a flying quarter mile, the tank was clocked at 64·3mph; which must have been a startling sight for the onlookers, and this was later confirmed in writing by Col. Martel. Although he felt that the British were duty bound to buy the tank, Christie had also invited representatives from the French Army to come over and look at it. Unfortunately before they arrived he was visited by people from the US Embassy in London who reminded him in no uncertain terms that it was illegal for US

148 The tank which J Walter Christie brought over to Britain in 1938, photographed at Farnborough. Its rakish lines promised speed, but no thought had been given to its combat potential.

citizens to export war materials, and would he kindly take it home at once. On 7 March the tank was taken down to Southampton for shipment, and the British relieved of an embarrassment. Even had it been permitted, it seems unlikely that the War Office would have wanted it. For all its detail improvements the tank was hardly different in principle from the earlier model, and engineers at Nuffields knew all they needed to know about that. What mattered now was what they did with that knowledge.

In the handbook for the Cruisers Mark III and IV, published in February 1940, the tanks are described as being 'medium weight, high-speed, reconnaissance machines', which appears to be rather a limited description of the cruiser role. However, it may be a reflection of another development, one which had actually been abandoned by that time. This was the so-called heavy, or battlecruiser tank. A number of such designs had been considered, two had even appeared as prototypes, but all are worth a brief examination as they appear to show certain trends in tank design which, had they been acted upon, might have provided the British Army with tanks of far greater promise than those actually taken into service: not just in 1940 but for most of the forthcoming war. The trend can first be detected towards the end of 1936 when Martel returned from a visit to Vickers where he had inspected the A17 design. He regarded it as underpowered and too small, remarking that service opinion still favoured something along the lines of A6, sub-turrets and all. Indeed it is worth noting just how popular the A6 type still seemed to be in the eyes of the users, and to emphasise how short-sighted was the planning that led to its abandonment. Certainly if sub-turrets meant firepower then a tank first outlined in February 1937 as the A15 had it all, and more. The main turret was to contain a 2pr gun, medium range howitzer and two air-cooled ZB machine-guns – one mounted for anti-aircraft use. In addition there would be two frontal turrets, each mounting a pair of ZB guns and a smoke mortar, plus a rear turret with two more machine-guns. Armour would be on the 30mm basis with a required top speed of 25mph while other matters considered were Horstmann suspension – like A6E3 – and Wilson steering. Such a tank would be high and wide, if not necessarily handsome, and the LMS, on being approached, expressed an interest. Yet, in a sense, railways were its downfall. Limitations set by the British railway loading gauge always had, and for a long time would continue to dictate the overall size of British tanks, and the projected A15 exceeded this. In an effort to get round this problem the War Office discussed the idea of building tanks to suit the continental loading gauge, which offered an advantage of about ten inches in width, but this was turned down by the more conservative element who, presumably, could not imagine British tanks operating in Europe, and the project was suspended in December 1937. To avoid confusion it should be noted that the GS specification A15 was later applied to another, slightly more successful design, the Crusader.

In June 1937 work began on a rival design under the designation A14, a slightly more modest proposal with the same armour thickness but only the two forward sub-turrets and a total crew of six. Again A6E3 suspension was considered suitable, along with the Thornycroft RY12 marine type engine which, as already noted, had been first tested in A6E3. It would be coupled to a new form of Wilson steering that offered a choice of seven speeds for each track, on a preselector basis, and provided a range of geared turning circles. Large, and extremely complicated as it was, this arrangement was a vast improvement on skid steering because it did not waste power, although the penalty in terms of weight was considerable. The Vulcan Foundry, at Newton-le-Willows first showed an interest, but eventually the contract for two tanks – dated March 1938 – was issued to the LMS when the A15 scheme was dropped. A14E1 was running by June 1939, but it was found to weigh 29 tons so work on A14E2 was slowed down while attempts were made to bring it down to 25 tons. An interesting phrase can be found in the papers relating to this tank, to the effect that it was 'capable of expansion to meet future GS requirements'. This might be taken to mean that there were those involved in tank design who appreciated that a tank could be built with the ability to take larger guns or thicker armour at some later stage. In the event, of course, no such thing happened and the project was abandoned with just the one prototype almost completed.

Not to be left out, Nuffields proposed their own heavy cruiser in October 1937, under the designation A16. It was effectively a heavy A13, with a crew of six and armour on a 30mm basis. A wooden mock-up, shown in December, revealed a hull and turret along the same lines as A14, (indeed the main turret was identical, and built for Nuffields by the LMS) but with a stronger version of the Christie suspension. Once again the phrase 'capable of expansion' appears, along with the suggestion that both it and an A14 should be made suitable for desert operations, which is rarely mentioned in respect of other tanks at this time. The engine was a Nuffield Liberty, naturally, and at first the standard A13 steering and transmission was employed; however, plans were drawn up for an altogether more sophisticated system, based on a controlled differential linked to a Maybach constant mesh gearbox, designed by Thompson and Taylor of Brooklands. The story of this Maybach connection and its ultimate use in the Tiger tank is told elsewhere*, but it should be noted that, according to MEE, there was no rigid obligation to use this box with the selected transmission. Fitted with the new gearbox the tank made a good road run from Brooklands to Farnborough, managing a top speed of 22mph and handling well in traffic; however, it broke down shortly afterwards and by the summer of 1940 had been abandoned.

The next project, which dates from June 1938, was actually for a light cruiser, described as of A13 type running on A17 suspension. Thus it would have featured the Tetrarch's warp steering on a larger scale. It would also have had the same type of Meadows engine as A17, although the actual layout was to be like A14 with sub-turrets. Indeed, when the mock-up was examined in February 1939, it had the mock-up sub-turrets from A16 fitted, but Vickers also showed the War Office party a design of their own in which pairs of machine-guns were mounted in a shallow, dome-shaped turntable faired into the sloping hull front on either side of the driver. This drew some favourable comments, and was even considered for A16E2, although that tank was never built. Papers relating to this tank do serve one other instructive purpose, since they reveal

---

*Fletcher, ed. *Tiger! The Tiger Tank: A British View*. HMSO, 1986.

something of the thinking then current in the military establishment on the future development of anti-tank weapons. One quite senior pundit placed it on record that a ·276in (8mm) armour piercing bullet was likely to become the normal anti-tank projectile in five years time – from 1939. Where he got the idea from is anybody's guess, but people take heed of those in authority whether they are speaking rubbish or not. Coincidentally another expert remarked on a recent test conducted with a 25pr field gun against armour, that showed it could penetrate 70mm at a range of 825 yards. This is a very close fighting range, but the 25pr was a relatively low-velocity weapon, yet there was then no tank in the world with armour that exceeded 70mm, so it is a bit surprising that someone did not immediately suggest mounting one in a tank. Again, however, it was firmly stated that anti-tank guns were unlikely to reach this calibre within five years. It should be noted, therefore, that the calibre of a 25pr was, as near as doesn't matter, 88mm. The fate of A18, as this design was known, was sealed when Vickers announced that it would take at least a year or more to develop. The War Office could not, or would not, wait that long, so this scheme was also terminated at the mock-up stage.

The last of these abortive schemes, A19, was outlined in December 1938. It was described as a heavy cruiser of the A14 type, but with the subsidiary turrets set on top of the main turret. While this implies problems of height it is nothing compared with the image raised of a main turret where the crew somehow have to contend with extra pairs of legs dangling down through the turret roof into the fighting space. This strange layout may have been chosen in an effort to reduce length, although this would have affected trench crossing too, and this theory is strengthened by the selection of a transverse engine layout. Thornycrofts were offering a shortened version of their RY12, yet despite the fact that Sir John Thornycroft had taken advice from Harry Ricardo, the Director of Mechanisation claimed that he was 'being asked to buy a pig in a poke'. Time wore on while details of engine design, never mind the actual tank, were settled, until, in May 1940, the project was abandoned.

In Sir Hugh Elles, as we have already seen, the War Office had a very cautious MGO, at least where tanks were concerned. In Maj-Gen. A E Davidson they had an equally cautious Director of Mechanisation. Davidson, a highly qualified engineer, based his reservations on technical matters, while Elles questioned the tactical side. He was not the least convinced by what had been happening on Salisbury Plain, and still saw warfare in terms of what he had known in 1917. As a result his ideas on future tank design came down strongly on the side of thick armour, since in his mind tanks should be used to assist infantry onto their objectives, and not go wandering off looking for other tanks to fight. What happened if enemy tanks came looking for them does not seem to have occured to him. Thus to Elles speed was of no great matter, or possibly even firepower come to that, just so long as they could slog forwards into the teeth of enemy anti-tank guns (of only 8mm calibre of course), to subdue the immediate opposition and pave the way for the infantry to move in. Among those consulted was Maj-Gen. P C S Hobart, the Inspector of the Royal Tank Corps in 1934. He offered two suggestions: one for a small, inconspicuous machine armed simply with a machine-gun, which would cover the infantry while they got their weapons on to the flanks and rear of the enemy position. Hobart specified large numbers of these tanks, on the grounds that a swarm would overwhelm the opposition allowing the majority to get through. His alternative was for a heavier tank, mounting a proper gun. This accorded with a long held opinion in RTC circles that a gun was essential in every tank; it is almost a rerun of the Medium D saga, and we should remember the attitude taken by Hugh Elles at that time. One could even say that the original Carden-Loyd concept had reappeared, and, given his success with the highly mobile Tank Brigade only a few years earlier, one even wonders what Hobart could be thinking of. Finally, as we shall see, Hobart's first suggestion implies a two-man tank, and what had the RTC learned, and Vickers-Armstrong preached on that subject following considerable experience of light tank design and operation?

The project, based on Hobart's first suggestion, originally took shape on 3 October 1935, when Sir John Carden produced a sketch for a two-man tank, mounting a single machine-gun, and running on four sets of Vickers double spring bogies per side. Clearly length was an important factor since the trench it is shown crossing is meant to be eight feet wide; hopefully it is not to scale, otherwise the tank shown here will be 32 feet long! A week later, on 10 October, Carden had a meeting with Col. M A Studd, Assistant Director of Mechanisation, at which he made the following notes, scribbled on a pad:

Code Word "Matilda"
Price £15,000
Delivery 6 months certain
(of serious importance)
May be kept secret from fighting soldier
Sample can be mild steel and cast turret
Spec. speed 5mph
        8mph hoped for
2 men = 1. 303" = 3000 rounds
No wireless
No look outs
We can try our idea of M/C gun but this is not so urgent
Order practically certain
        10.10.35 JVC

At the top another hand has added, 'Col. Studd, Sir John, Chertsey 10.10.35'

Many interesting points arise. The first dispels once and for all any suggestion that Hugh Elles coined the nickname when he saw the prototype waddling, it was a company code, chosen at the outset. The price includes development costs, individual machines worked out at around £5,000. No wireless might mean a space/weight saving factor or because the tanks would work in such large numbers over short distances that it would be superfluous. No lookout means no cupola, which in the same context seems to be removing from the gunner the obligations of command.

Vickers-Armstrong kept surprisingly close to the proposed timetable, especially considering that Carden died about two months after this meeting. The prototype, designated A11E1 by the General Staff, arrived at MEE in September 1936. Although similar in outline to Carden's sketch there were many detail differences. The compact, slightly coffin-shaped hull was of riveted construction, except on the nose where large bolts were used. Armour graduated from 10mm in less vulnerable

149/149A The original sketch and scribbled notes made by Sir John Carden which resulted in the design of the Infantry Tank Mark I. Notice the code word Matilda *and the date; precisely two months to the day before Sir John was killed.*

areas to 60mm where it mattered, while the small turret was a one-piece casting, capable of mounting a ·303 or ·5in Vickers water-cooled machine-gun. An internal bulkhead separated the crew from the rear engine compartment which contained a standard Ford V8 and Fordson four-speed gearbox driving the rear sprockets through clutch and brake steering, and A11E1 was first seen with toothed front idlers too. The tracks were totally exposed, but the greatest departure from Carden's sketch was the suspension, which was of the type used on the Mark IV artillery Dragon and itself derived from the type invented by Vickers-Armstrong for their famous six-tonner of 1929; a suspension which, it will be remembered, MWEE experts had condemned at that time for a number of reasons. Teething troubles are an inevitable part of any mechanical development, but A11 had relatively few. The exhaust pipe heated up the engine oil, as it did with the early carriers, until it was rerouted, and the tracks had a nasty habit of picking up stones which then jammed in the teeth of the drive sprockets. This was ultimately cured by raising the sprocket by five inches, and trouble with tyre wear on the rollers was corrected by making the rear ones with steel rims instead. An initial order for 60, now known as the Infantry Mark I, was placed with Vickers in 1938, and deliveries began in the following February with tanks going to 4th, 7th and 8th Battalions RTC. In the meantime the prototype had been used as a trial mounting for an anti-mine plough designed by Fowlers of Leeds, and tanks from a subsequent order came with the fittings to accept this item.

Once the prototype A11 appeared its effectiveness was questioned in RTC circles. It was no faster than a First World War Mark V and there were those who saw Hobart's scenario as a bit optimistic. If you introduced another element (enemy tanks) into the picture, what then? Demand began to grow for what was called Matilda Senior, being a faster, gun-armed version with, perhaps, a crew of three. Inevitably the question of a suitable power unit arose, and one suggestion involved a Napier-built version of the Junkers Jumo aircraft engine, although this was rejected in favour of an AEC unit, mounted crosswise, coupled to a Wilson gearbox and Rackham steering clutches. The weight was to be less than 14 tons, to conform with bridging requirements, and a speed of between 10 and 15mph was envisaged. A period of juggling now ensued, in an

effort to reconcile all these requirements. At various stages proposed armour thickness was reduced to 50mm, the armament changed to twin machine-gun and the engine layout reconsidered, but always the weight remained too great. Ultimately the specifications had to be entirely rewritten, to settle on a four-man crew, 2pr gun and maximum 70mm armour. Weight was now estimated at 16·5 tons. The most significant proposal at this stage was that the new tank should use Vickers' commercial suspension, known as the 'Japanese' type since it was used on the Medium Mark C supplied to that country. It was also agreed that armoured skirting plates ought to be fitted, to protect the suspension. As already recorded, one of the original Mark I Medium tanks had been modified by Vickers to take this suspension, and in June 1937 this tank was handed over to the design department at Vulcan Foundry, who had contracted to build the new Matilda under GS specification A12. Even so it was the engine problem that still dominated, and as weight progressively increased it was becoming obvious that a twin powerpack unit was the only effective answer, troublesome as it was. Six-cylinder AEC units were chosen and the company developed a special twin mounting to fit the tank. Meanwhile the Vulcan Foundry got on with the basic design. As with A11 the very thickness of the plate – a maximum of 78mm – made the use of a subframe unnecessary, so the plates and castings were bolted together, resulting in a very smooth finish. The main drawback was that this form of construction, the preparation of accurate castings and so on, demanded many skilled man-hours, on a type of machine which, in the event of war, would be needed quickly, and in large numbers.

Again, during the development stage, we find suggestions recorded that the tank should be capable of development as and when bigger guns became available. Yet the cast turret, as finally designed, could take a 2pr and co-axial Vickers gun comfortably, but nothing larger, while the turret ring diameter was equally limiting in this respect. It is just as surprising to discover that even on this new machine no thought was given to the provision of a hull machine-gun. Such a weapon would surely be of far greater use to a slow moving infantry tank than a fast cruiser, yet only the latter were built with extra machine-gun turrets sprouting all over the place. Study of the War Office reports for this period invites the conclusion that a form of tunnel vision was evident, focusing on each new type in turn with little or no cross-referencing, despite the fact that most of the designs were being developed at the same time. Clearly General Elles's wish that companies should pool information was not being fulfilled to any great extent, not even by the Department of Tank Design, which had no commercial axe to grind. Production of the pilot models A12E1 and A12E2 soon fell into arrears, mostly due to a shortage of components and even armour plate. It was not simply that new items needed to be developed, it was also due to an increasing workload falling on too few companies as production quickened for war. Thus it was that despite assurances, the first tank did not leave the factory, even for local trials, until April 1938, and it was the middle of that month before one got to MEE. However, when it did, testing officers were highly pleased. The AEC engines behaved beautifully, as did the six-speed Wilson pre-selector gearbox and Rackham clutches. Cooling, as ever, was the only major problem and once that was resolved, production could begin, with contracts being issued

150 A11E1, prototype for the Infantry Tank Mark I. This picture shows it in its earliest form, with toothed idler and sprocket, the latter set much lower than on production models.

151 King George VI visits the Vulcan Foundry at Newton-le-Willows to inspect the first prototype Matilda A12E1 which would enter production as the Infantry Tank Mark II and make a resounding name for itself in the imminent war.

to various firms including Fowlers of Leeds, Ruston Hornsby and the LMS, all under the parentage of the originators, Vulcan Foundry. A12 was duly designated Infantry Tank Mark II and later versions soon appeared with the Besa in the co-axial position, and with twin Leyland diesels replacing the AEC petrol units. Among the other engines considered at this stage were the Fowler-Sanders and Perkins, along with an automatic transmission by Freeborn, but all were rejected. Any tank can only be fairly judged on its ability to perform in the role for which it was designed, and by that criteria it has to be said that the Matilda was not only the best British tank, but one of the best in the world for its day.

This rash of development tended to eclipse Vickers-Armstrong to some extent, but they had not been idle. Sir Noel Birch's gloomy prognostications, recorded earlier, had certainly not come to pass, yet apart from Tetrarch, which was later transferred to another manufacturer anyway, all the other Vickers' designs, A9, A10 and A11, had been superseded by those of other manufacturers. Yet Sir John Carden's input was not entirely wasted, for in A9 he had combined a robust suspension, reliable engine and straightforward transmission into a thoroughly reliable unit. This was adopted as the basis for a new design, by Leslie Little, for an infantry tank known as Valentine, which was shown to War Office representatives in February 1938. However, since production did not get underway until just before war broke out it is covered, along with its contemporary, the Covenanter, in the next volume★.

Twenty years had passed since German aspirations to dominate her European neighbours had been crushed, thanks largely to the power of armoured vehicles. Now, in a malevolent new guise, she was about to try again. This time, however, the boot was on the other foot, at least where armoured fighting vehicles were concerned. Germany had embarked upon a logical programme of tank development, not over ambitious as it stood, but full of potential. Britain, at the same period, presented a picture of disarray. Theories were flying thick and fast, but many of the better ones were being deflected by a complacent establishment and there was no cohesive sense of direction. By the summer of 1939 there were two types of light tank, five types of cruiser tank and three models of infantry tank either in production or development, not counting designs that would be aborted. These various tanks used six different types of suspension, seven different makes of engine and four different systems of transmission, not to mention tracks and other detail features, all of which demanded different spare parts, different repair skills and even driving techniques. About all they had in common was the 2pr gun mounted in eight of them, yet not one of them was capable of being improved in this vital respect without taking serious liberties with the basic design, which were simply not worth taking. It was a sad verdict on 20 years of hard work and even harder thinking which, if nothing else, seems peculiarly British.

★*The Great Tank Scandal.*

Index